Ric Pimentel
Terry Wall

Cambridge

ENDORSED BY

NEW EDITION

HODDER
EDUCATION
AN HACHETTE UK COMPANY

Acknowledgements

The publishers would like to thank the following for permission to reproduce copyright material.

Photo credits

p.1 © Oleg Seleznev – Fotolia; **p.59** © Igor Pasechnik – Fotolia; **p.64** *l* © Interfoto/Sammlung Rauch/Mary Evans Picture Library, *r* © Rue des Archives/PVDE/Mary Evans Picture Library; **p.73** © nuttakit – Fotolia; **p.80** *both* © Photodisc/Photolibrary Group Ltd; **p.119** © jakezc – Fotolia; **p.120** © David Lees/CORBIS; **p.141** © cbomers – Fotolia; **p.177** © Rob Bouwman – Fotolia

l = left, *r* = right

Every effort has been made to trace all copyright holders, but if any have been inadvertently overlooked the publishers will be pleased to make the necessary arrangements at the first opportunity.

The authors and publishers would like to thank Adrian Metcalf for his help during the production of this book.

Hachette UK's policy is to use papers that are natural, renewable and recyclable products and made from wood grown in sustainable forests. The logging and manufacturing processes are expected to conform to the environmental regulations of the country of origin.

Orders: please contact Bookpoint Ltd, 130 Milton Park, Abingdon, Oxon OX14 4SB. Telephone: (44) 01235 827720. Fax: (44) 01235 400454. Lines are open 9.00–5.00, Monday to Saturday, with a 24-hour message answering service. Visit our website at www.hoddereducation.com

First published in 2011 by
Hodder Education, an Hachette UK Company,
Carmelite House, 50 Victoria Embankment,
London EC4Y 0DZ

Impression number 11
Year 2016

Cover photo © Macduff Everton/CORBIS
Illustrations by Barking Dog Art
Typeset in 11pt Palatino light by Pantek Arts Ltd, Maidstone, Kent
Printed in Dubai

A catalogue record for this title is available from the British Library

ISBN 978 1444 143 959

Contents

The chapters in this book have been arranged to match the Cambridge Secondary 1 Mathematics Curriculum Framework for stage 7 as follows:

- Number
- Algebra
- Geometry
- Measure
- Handling data
- Calculation and mental strategies
- Problem solving

Introduction

This series of books follows the Cambridge Secondary 1 Mathematics Curriculum Framework drawn up by University of Cambridge International Examinations. It has been written by two experienced teachers who have lived or worked in schools in many countries, and worked with teachers from other countries, including England, Spain, Germany, France, Turkey, South Africa, Malaysia and the USA.

Students and teachers in these countries come from a variety of cultures and speak many different languages as well as English. Sometimes cultural and language differences make understanding difficult. However, mathematics is largely free from these problems. Even a maths book written in Japanese will include algebra equations with x and y.

We should also all be very aware that much of the mathematics you will learn in these books was first discovered, and then built upon, by mathematicians from all over the world, including China, India, Arabia, Greece and Western countries.

Most early mathematics was simply game play and problem solving. Later this maths was applied to building, engineering and sciences of all kinds. Mathematicians study maths because they enjoy it.

We hope that you will enjoy the work you do, and the maths you learn in this series of books. Sometimes the ideas will not be easy to understand at first. That should be part of the fun. Ask for help if you need it, but try hard first. Write down what you are thinking so that others can understand what you have done and help to correct your mistakes. Most students think that maths is about answers, and so it is, but it is also a way to exercise our brains, whether we find the solution or not. Some questions throughout this book are starred (✪). This means that these questions go slightly beyond the content of the curriculum at this level and will be an enjoyable challenge for those of you who try them.

Ric Pimentel and Terry Wall

SECTION 1

1 Place value, ordering and rounding

- Interpret decimal notation and place value; multiply and divide whole numbers and decimals by 10, 100 or 1000.
- Order decimals, including measurements, changing these to the same units.
- Round whole numbers to the nearest 10, 100 or 1000 and decimals, including measurements, to the nearest whole number or one decimal place.
- Use the order of operations, including brackets, to work out simple calculations.

Place value

Our present number system originated in India with the Brahmi numerals in about 300 BCE.

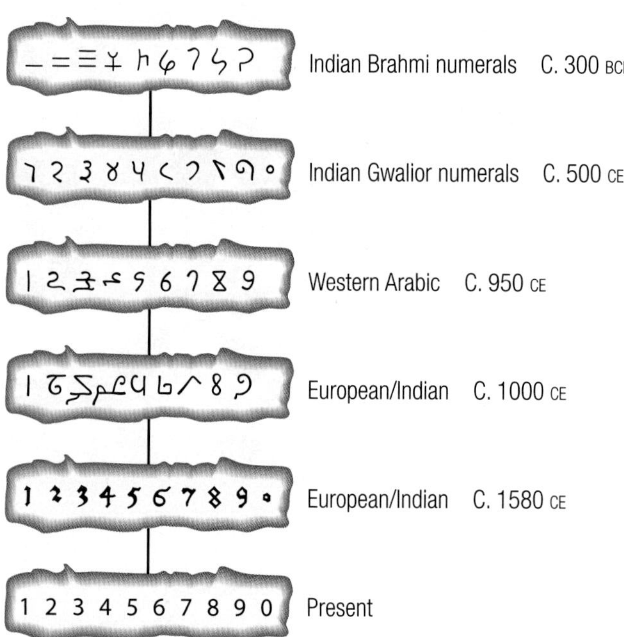

The position of a digit in our number system determines its value. For example, 6287.35 can be placed in a table like this:

Thousands	Hundreds	Tens	Units	Tenths	Hundredths
6	2	8	7	3	5

the decimal point

Looking at the table we can see that:

the 6 is worth	6000
the 2 is worth	200
the 8 is worth	80
the 7 is worth	7
the 3 is worth	0.3 or $\frac{3}{10}$
the 5 is worth	0.05 or $\frac{5}{100}$

EXERCISE 1.1A

1 What is the value of the 3 in the following numbers?
a) 37 **b)** 389 **c)** 2873 **d)** 6.13

2 What is the value of the 8 in the following numbers?
a) 0.8 **b)** 6.38 **c)** 0.048 **d)** 184 000

3 What is the value of the 5 in the following numbers?
a) 573 **b)** 8596 **c)** 0.54 **d)** 3.85

4 What is the value of the 1 in the following numbers?
a) 18 300 **b)** 0.71 **c)** 401 **d)** 0.041

5 Put the following sets of numbers in order, with the largest first.
a) 4.5, 7.2, 11, 0.9, 2.08, 0.07
b) 0.08, 0.008, 8, 80, 0.8
c) 4.6, 7.2, 6.7, 7.66, 4.07, 7.34
d) 0.1, 0.12, 0.09, 0.19, 0.92, 1.2
e) 1.12, 2.11, 3.1, 1.3, 2.13, 1.33, 3

6 Put the following sets of numbers in order, with the largest first.
a) 12.5, 7.67, 1, 3.59, 2.668, 0.097
b) 0.043, 0.009, 7.48, 8, 0.09, 20.8
c) 14.6, 25.2, 6.97, 7.0, 9.97, 7.34, 6.098
d) 0.31, 0.312, 0.309, 0.319, 0.392, 3.2
e) 0.512, 2.51, 0.1, 1.13, 1.113, 1.33, 1.433

7 Put the following sets of numbers in order, with the largest first.
a) 14.5, 372, 31, 10.9, 12.08, 10.07
b) 0.308, 0.3008, 3.8, 8, 0.88, 0.898
c) 74.6, 77.2, 76.7, 77.66, 74.07, 77.34
d) 0.91, 0.12, 0.909, 0.919, 0.992, 1.92
e) 31.12, 62.11, 33.81, 101.3, 52.13, 18.33, 3.98

8 Put the following sets of quantities in order, with the largest first.
a) 3 cm, 1.3 cm, 5.3 cm, 3.5 cm, 5.6 cm, 2.55 cm
b) 5 g, 6.4 g, 3.4 g, 8.75 g, 5.5 g, 0.9 g, 4.25 g
c) 30 cm, 0.4 m, 8.9 m, 2 m, 0.1 m, 250 cm
d) 400 g, 80 g, 2 kg, 1.3 kg, 2500 g
e) 2 litres, 0.6 litre, 400 m*l*, 0.5 litre, 550 m*l*

Multiplying and dividing by 10, 100 and 1000

Multiplying a number by 10, 100 or 1000 results in the digits moving one, two or three places to the left respectively. For example,

$28 \times 10 = 280$ $\quad 34.56 \times 10 = 345.6$
$28 \times 100 = 2800$ $\quad 34.56 \times 100 = 3456$
$28 \times 1000 = 28\,000$ $\quad 34.56 \times 1000 = 34\,560$

Similarly, dividing a number by 10, 100 or 1000 results in the digits moving one, two or three places to the right respectively. For example,

$28 \div 10 = 2.8$ $\quad 34.56 \div 10 = 3.456$
$28 \div 100 = 0.28$ $\quad 34.56 \div 100 = 0.3456$
$28 \div 1000 = 0.028$ $\quad 34.56 \div 1000 = 0.034\,56$

EXERCISE 1.1B

1 Multiply the following numbers by 10.
a) 63 **b)** 4.6 **c)** 0.84 **d)** 0.065 **e)** 1.07

2 Multiply the following numbers by 100.
a) 45 **b)** 7.2 **c)** 0.96 **d)** 0.0485 **e)** 6.033

3 Find the value of the following.
a) 46×1000
b) 6.8×1000
c) 3.8×1000
d) 0.0084×1000
e) 0.7×1000

4 Divide the following numbers by 10.
a) 680 **b)** 72 **c)** 8.9 **d)** 0.64 **e)** 0.054

5 Divide the following numbers by 100.
a) 3500 **b)** 655 **c)** 5.62 **d)** 0.8 **e)** 0.034

6 Find the value of the following.
a) $6.4 \div 1000$
b) $46 \div 1000$
c) $950 \div 1000$
d) $0.0845 \div 1000$
e) $4 \div 1000$

Rounding

A large school has 1746 students. This figure can be **rounded** (approximated) in several ways by showing its position on a number line.

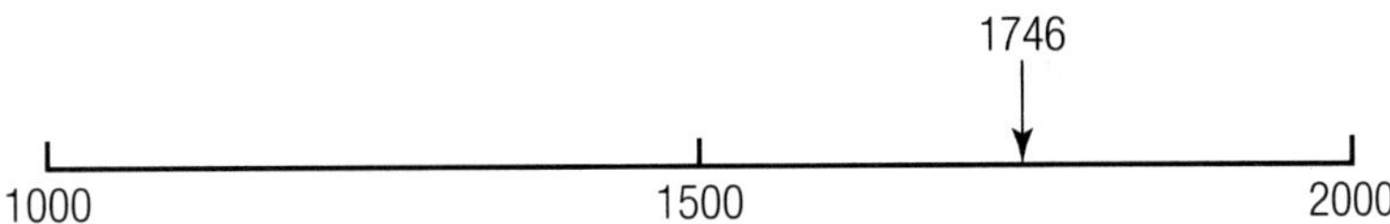

If 1746 is rounded to the nearest **thousand**, then it is written as 2000, because 1746 is closer to 2000 than it is to 1000.

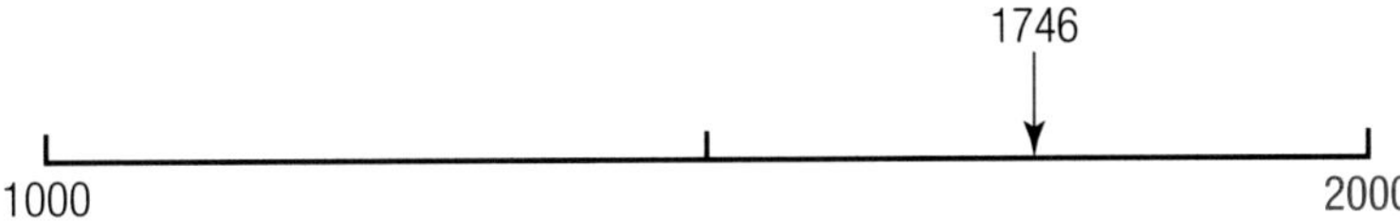

If 1746 is rounded to the nearest **hundred**, then it is written as 1700, because 1746 is closer to 1700 than it is to 1800.

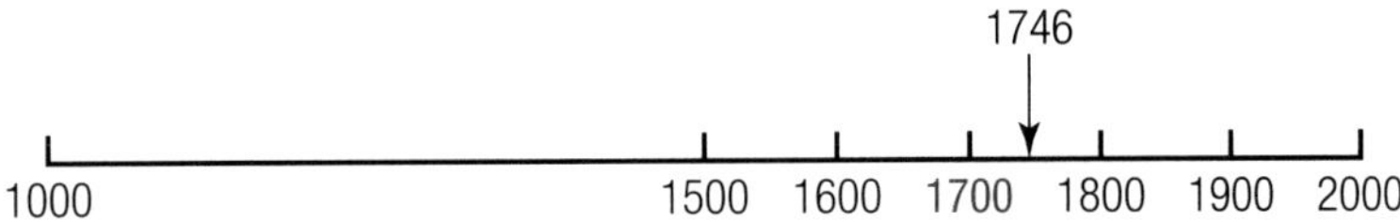

If 1746 is rounded to the nearest **ten**, then it is written as 1750, because 1746 is closer to 1750 than it is to 1740.

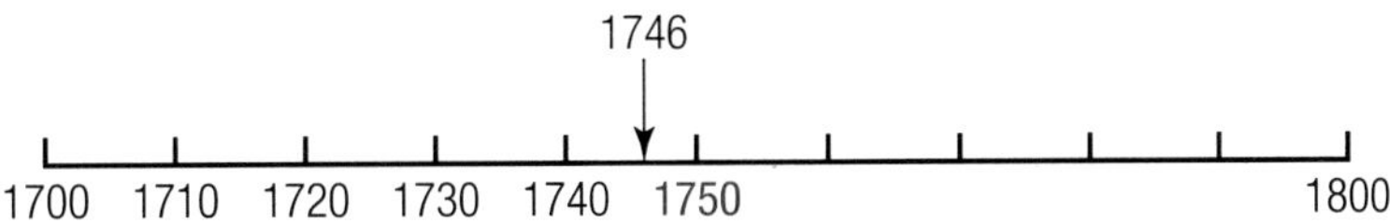

If a number is half way, then it is rounded up. For example, 1745 rounded to the nearest ten would be 1750 even though it is half way between 1740 and 1750.

EXERCISE 1.2

1 Draw number lines similar to those above and use them to round the following numbers **(i)** to the nearest thousand, **(ii)** to the nearest hundred and **(iii)** to the nearest ten.

a) 38 273 **b)** 21 793 **c)** 15 476 **d)** 58 437

→

2 107 638 people attended a football match in Madrid.
a) This was reported in the programme as 100 000 attendance.
b) The club estimate was 110 000 in the crowd.
c) A closer estimate in a newspaper was 108 000.

All of these estimates were acceptable. However, they are to different degrees of accuracy.
Write down the degree of accuracy for each one.

3 Round the following numbers to the nearest thousand.
a) 58 437 **b)** 9288 **c)** 68 400 **d)** 72 985

4 Round the following numbers to the nearest hundred.
a) 483 **b)** 1692 **c)** 93 **d)** 12 763

5 Round the following numbers to the nearest ten.
a) 63 **b)** 846 **c)** 5839 **d)** 8

Decimal places

Another way of *rounding* a number is to write it to a given number of **decimal places.** This refers to the number of digits written after the decimal point.

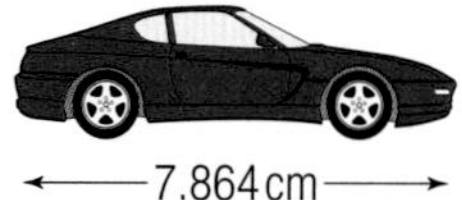

Worked example

The length of this model car is 7.864 cm.
Write 7.864

a) to the nearest whole number
b) to one decimal place.

A number written to one decimal place has one digit after the decimal point.

Draw a number line to help you.

a)

7.864
7
8

7.864 is closer to 8 than it is to 7, so 7.864 written to the nearest whole number is 8.

b)

7.864
7.8
7.9

7.864 is closer to 7.9 than it is to 7.8, so 7.864 written to one decimal place is 7.9.

To round to a whole number or to a certain number of decimal places, look at the next digit after the one in question. If that digit is 5 or more, round up. If it is 4 or less, round down.

EXERCISE 1.3

1 Round the following numbers **(i)** to the nearest whole number and **(ii)** to one decimal place.

a) 6.37 **b)** 4.13 **c)** 0.85
d) 8.672 **e)** 1.093 **f)** 0.063

2 Round the following numbers **(i)** to the nearest whole number and **(ii)** to one decimal place.

a) 4.383 **b)** 5.719 **c)** 5.803
d) 1.477 **e)** 3.999 **f)** 6.273

3 Round the following numbers **(i)** to the nearest whole number and **(ii)** to one decimal place.

a) 0.5682 **b)** 3.4765 **c)** 8.8467 **d)** 3.6543 **e)** 3.4567

Estimating answers to calculations

Even though calculators are a quick and easy way of solving arithmetical problems, an **estimate** can be a useful check.

Worked examples

a) Estimate the answer to

18×71.

To the nearest ten, 18 is 20 and 71 is 70.
So an easy estimate is

$20 \times 70 = 1400$.

b) Estimate the answer to

$3568 \div 28$.

To the nearest hundred, 3568 is 3600.
To the nearest ten, 28 is 30.

So a good estimate would be

$3600 \div 30 = 120$.

If 3568 was rounded to 4000 then 4000 ÷ 30 = 133 is still a reasonable estimate.

EXERCISE 1.4

1 Estimate the answers to the following calculations.

a) 42×19 **b)** 63×27
c) 198×39 **d)** 8.9×384
e) 55×77

2 Estimate the answers to the following calculations.

a) $3984 \div 41$ **b)** $5872 \div 32$
c) $8.972 \div 2.8$ **d)** $0.414 \div 2.1$
e) $0.414 \div 0.21$

3 Using estimation, write down which of these calculations are definitely wrong.

a) $6357 \div 21 = 30.27$ **b)** $834 \times 7.9 = 6588$
c) $189 \div 8.9 = 212$ **d)** $78.3 \times 11.2 = 8769$

Order of operations

The order in which mathematical calculations are done depends on the operations being used.

Look at this calculation:

$6 + 3 \times 2 - 1$.

Carrying out the calculation from left to right would give an answer of 17. However, if you do the calculation on a calculator, the answer it gives is 11.

This is because mathematical operations are carried out in a particular order:

- **B**rackets — Any operation in brackets is done first.
- **I**ndices — A number raised to a power (index) is done next.
- **D**ivision and/or **M**ultiplication — Multiplications and divisions are done next. Their order does not matter.
- **A**ddition and/or **S**ubtraction — Additions and subtractions are carried out last. Again, their order is not important.

A way of remembering this order is with the shorthand **BIDMAS**.

The correct answer to the calculation $6 + 3 \times 2 - 1$ is 11, because the 3×2 must be done first, followed by addition of the 6 and subtraction of the 1.

The 1 can be subtracted before the 6 is added; the answer is still 11.

Worked examples

a) Calculate

$7 + 4 \times 9 - 8$.

$7 + 4 \times 9 - 8$
$= 7 + 36 - 8$
$= 35$

The multiplication is done first.

b) Calculate

$25 - (2 + 3) \times 4$.

$25 - (2 + 3) \times 4$ — *The brackets are done first, (2 + 3) = 5.*

$= 25 - 5 \times 4$ — *This is multiplied by 4 next, giving 20.*

$= 25 - 20$ — *Lastly this is subtracted from 25.*

$= 5$

c) Calculate

$101 - (11 - 7) - 3 \times 8$.

$101 - (11 - 7) - 3 \times 8$
$= 101 - 4 - 3 \times 8$
$= 101 - 4 - 24$
$= 101 - 28$
$= 73$

EXERCISE 1.5

Work out the following.

1 $4 + 3 \times 2 - 1$

2 $6 \times 2 + 4 \times 3$

3 $3 \times 5 - 2 - 7$

4 $8 + 4 \times 8 - 40$

5 $6 - 2 \times 3 \times 4$

6 $7 \times (4 + 2) - 3$

7 $8 + (6 + 3) \div 3$

8 $16 \div (2 + 6) + 8$

9 $4 + 4 \times 4 - 4$

10 $(4 + 4) \div (8 - 4)$

2 Expressions

- Use letters to represent unknown numbers or variables; know the meanings of the words *term*, *expression* and *equation*.
- Know that algebraic operations follow the same order as arithmetic operations.
- Construct simple algebraic expressions by using letters to represent numbers.
- Simplify linear expressions, e.g. collect like terms; multiply a constant over a bracket.

'The yield of two sheaves of superior grain, three sheaves of medium grain and four sheaves of inferior grain is each less than one tou. But if one sheaf of medium grain is added to the superior grain, or if one sheaf of inferior grain is added to the medium, or if one sheaf of superior grain is added to the inferior, then in each case the yield is exactly one tou.

What is the yield of one sheaf of each grade of grain?'

The problem above comes from the most important book of ancient Chinese mathematics. The book was called *Nine Chapters on the Mathematician's Art*. It was written approximately 2000 years ago. As its name suggests, it consists of nine chapters. Each chapter presents a series of mathematical problems related to life in China at the time.

Expressions

An **expression** is used to represent a value in algebraic form. For example,

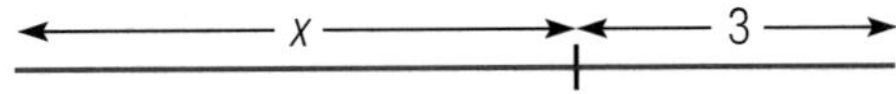

The length of the line is given by the expression $x + 3$.

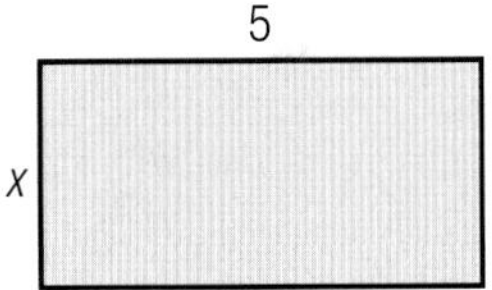

The perimeter of the rectangle is given by the expression $x + 5 + x + 5$. This can be simplified to $2x + 10$.

The area of the rectangle is given by the expression $5x$.

In the examples above, x, $2x$ and $5x$ are called **terms** in the expressions.

In the expression $2a + 3b + 4c - 5$, each of $2a$, $3b$, $4c$ and -5 is a term in the expression.

An expression is different from an **equation**. An equation contains an equals sign (=), which shows that the expressions either side of it are equal to each other. For example, the equation

$$x + 1 = y - 2$$

tells us that the expressions $x + 1$ and $y - 2$ are equal to each other.

Order of operations when simplifying expressions

In Chapter 1 you saw that calculations need to be carried out in a particular order. This order is not necessarily from left to right.

For example, the calculation $2 + 3 \times 4$ has the answer 14 (rather than 20) because the multiplication is done before the addition.

The order in which operations are carried out is as follows:

Brackets
Indices
Division/**M**ultiplication
Addition/**S**ubtraction

A useful way of remembering the order is with the shorthand **BIDMAS**.
The same order of operations applies when working with algebraic expressions.

Worked examples

a) Simplify the expression
$2a + 3 \times 4a - a$

$2a + 3 \times 4a - a$

The multiplication is done first.

$= 2a + 12a - a$

Additions and subtractions can be done in any order.

$= 13a$

b) Simplify the expression
$2b + 3(5b + 2c) - 5c$

$2b + 3(5b + 2c) - 5c$

The brackets are done first.

$= 2b + 15b + 6c - 5c$
$= 17b + c$

EXERCISE 2.1A

Simplify the following expressions using the correct order of operations.

1 $2a + 3a - 4a$

2 $2b - 5b + 7b - b$

3 $3c + 2b + 2c - 4b$

4 $5d - 4f + 3e - 2d + f - 2e$

5 $4g + 2(3g - 4h) + 2h$

6 $3(2j - k) - 4(j - 2k)$

7 $4m + 5(2n + 3p) - 4(n - m - p)$

8 $8q + 6(4q - 3r + 5t) + 2(r - 7t)$

9 $5u - 8v + 9(2u - 3v) - 4(2v - 5u)$

10 $7(4w + x + 2y) - 5(w - x + 3y)$

EXERCISE 2.1B

a) Write an expression for the distance around the edge of each of these shapes.

This is called the perimeter of the shape.

b) Simplify your expression where possible.

1

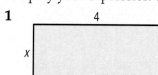

4

x

2

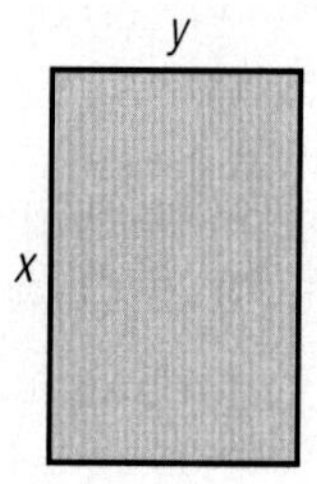

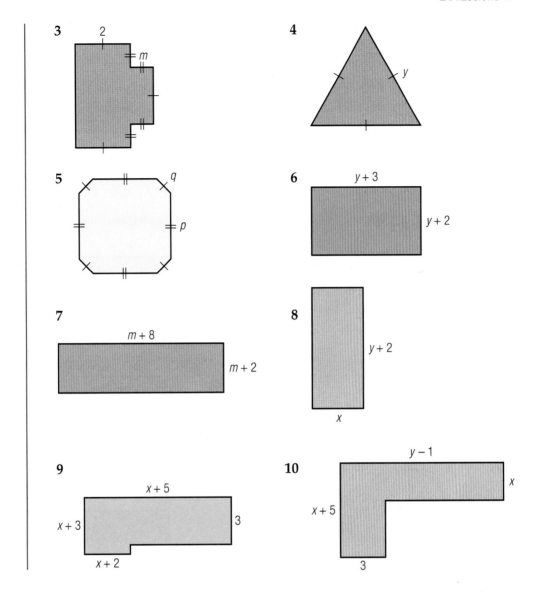

3 2, m

4 y

5 q, p

6 $y + 3$, $y + 2$

7 $m + 8$, $m + 2$

8 $y + 2$, x

9 $x + 5$, $x + 3$, 3, $x + 2$

10 $y - 1$, x, $x + 5$, 3

Expanding two linear expressions

An expression for the area of this shape is more complicated.
(Note: Areas of rectangles and composite shapes made of rectangles are covered in Chapter 18.)

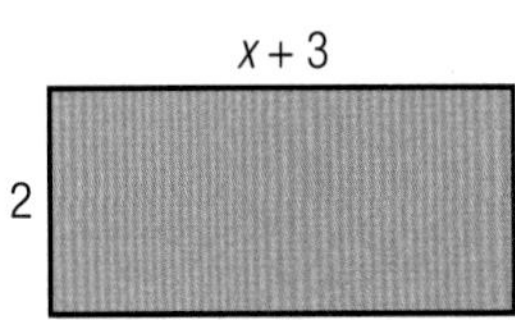

The rectangle can be split in two as shown.

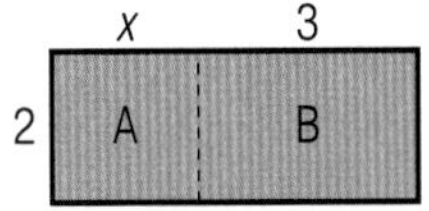

The area of A can be expressed as $2x$.
The area of B can be expressed as 6.
The total area of the rectangle is $2x + 6$.

The area of the rectangle can also be expressed using brackets as $2(x + 3)$.
Therefore

$$2(x + 3) = 2x + 6.$$

Remember that, to expand brackets, you multiply the terms inside the brackets by the term outside. So with $2(x + 3)$, the 2 multiplies both the x and the 3:

$$\mathbf{2(x + 3) = 2 \times x + 2 \times 3}$$
$$\mathbf{= 2x + 6}$$

EXERCISE 2.2

Write an expression for the area of each of these shapes.

1

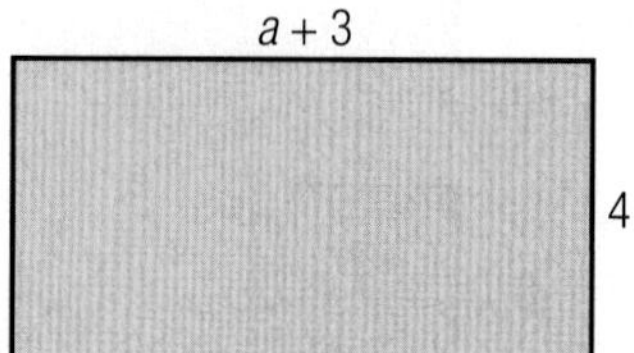

2

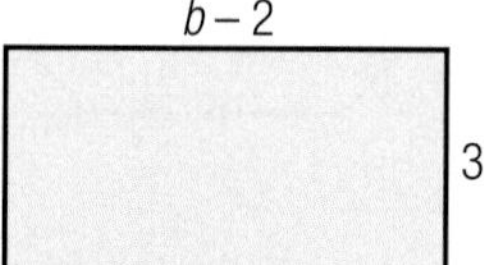

3

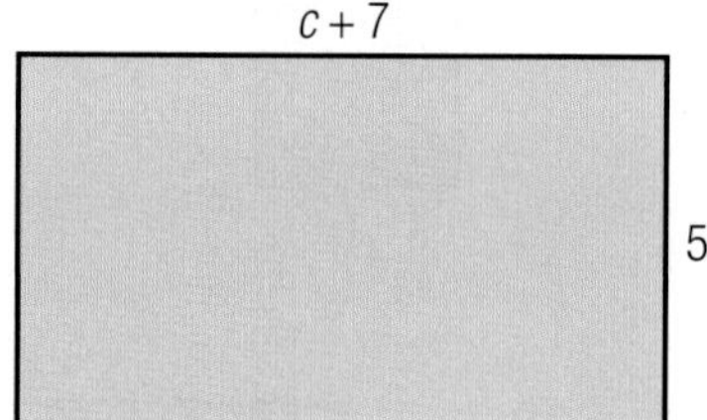

4

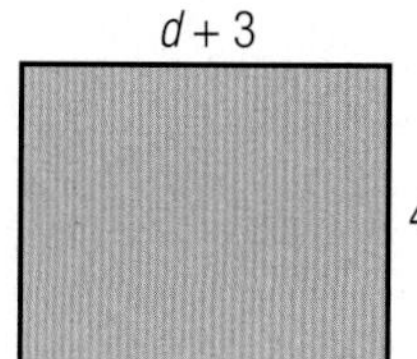

5

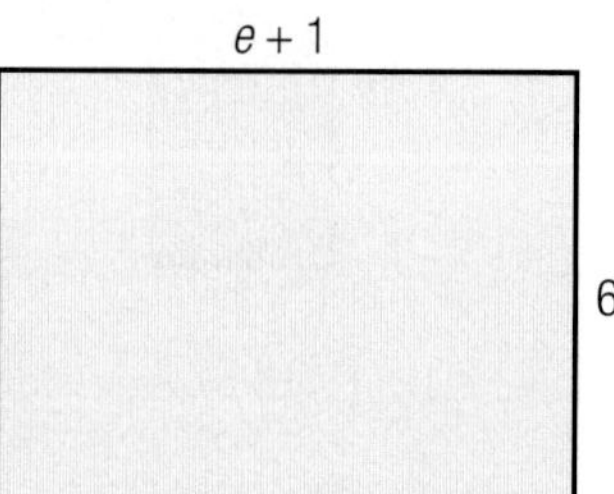

6

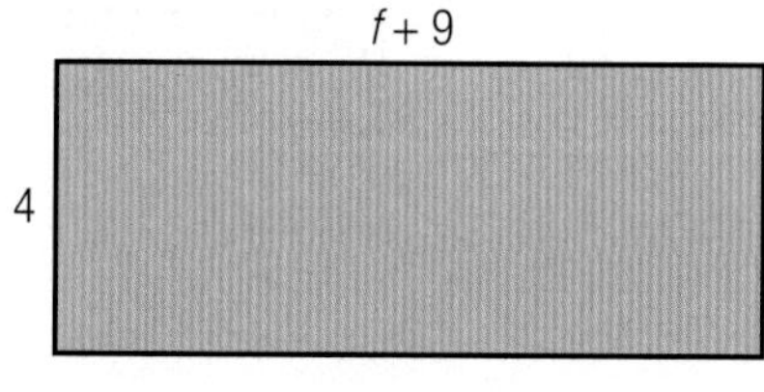

7

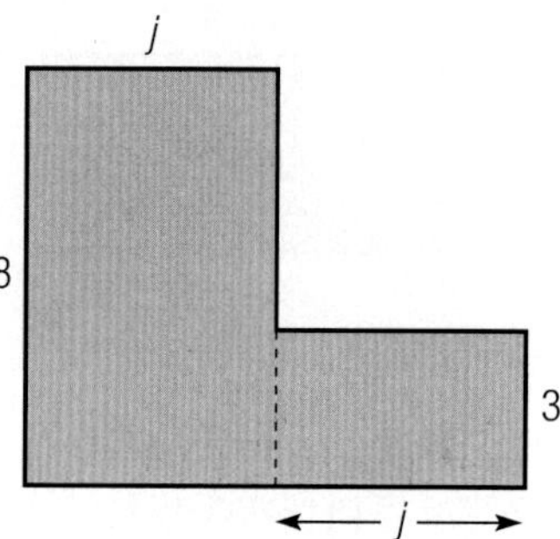

8

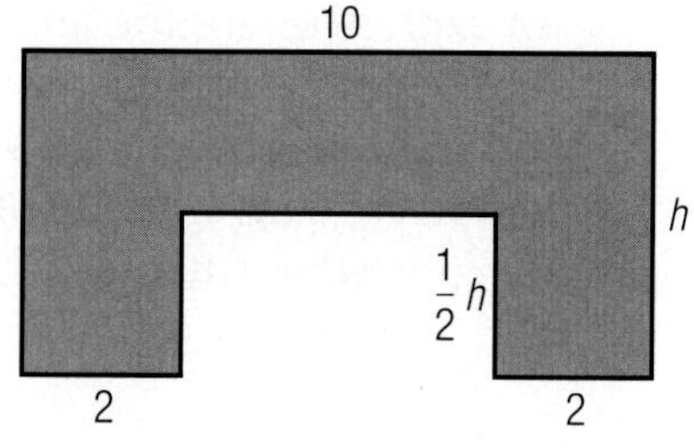

3 Shapes and geometric reasoning

- Identify, describe, visualise and draw 2-D shapes in different orientations.
- Use the notation and labelling conventions for points, lines, angles and shapes.
- Name and identify side, angle and symmetry properties of special quadrilaterals and triangles, and regular polygons with 5, 6 and 8 sides.
- Recognise and describe common solids and some of their properties, e.g. the number of faces, edges and vertices.
- Recognise line and rotation symmetry in 2-D shapes and patterns; draw lines of symmetry and complete patterns with two lines of symmetry; identify the order of rotation symmetry.
- Transform 2-D points and shapes by:
  - reflection in a given line
  - rotation about a given point
  - translation.

  Know that shapes remain congruent after these transformations.

Transformations

If an **object** is **transformed** it can change either its position or its shape. The new shape after the transformation is known as the **image**.

The simplest forms of transformations include **reflection**, **rotation** and **translation**. With these transformations, only the position of the object changes, as its shape and size remain the same. So the object and the image are **congruent** (the same shape and size).

Reflection

If an object is reflected it is *flipped* about a line. This line is known as the **mirror line**. On a diagram it is usually drawn as a dotted line, as shown.

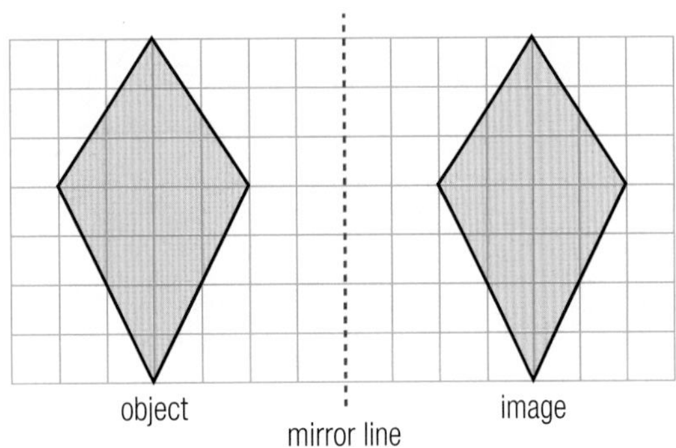

EXERCISE 3.1A

In the following questions, the object and mirror line(s) are given. Copy each diagram on to squared paper and draw in the position of the image(s).

1

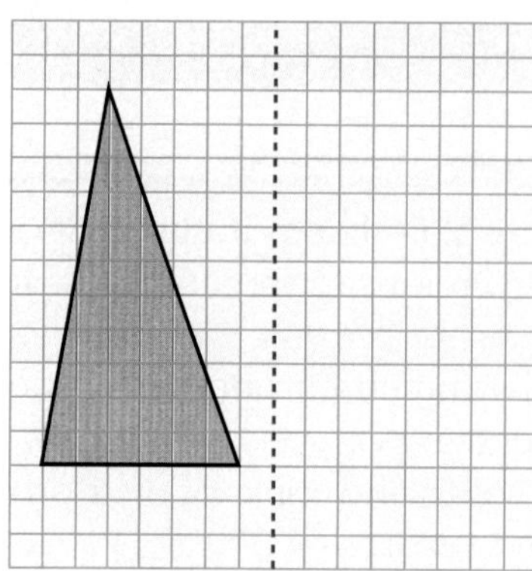

2

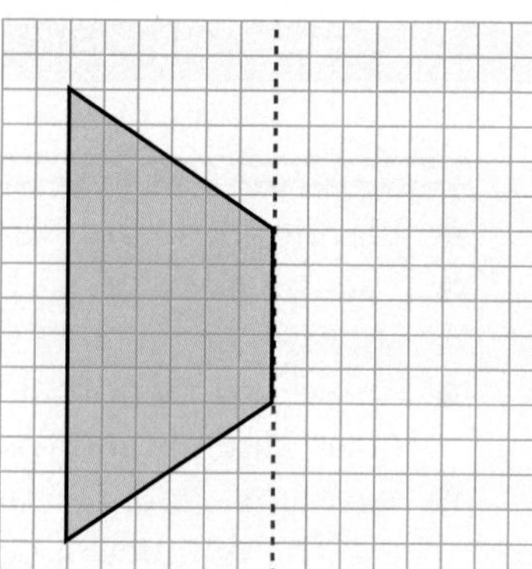

3

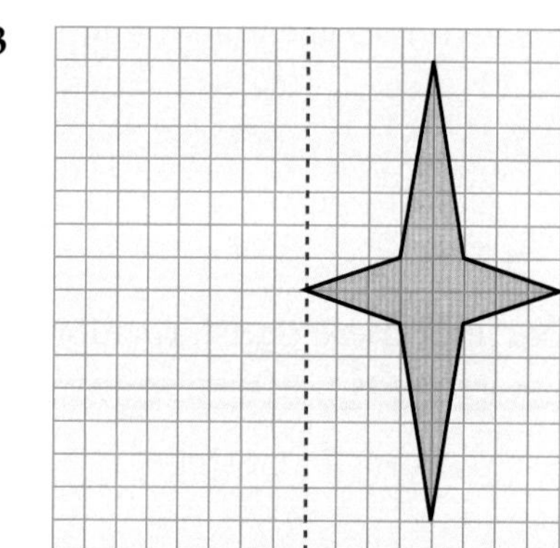

4

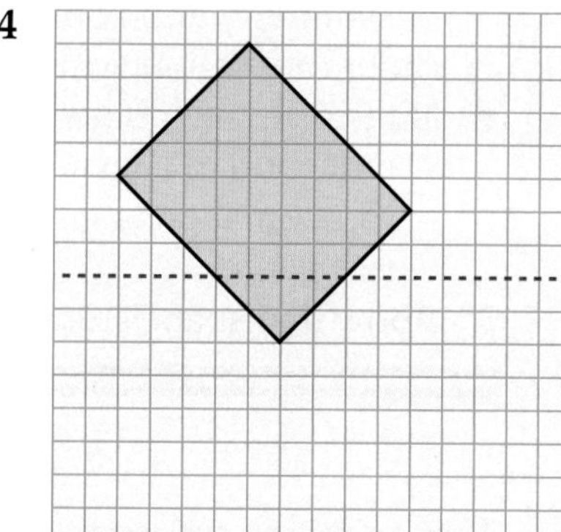

5

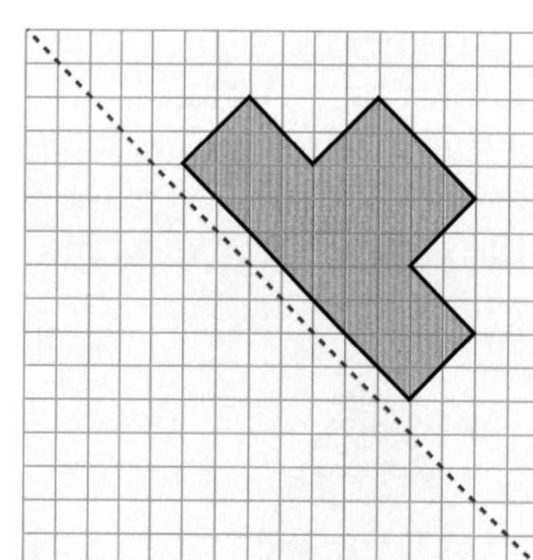

6

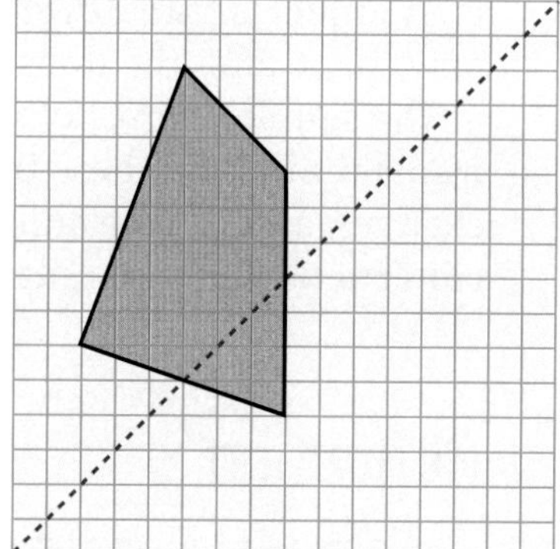

7

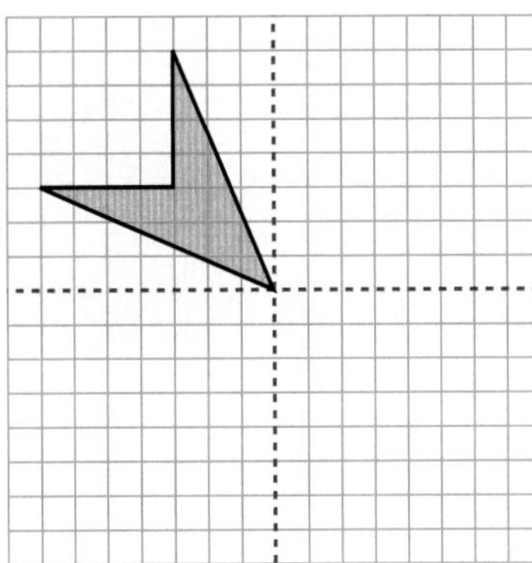

8

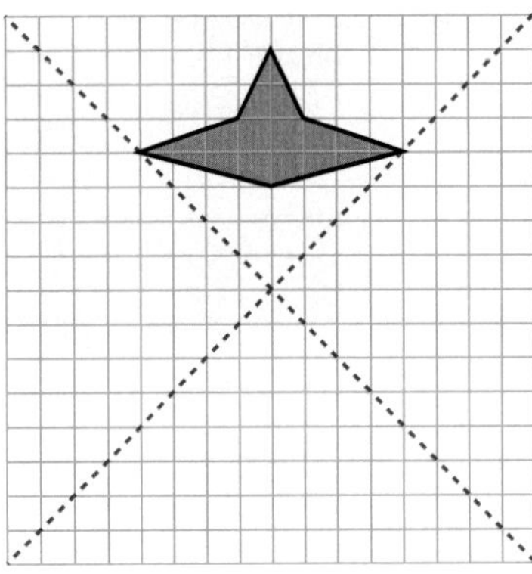

EXERCISE 3.1B

In the following questions, the objects and images are given. Copy each diagram on to squared paper and draw in the position of the mirror line(s).

1

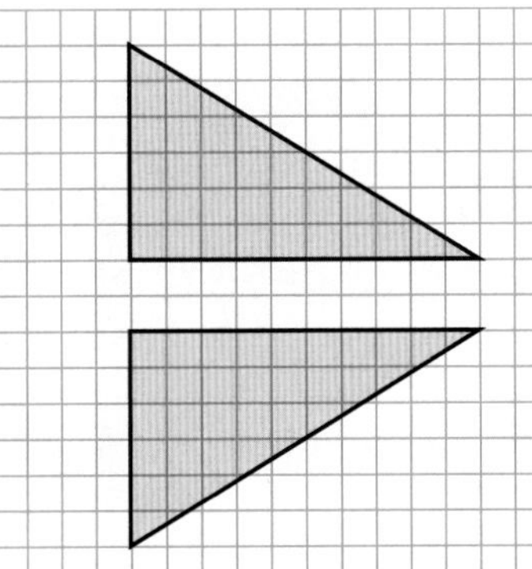

2

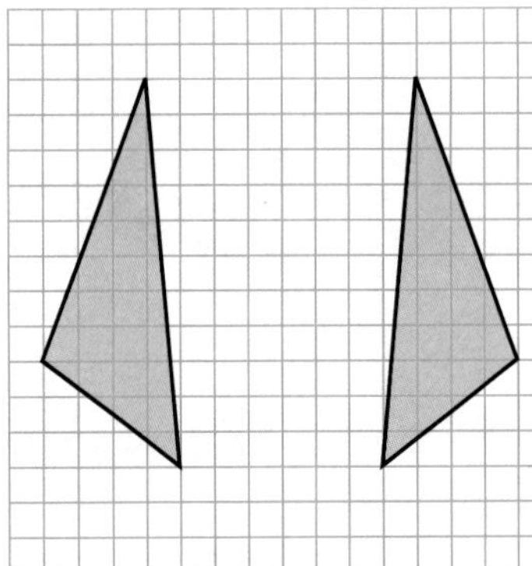

3

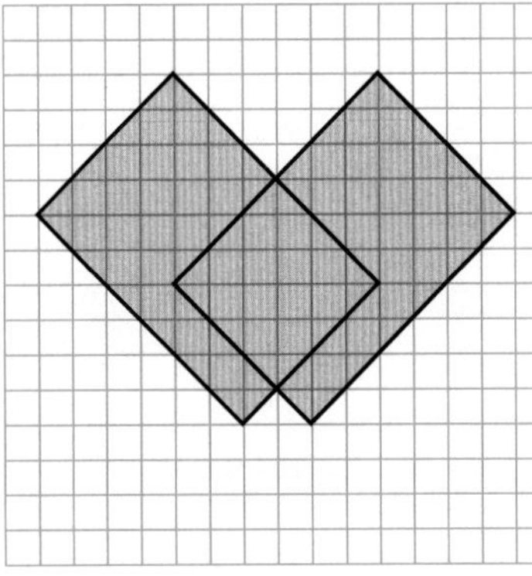

4

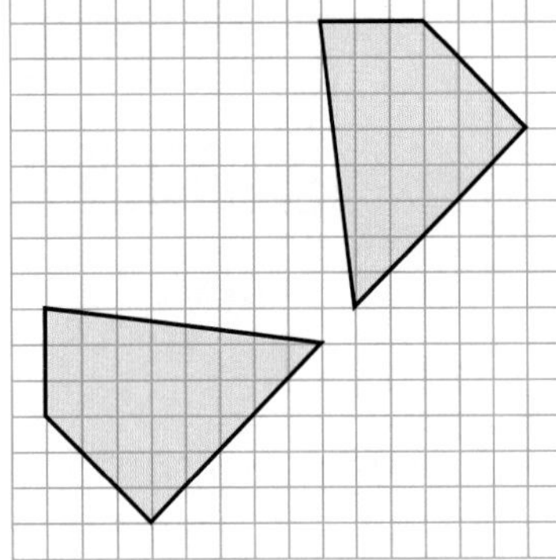

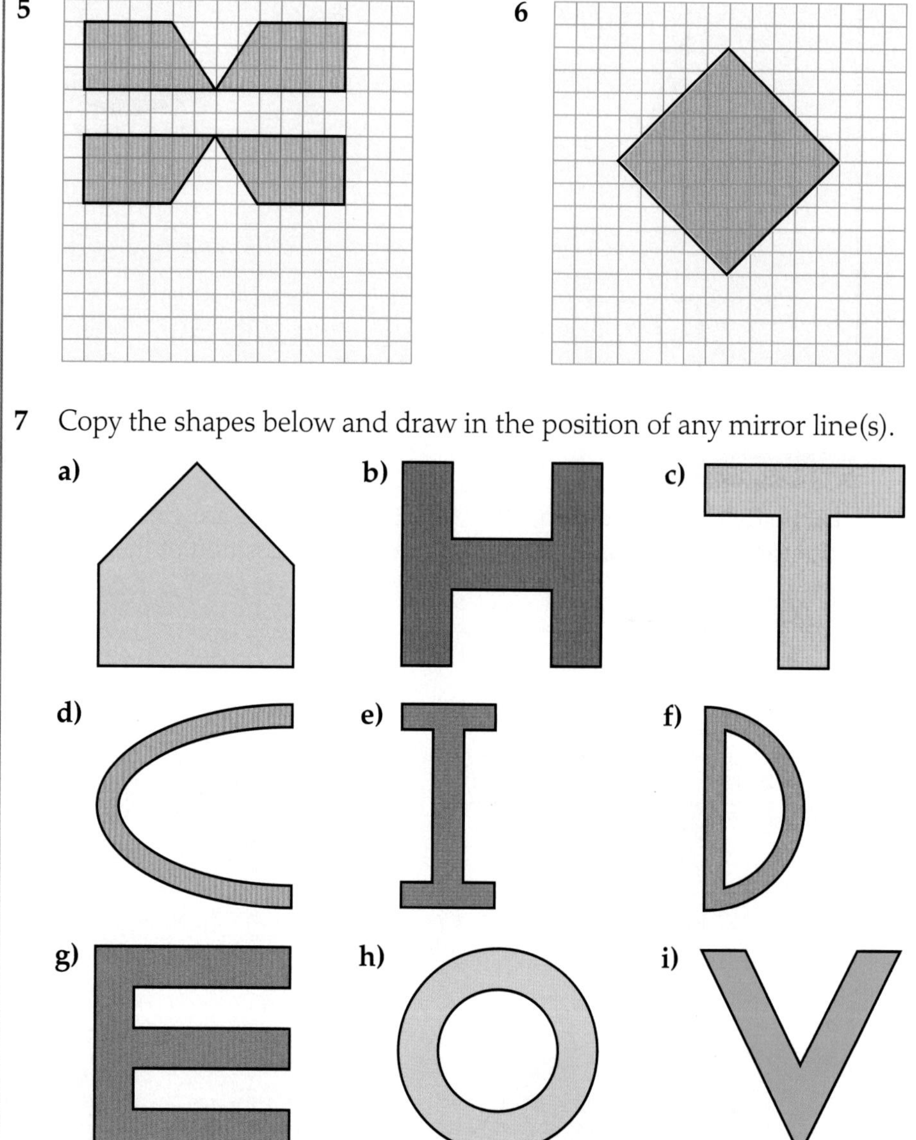

Rotation

If an object is rotated, it undergoes a *turning* movement about a specific point known as the **centre of rotation**.

If an object has **rotational symmetry**, then the image will look identical to the object more than once during a full rotation of 360°. The number of times an object looks the same in a complete rotation is known as the **order of rotational symmetry**.

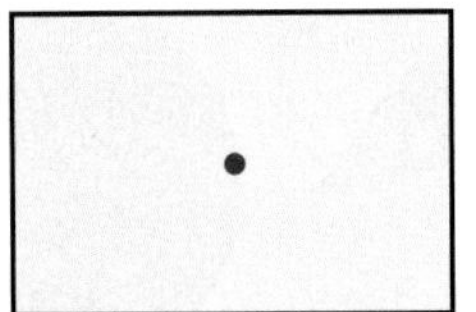

This shape has rotational symmetry of order 2.

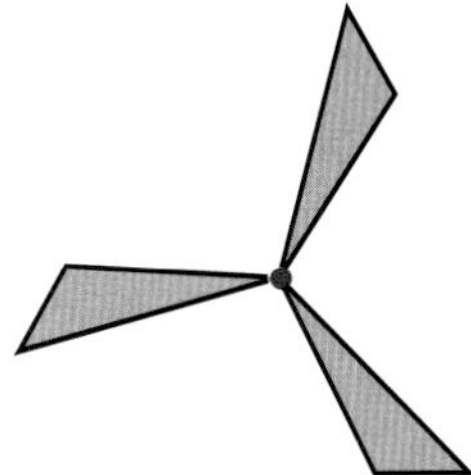

This shape has rotational symmetry of order 3.

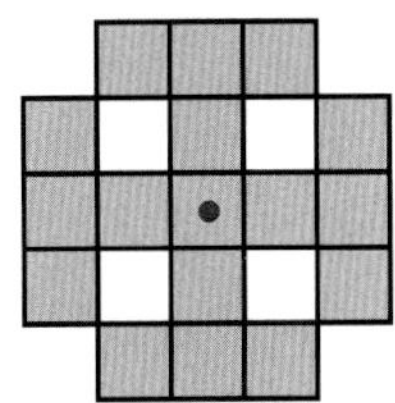

This shape has rotational symmetry of order 4.

All shapes and patterns have rotational symmetry of at least order 1, because *any* shape or pattern will look the same after a full rotation of 360°. So a shape or pattern which only has rotational symmetry of order 1 is considered not to have rotational symmetry.

This shape has no rotational symmetry, as it only has rotational symmetry of order 1.

EXERCISE 3.2A

Write down the order of rotational symmetry for each of the following shapes.

1

2

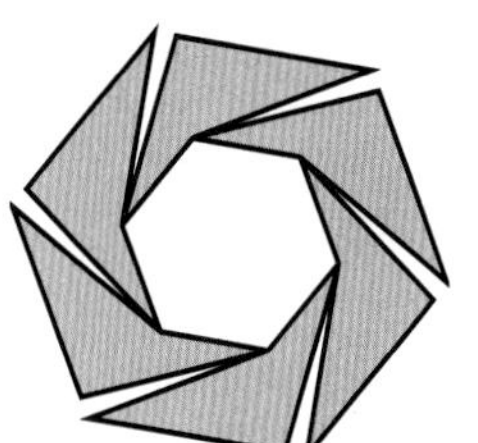

3

4 5 6

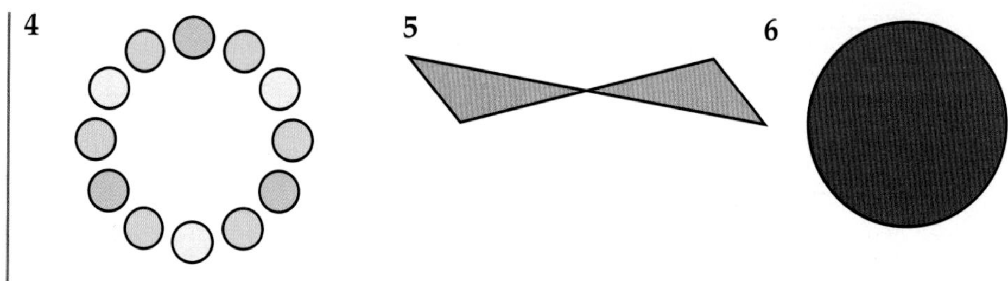

7 Copy the shapes below. Indicate the centre of rotation and write down the order of rotational symmetry.

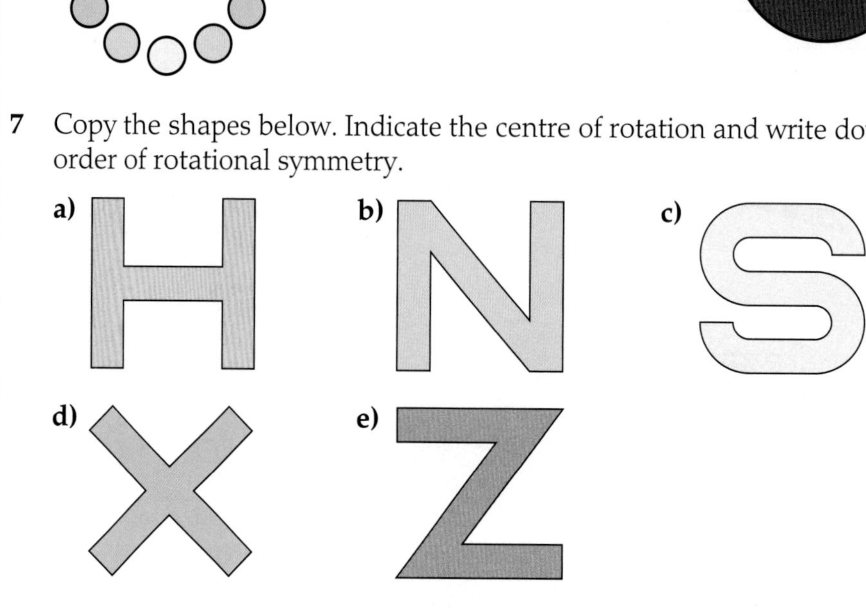

For a pattern to have rotational symmetry, the angle between each pair of the images must be constant (the same). For example,

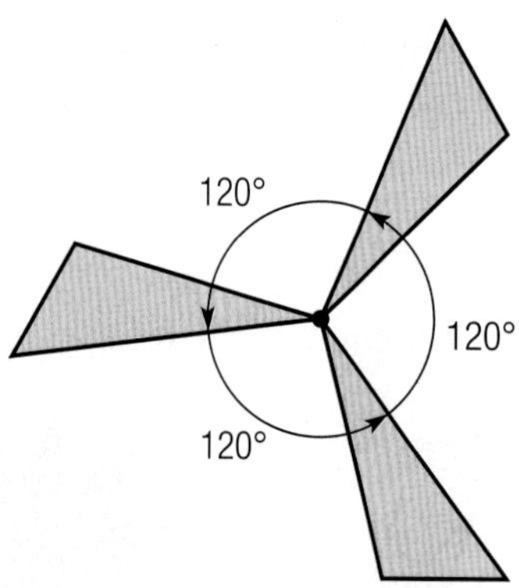

As the diagram has rotational symmetry of order 3, the full turn of 360° is divided by 3. $360° \div 3 = 120°$, so the angle between the images is 120°.

EXERCISE 3.2B

1 Copy and complete this table.

Order of rotational symmetry	Angle between images
2	
3	
4	
5	
6	
8	
9	
10	
12	
20	

2 Design a rotation pattern of your own with each of the following orders of rotational symmetry.
a) 5 **b)** 8 **c)** 10 **d)** 12

3 Collect pictures from various sources, such as magazines, the internet, etc., which have rotational symmetry.

Rotation about a point

So far we have looked at shapes with rotational symmetry. However it is also possible to rotate shapes about a point known as the **centre of rotation**.

In the diagrams below, an object A is rotated by different angles about the centre of rotation O, to produce the image B.

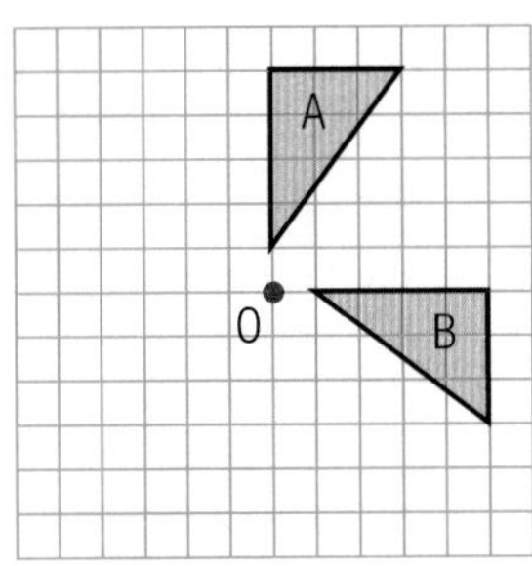

Rotation 90° clockwise

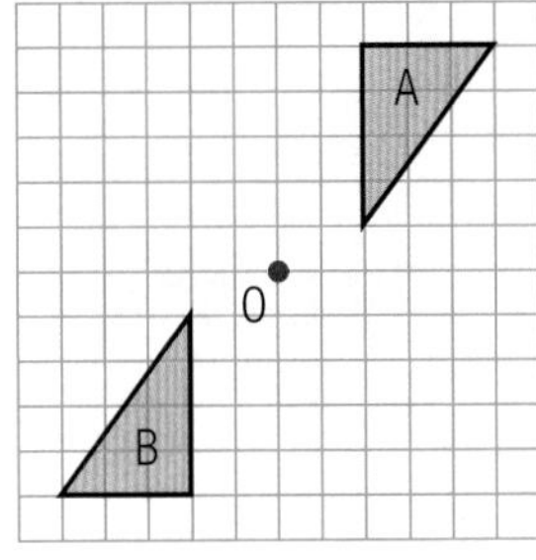

Rotation 180°

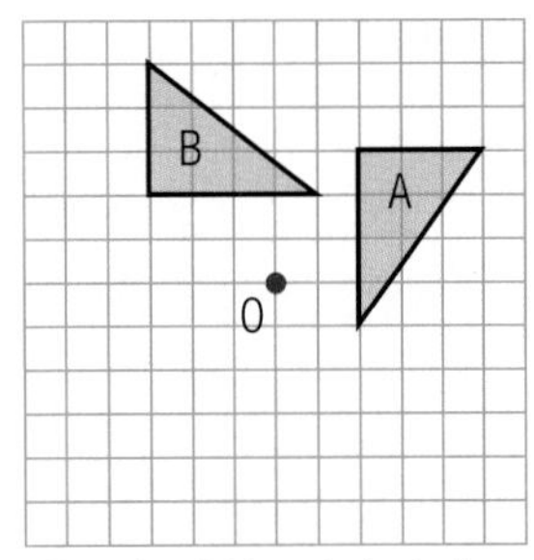

Rotation 90° anti-clockwise

As a way of checking, the angle between each point on the object and its corresponding point on the image must be the same about the centre of rotation.

The diagram below shows this for the 90° anti-clockwise rotation.

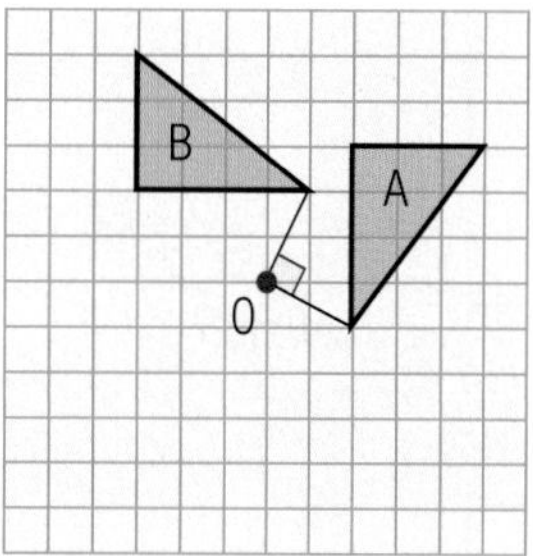

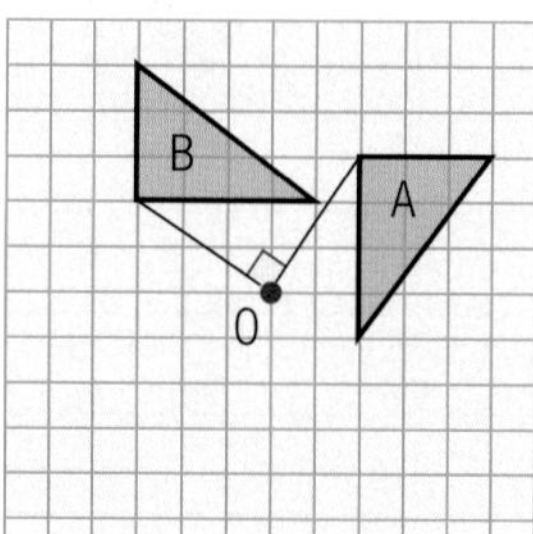

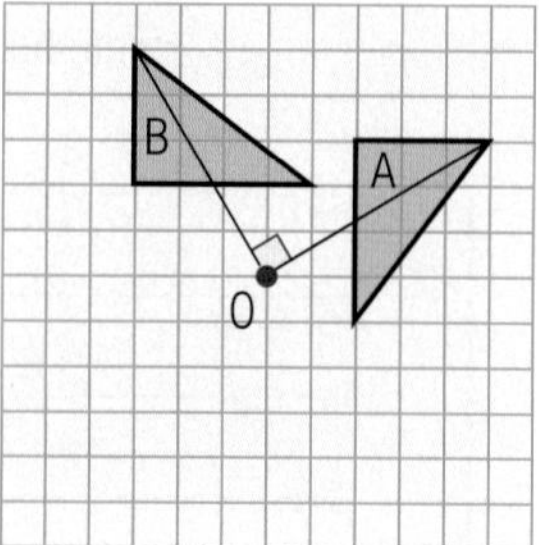

EXERCISE 3.2C

In each of the following questions, copy the grid and the object.

a) Rotate the object by the angle and direction stated about the centre of rotation O.

b) Label your image in each case P.

Note: A piece of tracing paper may help.

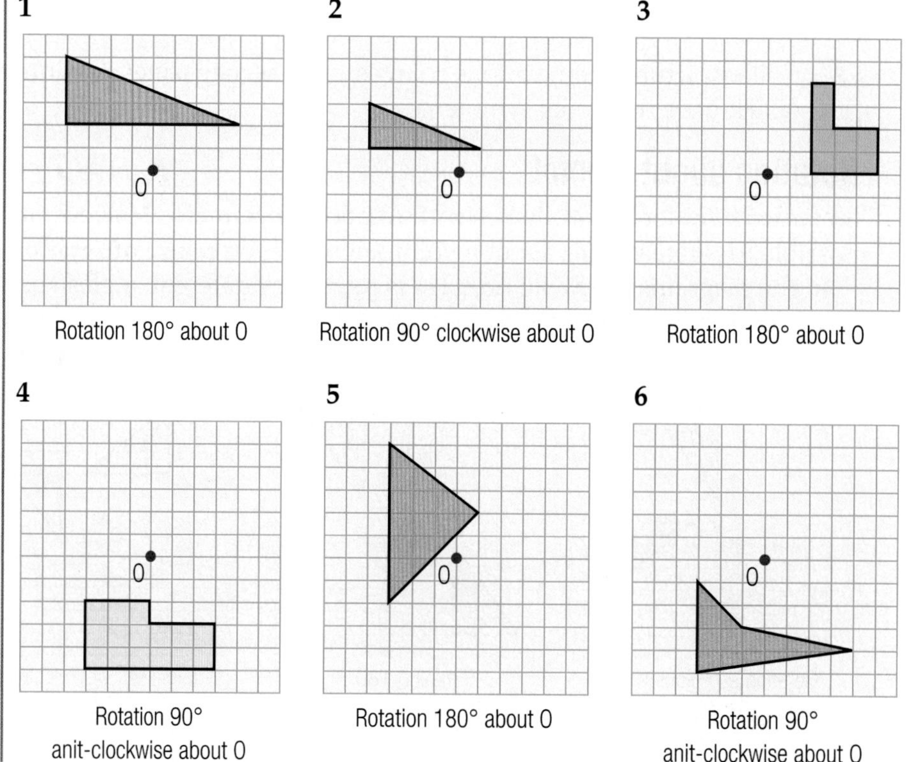

1 Rotation 180° about 0

2 Rotation 90° clockwise about 0

3 Rotation 180° about 0

4 Rotation 90° anit-clockwise about 0

5 Rotation 180° about 0

6 Rotation 90° anit-clockwise about 0

Translation

Translation symmetry occurs when an object *slides* to a new position. The sliding movement involves no rotation or reflection.

Translation symmetry is commonly found on patterned material or paper as these usually involve using patterns which repeat. For example,

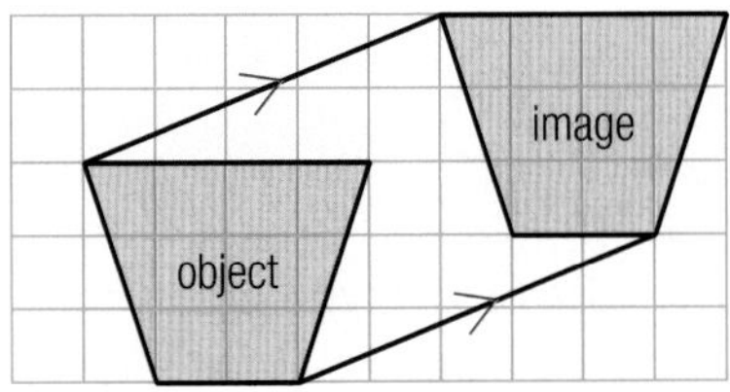

The object is translated to a new position.

To describe a translation, it is necessary to describe how far the object moves horizontally and also how far it moves vertically. In the example above, the translation is described as 5 units to the right and 2 units upwards.

EXERCISE 3.3

1 Copy the diagram (right) on to squared paper and translate the object according to each set of instructions given.

a) 4 units to the right and 2 units upwards
b) 3 units to the left
c) 2 units to the right and 3 units downwards
d) 5 units to the left and 4 units downwards

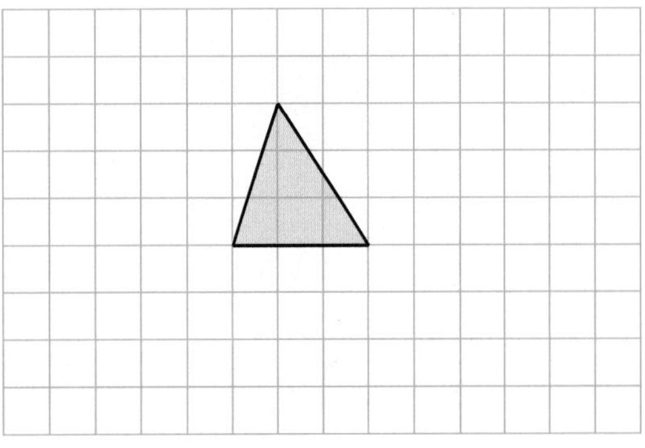

2 For the grid below, describe the translation which takes the given object to each of the images **a)**, **b)**, **c)**, **d)**, and **e)**.

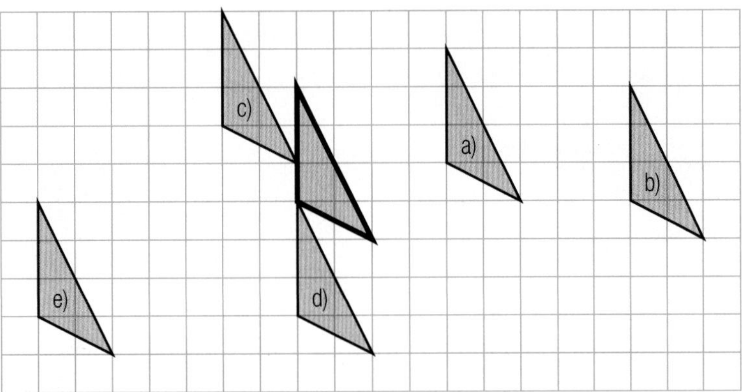

3 The diagram below shows a translation, but the arrows showing the direction of the movement are drawn incorrectly.

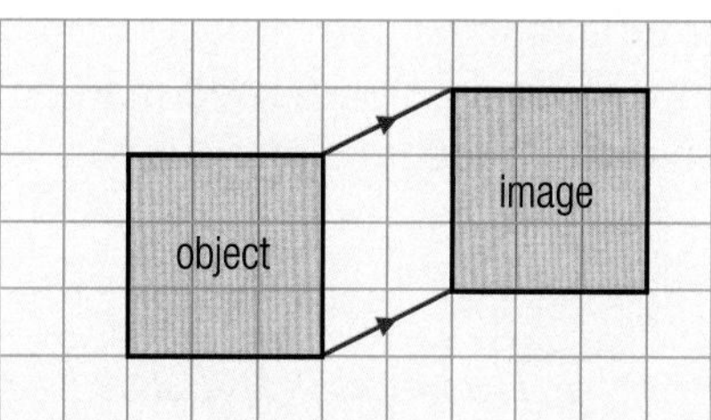

a) In your own words, write down why the arrows are incorrect.
b) Copy the diagram. On your copy, draw an arrow which shows the translation correctly.

Labelling of shapes, points, lines and angles

This shape is a triangle. Its sides are all of different lengths and its angles are all of different sizes.

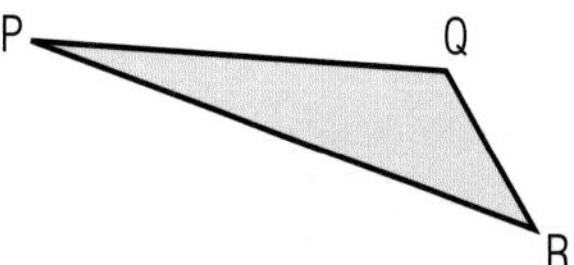

There is a special notation that is used for describing a shape and its different parts. It is useful to become confident with the notation.

The triangle above can be described as triangle *PQR* or $\triangle PQR$.

The angle at point *R* can be described as $\angle PRQ$ or $\angle QRP$.

The angle at point *Q* can be described as $\angle PQR$ or $\angle RQP$.

The sides of the triangle are described by the two points at the ends of the side, for example as *PQ*, *QR* and *PR*.

Each of the corners *P*, *Q* and *R* is known as a **vertex**. A triangle therefore has three **vertices** and a square has four vertices.

There are other ways of labelling shapes, though. The triangle *ABC* is labelled slightly differently from the one above.

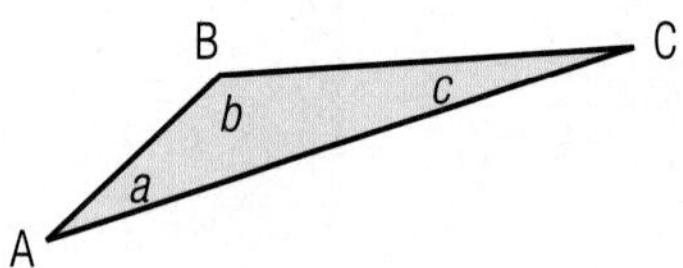

The vertices have been labelled with capital letters whilst the angles are labelled with lower-case (small) letters. Therefore $\angle BAC = \angle a$.

Two-dimensional shapes

Triangles

Triangles can be described in terms of their sides or their angles, or both.

An **acute-angled** triangle has all its angles less than 90°.

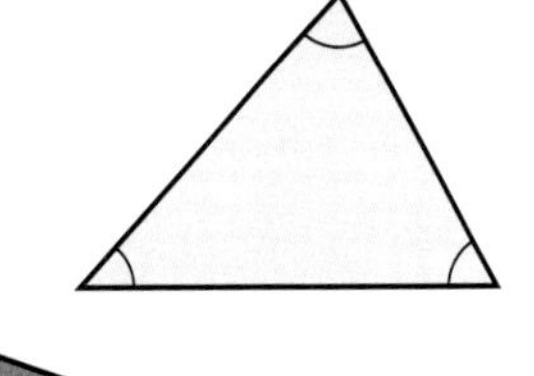

A **right-angled** triangle has one angle of 90°.

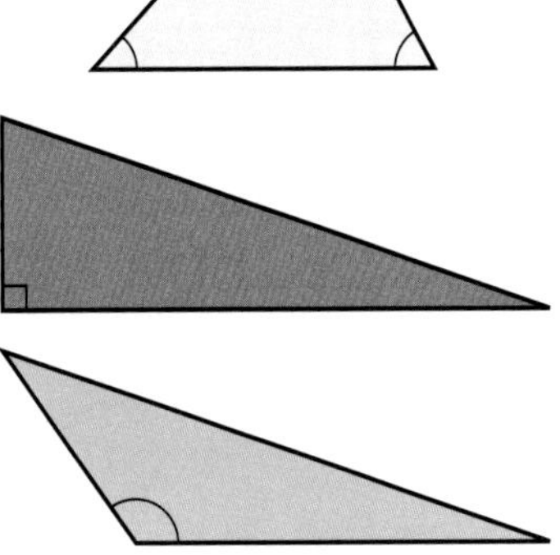

An **obtuse-angled** triangle has one angle greater than 90°.

An **isosceles** triangle has two sides of equal length, and the angles opposite the equal sides are equal.

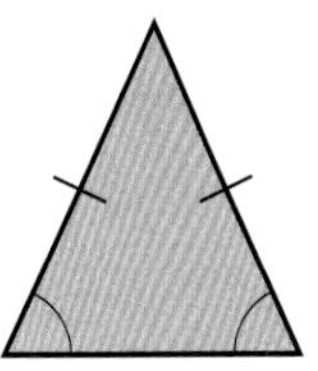

An **equilateral** triangle has three sides of equal length and three equal angles.

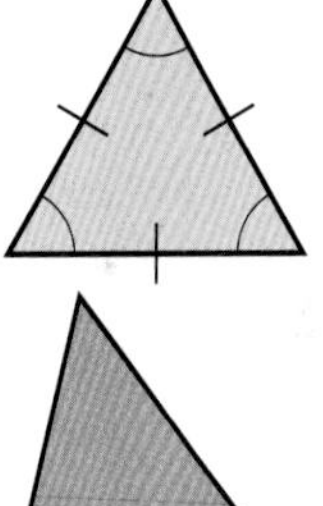

A **scalene** triangle has three sides of different lengths, and all three angles are different.

EXERCISE 3.4A

1 Describe each of the triangles below in two ways.

For example, this triangle shows an ***acute-angled isosceles*** *triangle.*

a)

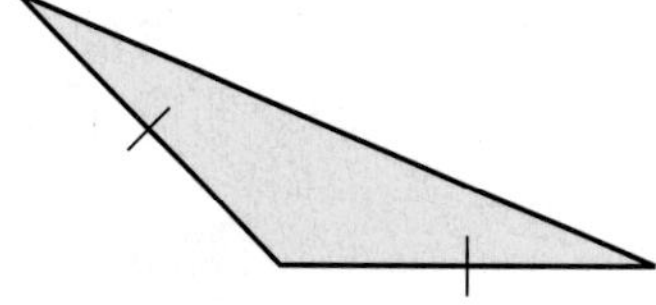

b)

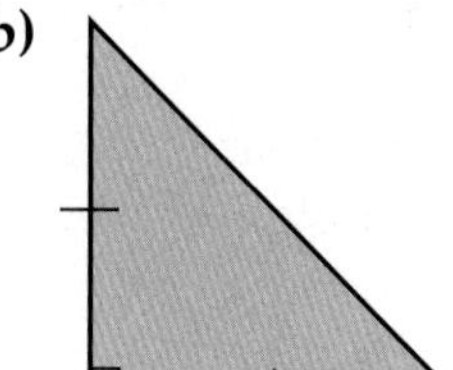

c)

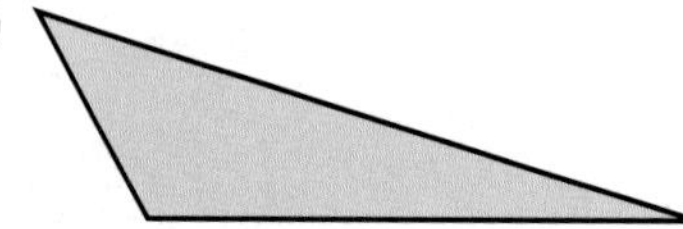

d)

e)

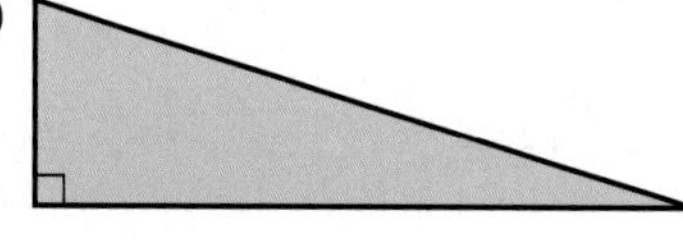

f)

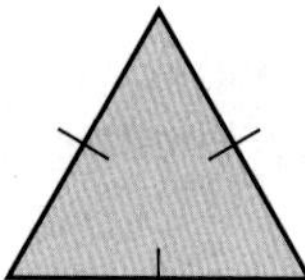

2 Look at these triangles and answer the following questions.

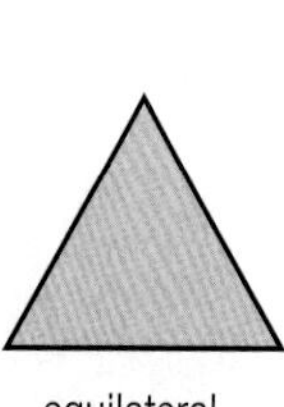

equilateral

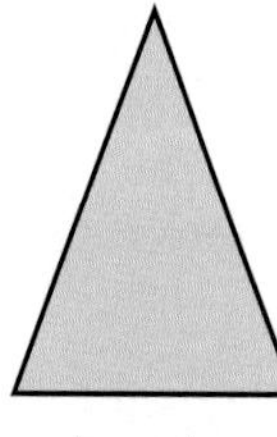

isosceles

scalene

a) How many lines of symmetry has an equilateral triangle?
b) What is the order of rotational symmetry of an equilateral triangle?
c) How many lines of symmetry has an isosceles triangle?
d) What is the order of rotational symmetry of an isosceles triangle?
e) How many lines of symmetry has a scalene triangle?
f) What is the order of rotational symmetry of a scalene triangle?

Quadrilaterals

A **quadrilateral** is any four-sided, closed shape consisting only of straight lines. There are many different types of quadrilaterals, each with their own special properties.

- A **square** has four sides of equal length and four right-angled corners.
- A **rectangle** has two pairs of sides of equal length, and four right-angled corners.
- A **parallelogram** has two pairs of sides of equal length, and two pairs of opposite angles which are equal.
- A **rhombus** is a parallelogram with all its sides of equal length.
- A **trapezium** is a quadrilateral with one pair of parallel sides.
- An **isosceles trapezium** has one pair of parallel sides, and the other pair of sides are equal in length.
- A **kite** has two pairs of adjacent sides which are equal in length.

Polygons

Both triangles and quadrilaterals belong to the family of **polygons**. Any closed shape made up of straight lines is called a polygon. If all the sides are the same length and all the interior angles are equal, the shape is called a **regular polygon**. A square and an equilateral triangle are examples of regular polygons.

The names of some other common polygons are:

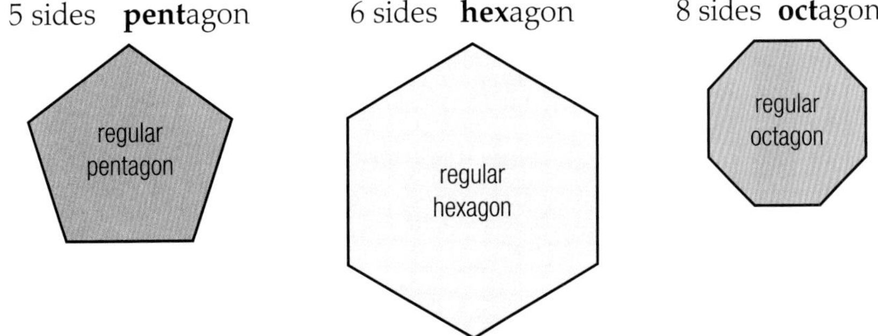

EXERCISE 3.4B

1 Look at the shapes below and name each shape according to the quadrilateral definitions given on page 27.

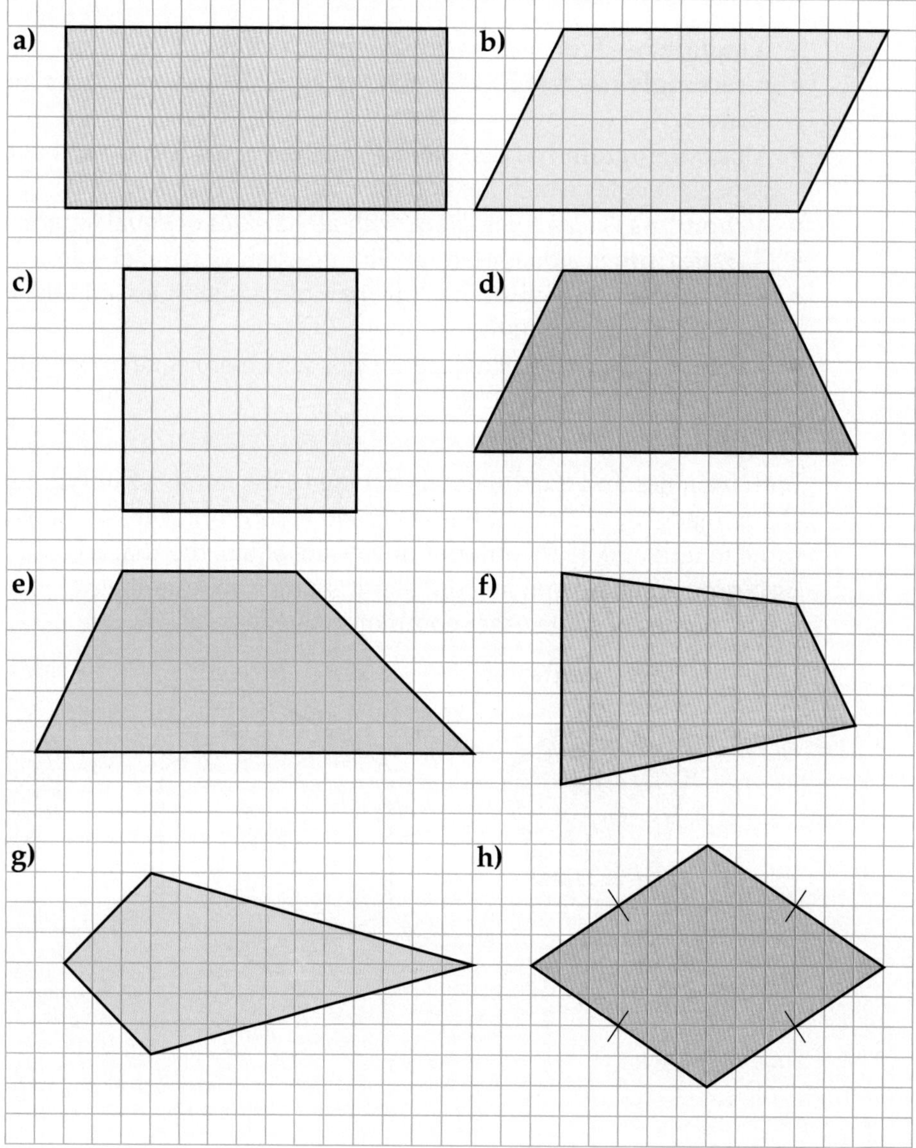

2 Copy and complete the following table. The first line has been started for you.

	Rectangle	Square	Parallelogram	Kite	Rhombus	Trapezium
Opposite sides equal in length	Yes		Yes			
All sides equal in length						
All angles right angles						
Both pairs of opposite sides parallel						
Diagonals equal in length						
Diagonals intersect at right angles						
All angles equal						

3 For this regular hexagon write down:
a) the number of lines of symmetry
b) the order of rotational symmetry.

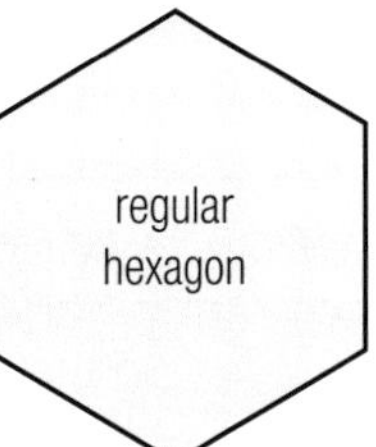

4 **a)** For this regular octagon write down:
(i) the number of lines of symmetry
(ii) the order of rotational symmetry.
b) Is it possible for an octagon to have only two lines of symmetry?
Explain your answer clearly.

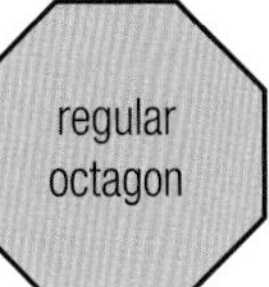

Solid shapes

All polygons are *flat*. They are examples of **two-dimensional** (2-D) shapes. Many shapes in the world about you are **three-dimensional** (3-D) shapes. Some of the basic three-dimensional shapes are shown below.

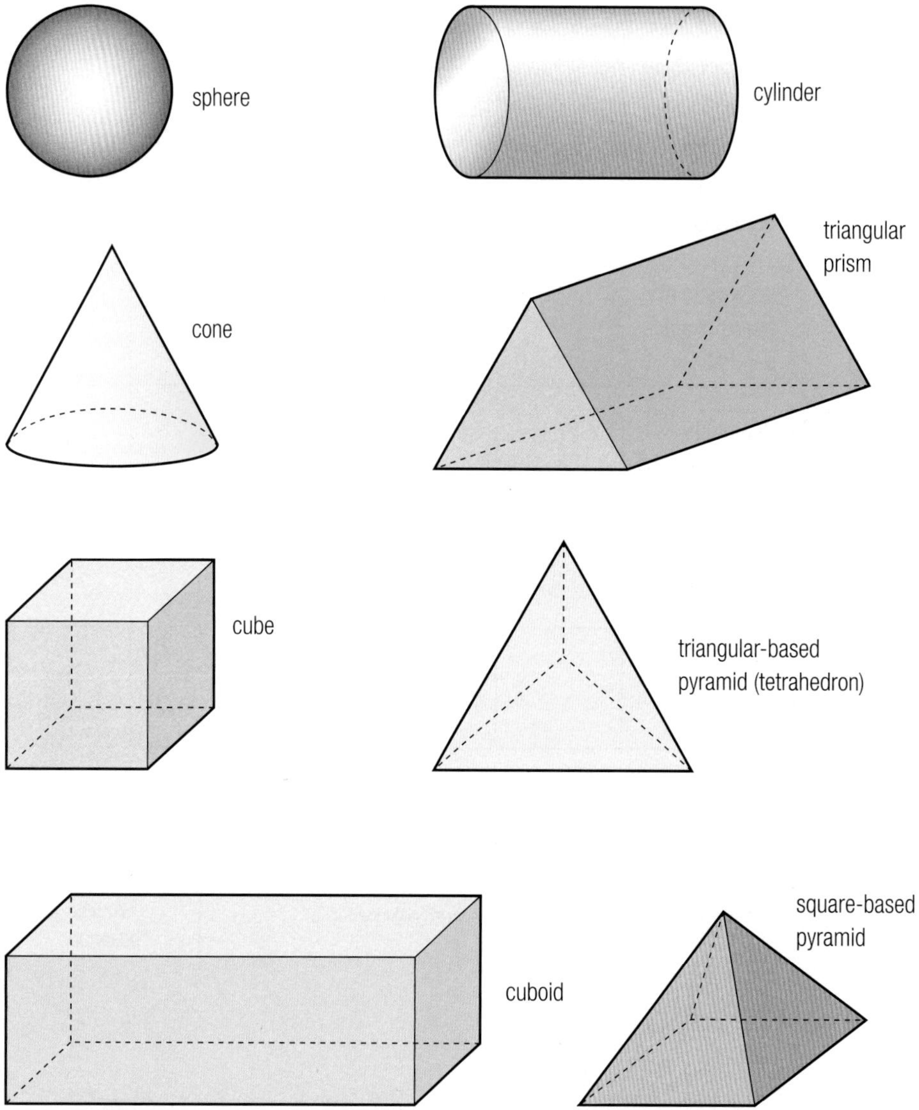

In three-dimensional shapes, each side is known as a **face**. Two faces meet to form an **edge**, and edges meet to form a **vertex**. For example,

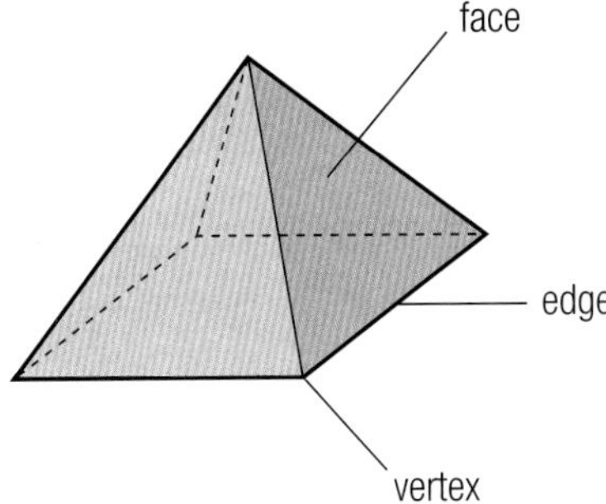

A three-dimensional shape in which all the faces are polygons is called a **polyhedron** (**polyhedra** if there is more than one polyhedron). A **regular polyhedron** is one in which all the faces are identical regular polygons.

EXERCISE 3.5

1 Look at the eight three-dimensional shapes shown on page 30. Write down which are polyhedra, which are regular polyhedra and which are neither.

2 For each of the following shapes write down the number of:

(i) vertices
(ii) faces
(iii) edges.

a) cube
b) triangular prism
c) triangular-based pyramid (tetrahedron)
d) square-based pyramid

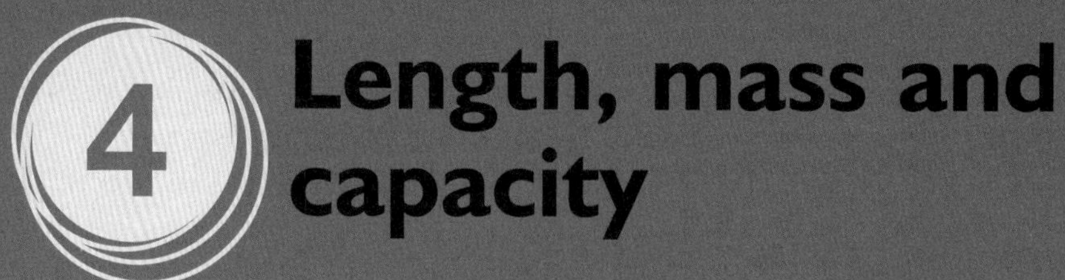

4 Length, mass and capacity

- Choose suitable units of measurement to estimate, measure, calculate and solve problems in everyday contexts.
- Know abbreviations for and relationships between metric units; convert between:
  - kilometres (km), metres (m), centimetres (cm) and millimetres (mm)
  - tonnes (t), kilograms (kg) and grams (g)
  - litres (*l*) and millilitres (m*l*).
- Read the scales on a range of analogue and digital measuring instruments.

In one day a soldier in Julius Caesar's army could comfortably march 20 miles wearing full kit, and then help to build a defensive stockade.

The mile was a unit of length based upon 1000 strides of a Roman legionary. The measurement was sufficiently accurate for its purpose but only an approximate distance.

Most measures started as rough estimates. The yard (3 feet or 36 inches) was said to be the distance from the English king's nose (reputed to be Edward I) to the tip of his extended finger.

As it became necessary to have standardisation in measurement, the measures themselves became more exact.

In 1791 during the French Revolution, a new unit of measurement, the metre, was defined in France. Originally it was defined as 'one ten-millionth of the length of the quadrant of the Earth's meridian through Paris'. The use of this unit of measurement became law in France in 1795.

However, later, this measurement was not considered sufficiently accurate and further definitions were required.

In 1927 a metre was defined as the distance between two marks on a particular platinum-iridium bar. This bar is kept in Paris.

In 1960 the definition was based on the emission of a krypton-86 lamp.

At the 1983 General Conference on Weights and Measures, the metre was re-defined as the length of the path travelled by light in a vacuum in $\frac{1}{299\,792\,488}$ second. This definition, though not very neat, can be considered to be one of the few *accurate* measures. Most measures are defined less accurately than this.

The metric system

The metric system uses a number of units for length. They are:

kilometre (km), metre (m), centimetre (cm) and millimetre (mm)

The units for mass are:

tonne (t), kilogram (kg), gram (g) and milligram (mg)

The units for capacity are:

litre (l) and millilitre (ml)

centi comes from the Latin 'centum' meaning hundred, milli comes for the Latin 'mille' meaning thousand, kilo comes from the Greek 'khilioi' meaning thousand.

EXERCISE 4.1A

1 Copy and complete the sentences below.

a) There are ______ centimetres in one metre.

b) A centimetre is ______ part of a metre.

c) There are ______ metres in one kilometre.

d) A metre is ______ part of a kilometre.

e) There are ______ grams in one kilogram.

f) A gram is ______ part of a kilogram.

g) A kilogram is ______ part of a tonne.

h) There are ______ millilitres in one litre.

i) One thousandth of a litre is ______.

j) There are ______ grams in one tonne.

2 Which of the units below would you use to measure each of the following?

mm cm m km mg g kg tonne m*l* litre

a) your mass (weight)
b) the length of your foot
c) your height
d) the amount of water in a glass
e) the mass of a ship
f) the height of a bus
g) the capacity of a swimming pool
h) the length of a road
i) the capacity of the fuel tank of a truck
j) the size of your waist

3 Draw ten lines of different lengths.
a) Estimate the length of each line in millimetres.
b) Measure the length of each line to the nearest millimetre.

4 Write an estimate for each of the following using a sensible unit.
a) your height
b) your mass (weight)
c) the capacity of a cup
d) the distance to the nearest town
e) the mass of an orange
f) the quantity of blood in the human body
g) the depth of the Pacific Ocean
h) the distance to the Moon
i) the mass of a car
j) the capacity of a swimming pool

Converting from one unit to another

Length

1 km is 1000 m, so

to change from km to m, multiply by 1000
to change from m to km, divide by 1000.

Worked examples

a) Change 5.84 km to metres.

1 km = 1000 m, so multiply by 1000.
$5.84 \times 1000 = 5840$ m

b) Change 3640 mm to metres.

1 m = 1000 mm, so divide by 1000.
$3640 \div 1000 = 3.64$ m

Mass

1 tonne is 1000 kg, so
to change from tonnes to kg, multiply by 1000
to change from kg to tonnes, divide by 1000.

Worked examples

a) Change 0.872 tonne to kilograms.
1 tonne = 1000 kg, so multiply by 1000.
$0.872 \times 1000 = 872$ kg

b) Change 4200 kg to tonnes.
1 tonne = 1000 kg, so divide by 1000.
$4200 \div 1000 = 4.2$ tonnes

Capacity

1 litre is 1000 m*l*, so
to change from litres to m*l*, multiply by 1000
to change from m*l* to litres, divide by 1000.

Worked examples

a) Change 2.4 litres to millilitres.
1 litre is 1000 m*l*, so multiply by 1000.
$2.4 \times 1000 = 2400$ m*l*

b) Change 4500 m*l* to litres.
1 litre is 1000 m*l*, so divide by 1000.
$4500 \div 1000 = 4.5$ litres

EXERCISE 4.1B

1 Copy and complete the sentences below.

a) 1 m is _______ cm, so
to change from m to cm _______
to change from cm to m _______.

b) 1 m = _______ mm, so
to change from m to mm _______
to change from mm to m _______.

c) 1 cm = _______ mm, so
to change from cm to mm _______
to change from mm to cm _______.

2 Convert these to millimetres.
a) 4 cm **b)** 6.2 cm **c)** 28 cm **d)** 1.2 m
e) 0.88 m **f)** 3.65 m **g)** 0.008 m **h)** 0.23 cm

3 Convert these to metres.
a) 260 cm **b)** 8900 cm **c)** 2.3 km **d)** 0.75 km
e) 250 cm **f)** 0.4 km **g)** 3.8 km **h)** 25 km

4 Convert these to kilometres.
a) 2000 m **b)** 26 500 m **c)** 200 m **d)** 750 m
e) 100 m **f)** 5000 m **g)** 15 000 m **h)** 75 600 m

5 Copy and complete the sentences below.

1 kg is ______ g, so

to change kg to g ______

to change g to kg ______.

6 Convert these to kilograms.
a) 2 tonne **b)** 7.2 tonne
c) 2800 g **d)** 750 g
e) 0.45 tonne **f)** 0.003 tonne
g) 6500 g **h)** 7 000 000 g

7 Convert these to millilitres.
a) 2.6 litres **b)** 0.7 litre **c)** 0.04 litre **d)** 0.008 litre

8 Convert these to litres.
a) 1500 m*l* **b)** 5280 m*l* **c)** 750 m*l* **d)** 25 m*l*

9 How much water is left in a 1-litre bottle after 400 m*l* is drunk?

10 How much water is left in a 1.5-litre bottle after 750 m*l* is drunk?

11 A pile of bricks weighs 16 kg.
9450 g of bricks are removed. What weight is left?

12 I am travelling to a city 250 km away.
I take a break after 173 km. How many kilometres do I have left to travel?

13 A cyclist travels for five days, and covers 375 km in total.
He covers 67 km, 78 km, 46 km and 89 km on the first four days.
How far does he travel on day 5?

14 The masses of four containers loaded on a ship are 28 tonnes, 45 tonnes, 16.8 tonnes and 48 500 kg. What is the total mass in tonnes?

15 Three test tubes contain 0.08 litre, 0.42 litre and 220 m*l* of solution.
a) What is the total volume of solution in millilitres?
b) How many litres of water need to be added to make the volume of solution up to 1.25 litres?

Reading scales

Scales are used in everyday life to measure a variety of different quantities, for example on weighing scales, measuring cylinders and rulers. It is important to be able to read scales accurately.

There are two things to remember in order to read a scale accurately:

- Work out the value of each division on the scale before trying to take the reading.

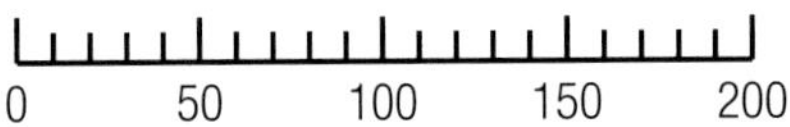

On this scale, the value of each small division is 10. This is calculated by dividing the difference between two consecutive numbers on the scale by the number of divisions between them, i.e.

$$\frac{100 - 50}{5} = 10$$

On the scale below, however, the value of each small division is 0.5.

5 10

$$\frac{10 - 5}{10} = 0.5$$

- Always read a scale by looking straight at it, rather than at an angle.

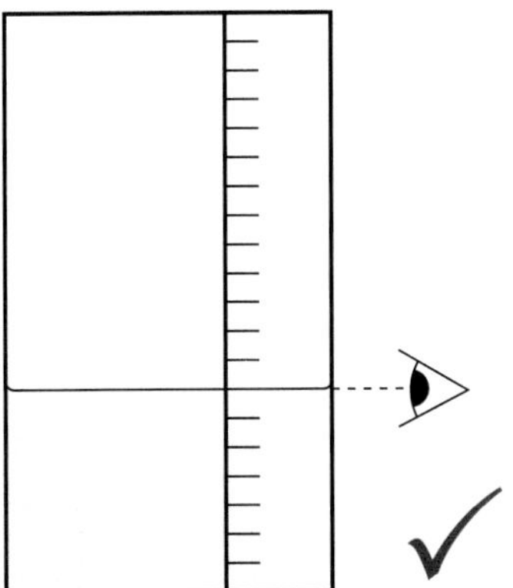

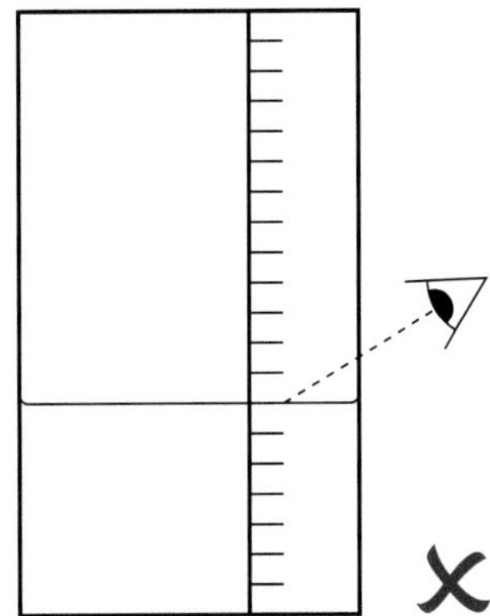

EXERCISE 4.2A

Work out the value shown by the arrow on each of the following scales.

1

0 50 100 150 200

2

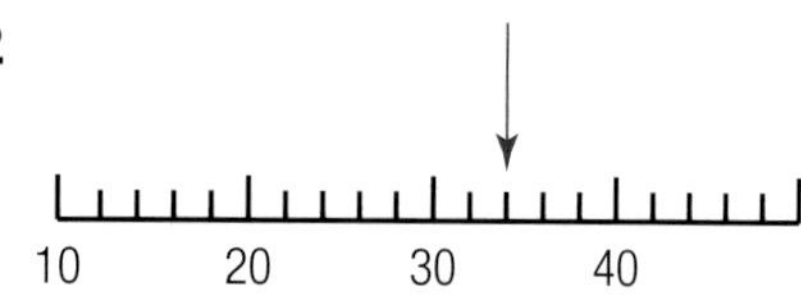

3

15 25 35 45

4

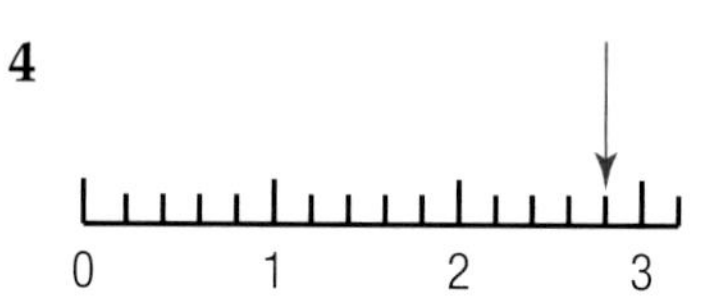

5

100 200 300 400

6

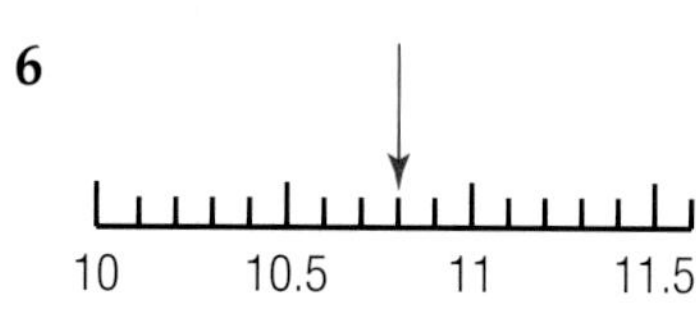

7

–50 –40 –30 –20

8

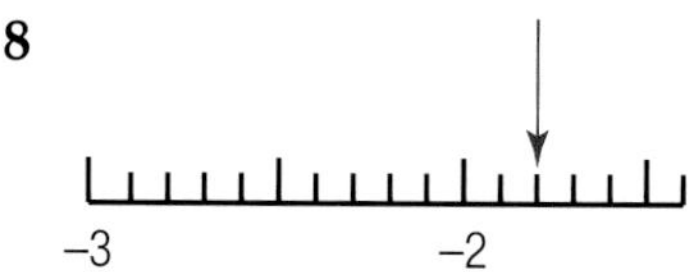

EXERCISE 4.2B

1 How heavy is the man?

2 How tall is the girl?

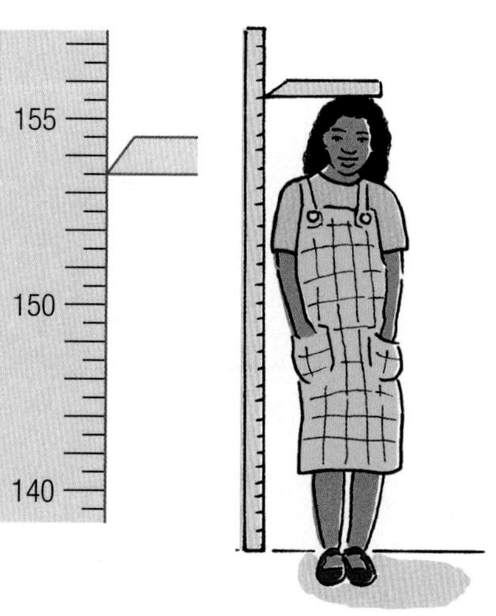

3 How fast is the car travelling?

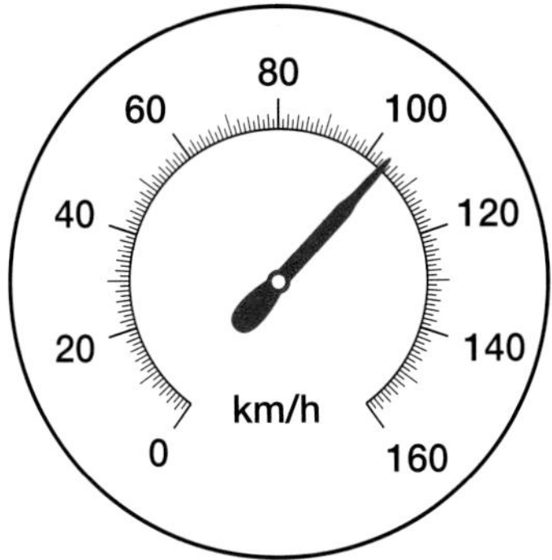

4 How much liquid is in the measuring cylinder?

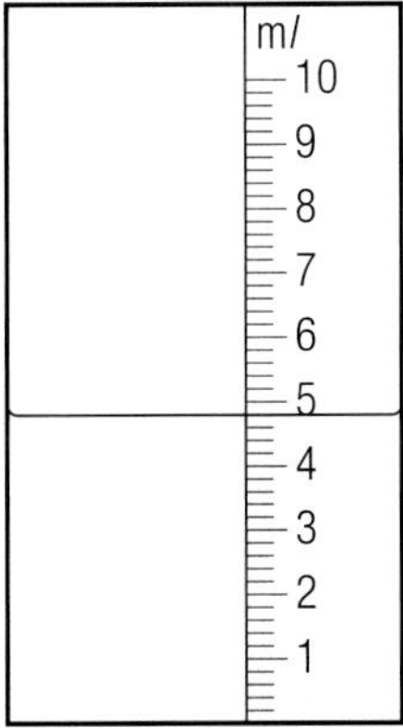

5 What is the temperature?

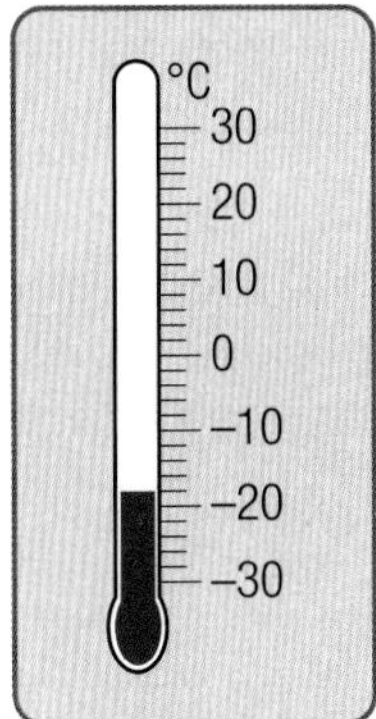

5 Collecting and displaying data

- Decide which data would be relevant to an enquiry and collect and organise the data.
- Design and use a data collection sheet or questionnaire for a simple survey.
- Construct and use frequency tables to gather discrete data, grouped where appropriate in equal class intervals.
- Draw and interpret:
  - bar-line graphs and bar charts
  - frequency diagrams for grouped discrete data
  - simple pie charts
  - pictograms.

Collecting data

Pieces of information are often called **data**. **Primary data** is information you collect yourself. **Secondary data** is data which somebody else has collected, for example information you may find on the internet or in newspaper articles.

This chapter looks at how to collect primary data through surveys and at different methods for displaying the data when it has been collected.

Surveys are needed by companies and organisations for a number of reasons. For example, if a government wishes to spend more money on schools it may need to raise more money through taxes to achieve this. It may want to carry out a survey to find out what people think of that idea.

Discuss in groups.

Q Which of the following questions do you think would be the best one for the government to use in a questionnaire?

a) Do you think you pay too much tax?

b) Do you think our schools are good?

c) Would you be prepared to pay more tax if the money raised was spent on improving schools?

d) Do you think the government spends too much money on offices for politicians and not enough on new schools?

A car manufacturer wants to know which things (electric windows, air conditioning, heated seats, etc.) people expect to have in a car and which are seen as extras.

Q What sort of questions might be asked in a questionnaire?

A television company wants to find out which are its five most popular programmes.

Q What sort of questions might the television company ask in a questionnaire?

Your discussion may have shown that asking the *right* question to give a *meaningful* and *useful* answer is not as easy as it seems.

The design of questionnaires is very important. There are some simple rules which you need to think about so that:

- people will co-operate and try to answer your questions
- people will answer honestly
- the answers you get can be presented and understood easily.

The rules are as follows.

1. Make it clear what it is you are trying to find out.

For example, 'Excuse me. I am conducting a survey to find out if people would like to see new traffic lights at these crossroads. Please would you help by answering a few simple questions?'

2. Make the questions simple and give a choice of answer.

For example, a television company wishes to know how much its coverage of the athletics events in the Beijing Olympics was watched.

An example of a bad question would be:
Did you watch much of the Beijing Olympics on TV?
A better question might be:
The Beijing Olympics were shown on TV. How many hours did you watch of the athletics events?

a) none **b)** 1–5 hours **c)** 6–10 hours **d)** 11–15 hours **e)** 16–20 hours

3. Make your question ask for the other person's opinion. Do not make it clear what your own opinion is (this would be called a *biased question* or a *leading question*).

A bad example would be: Fishing is a very cruel pastime. Do you agree?
A better question might be: Do you think that fishing is a cruel pastime?

a) strongly agree **b)** agree **c)** neutral **d)** disagree **e)** strongly disagree

4. Do not ask sensitive or embarrassing questions.

EXERCISE 5.1A

Re-write the questions below so that they could be used in a questionnaire.

1 Do you have too much homework?

2 Maths is the most important subject at school, isn't it?

3 What is the food like at this school?

4 Do you go to the cinema?

5 Do you think children spend too much time playing computer games?

6 Are boys in this class taller than girls?

7 The eight o'clock bus is always late. Do you agree?

8 How many languages do you speak?

9 Television is boring. Do you agree?

10 Do you agree that people only use supermarkets because it is easy to park there?

Discuss and compare your answers with friends.

EXERCISE 5.1B

1 A mobile telephone company thinks that younger people use mobile telephones more than older people do.
  - **a)** Suggest five questions which could be used in a suitable questionnaire.
  - **b)** Use your questionnaire to conduct a survey to test the statement 'Young people are always on the mobile phone. Older people do not use them.'

2 Suggest five questions for a questionnaire to discover what opinions people in your class have about school.

3 **a)** Write some suitable questions for a questionnaire to discover which students in your class are interested in football, whether they go to matches or watch it on TV, which team they support and whether they buy things to show their support for a team.
  - **b)** Use your questionnaire to conduct a survey to test the statement 'Students in this class are not interested in football.'

4 Construct a suitable questionnaire to carry out a survey on a subject of your own choice. Discuss and compare your questionnaire with friends and suggest ways of improving it.

Organising data

Data can be organised in several ways. Which method is chosen depends largely on the type of data being collected.

Constructing a **tally and frequency table** is a simple way of recording the number of results in each category.

For example, a survey is carried out to test the manufacturer's claim that there are 'about 36 chocolate buttons in each packet'. The number of buttons in each of 25 packets is counted, giving the figures below.

35 36 34 37 36 36 38 37 36 35 38
34 35 36 36 34 37 38 37 36 35 36
36 37 36

Displayed as a list, the numbers are not clear. However, they are easier to analyse if they are recorded in a tally and frequency chart like this.

Number	Tally	Frequency
34	III	3
35	IIII	4
36	~~IIII~~ ~~IIII~~	10
37	~~IIII~~	5
38	III	3

The tally column is filled in as the survey is being carried out. The frequency column is completed by counting up the tally marks at the end of the survey.

Sometimes, if there is a big range in the data, it is more useful to group the data in a **grouped frequency table**. The groups are chosen so that no data item can appear in two groups.

For example, the ages of 30 residents in a care home are shown below.

98 71 76 77 72 78 77 73 76 86
75 79 81 105 100 74 82 88 91 96
85 90 97 102 83 101 83 84 80 95

Constructing a tally and frequency table with a list of individual ages will not be very useful as most ages in the range will only have one or two results. Grouping the data into the age ranges 71–80, 81–90, etc. produces this more useful table.

Age	Tally	Frequency
71–80	~~IIII~~ ~~IIII~~ II	12
81–90	~~IIII~~ IIII	9
91–100	~~IIII~~ I	6
101–110	III	3

The ages could have been grouped 71–75, 76–80, 81–85, etc. The group size is the decision of the person collecting the data, but it is important that the groups are all the same size and do not overlap.

Displaying data

Once the data has been collected, it can be displayed in several ways. Which method is chosen depends on the type of data collected and the audience it is intended for.

One of the simplest and most effective is to use a **pictogram**.

This method uses pictures to represent the frequency. The chocolate button data can be displayed on a pictogram like this, using one circle to represent one chocolate button.

Number of chocolate buttons	Frequency
34	●●●
35	●●●●
36	●●●●●●●●●●
37	●●●●●
38	●●●

Sometimes one symbol represents more than one item. In the pictogram below, for example, each circle represents four chocolates and fractions of a circle represent smaller amounts.

Number of chocolate buttons	Frequency
34	◕
35	●
36	●●◑
37	●◔
38	◕

Key

● = 4 chocolates

Look at the key to see what each symbol represents.

Probably the most common way of displaying data is the **bar graph** or **frequency diagram**. It is quick and easy to draw, and straightforward to understand.

Worked example

A school of 120 students carry out a survey to see which subjects are most popular. Their results are shown in the frequency table.
Show this information on a frequency diagram.

Subject	Frequency
Sport	40
Science	20
Maths	30
Art	15
Languages	15
Total	120

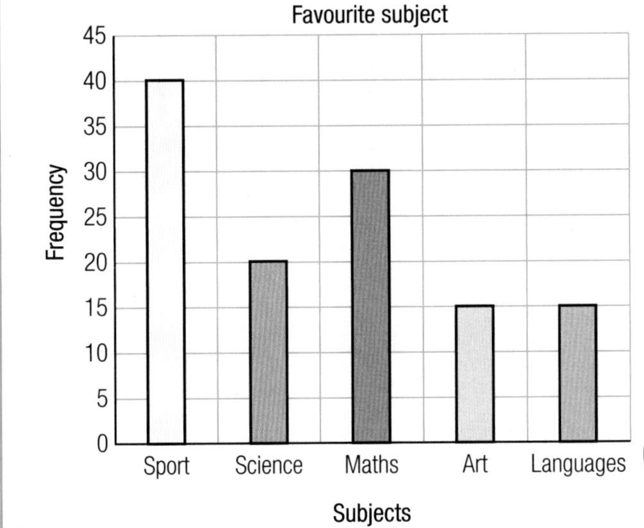

The graph is fully labelled.

The bars are all the same width and do not touch. The height of each bar represents the frequency.

Frequency diagrams can also be used to display grouped data, such as the ages of the residents in the care home.

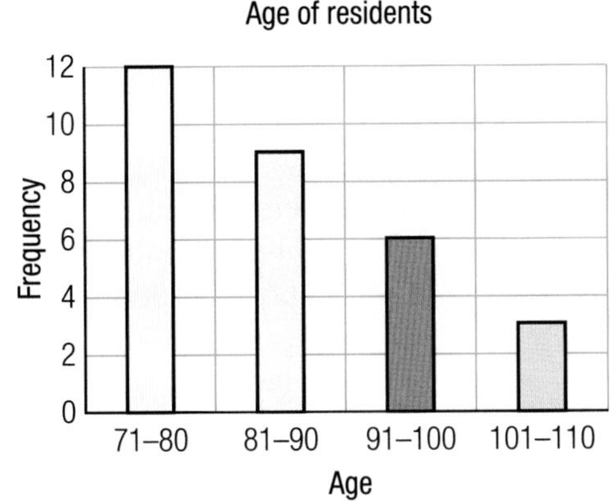

As before, the bars are all the same width and do not touch.

An alternative to a frequency diagram is a **bar-line graph**. Instead of bars, lines are drawn to represent the frequencies. The height of each line indicates the frequency.

The data about students' favourite subjects can be shown on a bar-line graph like this.

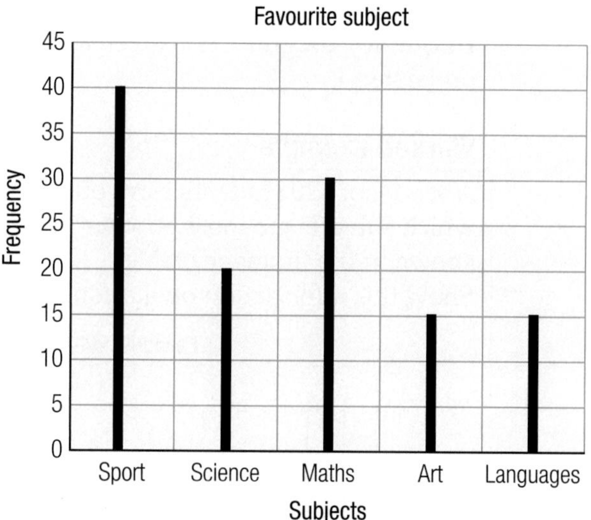

In frequency diagrams and bar-line graphs, each frequency is represented by the *height* of a bar or line. Another way of displaying data is on a **pie chart**. On these, each frequency is represented by a *fraction of a circle*.

Worked example

Look again at the data about students' favourite subjects. Show this information on a pie chart.

- First you need to express the frequency of each subject as a fraction of the total number of students.

  Sport is $\frac{40}{120} = \frac{1}{3}$ of the total,

  Science is $\frac{20}{120} = \frac{1}{6}$,

  Maths is $\frac{30}{120} = \frac{1}{4}$ of the total

  and Art and Languages are $\frac{15}{120} = \frac{1}{8}$ each.

- To draw the pie chart without a protractor, an understanding of fractions helps. For example, Sport and Science together represent half of the total, and Maths, Art and Languages represent the other half of the total.

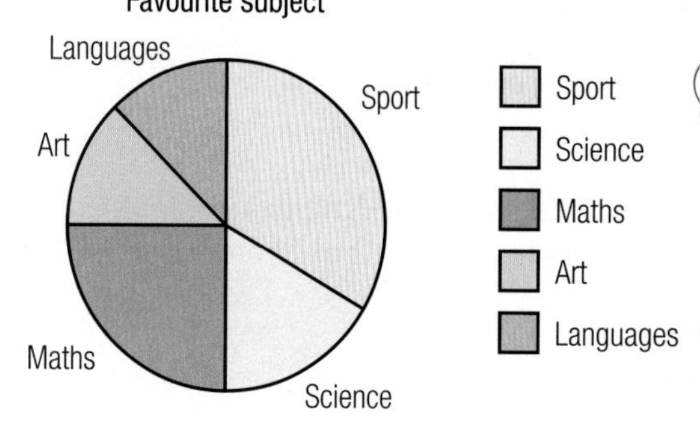

The pie chart has a heading and a key, and each slice is clearly labelled.

The pie chart is divided into slices, which are fractions of the circle. The size of each slice represents the frequency, as a fraction of the total number of students.

EXERCISE 5.2

1 Twelve people were asked which sandwiches they had bought from a sandwich shop. Their answers were:

Chicken	Tuna	Egg	Chicken
Egg	Tomato	Chicken	Tuna
Tomato	Egg	Chicken	Chicken

Show this information on a pictogram.

2 A baker's shop sells brown (B), white (W), wholemeal (M) and soda (S) bread. It keeps a record of the types of loaves it sells. The data is shown below.

B	B	W	W	W	M	B	W	M	S
B	B	B	W	M	W	M	B	M	B
S	W	W	B	B	W	M	M	M	M
B	M	M	W	M	W	B	S	M	M

a) Construct a tally and frequency table of the results.
b) Draw a pictogram of the results.
c) Draw a bar-line graph of the results.

3 A fitness club carries out a survey to find out the ages of its members. Here are the results.

22	18	23	17	44	42	50	19	21	23	11	16
38	55	62	41	17	19	23	36	38	42	35	33
18	22	63	48	9	7	17	23	36	48	54	60

a) Make a grouped tally and frequency table using the age groups 1–10, 11–20, 21–30, etc.
b) Draw a frequency diagram of the data.
c) What does the data tell you about the ages of people at the fitness club?

4 A class of 30 students were asked how many brothers and sisters they have. Here are the results.

2	4	0	1	1	4	1	1	2	2	2	5	2	3	0
1	2	1	2	3	1	1	2	3	2	0	2	0	2	5

a) Draw a tally and frequency table of the results.
b) Use your table to draw a frequency diagram.
c) Interpret the results and comment on the numbers of brothers and sisters that the students have.

5 The numbers of litres of milk consumed in a group of 150 houses are shown in the table.

Number of litres	1	2	3	4	5	6
Frequency	27	54	34	16	15	4

Show this information on a frequency diagram.

6 90 students sat a maths exam. On the way out of the hall, they were asked whether they found it hard, OK or easy. Here are the results.

Response	Easy	OK	Hard
Frequency	15	45	30

Show the results on a pie chart.

7 Two football teams have the results shown in the table.

	Total	Win	Draw	Lose
Spain	36	27	9	0
England	36	6	18	12

Illustrate these on two pie charts.

6 Addition and subtraction

- Consolidate the rapid recall of number facts, including positive integer complements to 100.
- Add and subtract integers and decimals, including numbers with different numbers of decimal places.

Being able to carry out calculations without the help of a calculator is an important skill. This chapter looks at some methods for doing additions and subtractions mentally and on paper.

Mental skills

EXERCISE 6.1A

Work with a friend and ask each other the following questions.
Write down your answers.

1 **a)** 3 + 8 **b)** 12 + 4 **c)** 15 + 3 **d)** 6 + 9
e) 13 + 6 **f)** 5 + 14 **g)** 3 + 17 **h)** 9 + 8

2 **a)** 7 – 4 **b)** 12 – 8 **c)** 14 – 6 **d)** 18 – 11
e) 19 – 13 **f)** 14 – 8 **g)** 20 – 14 **h)** 17 – 9

3 **a)** 34 + 12 **b)** 45 + 25 **c)** 67 + 34 **d)** 23 + 23 **e)** 56 + 34
f) 34 – 12 **g)** 45 – 34 **h)** 98 – 65 **i)** 54 – 48 **j)** 81 – 55

4 **a)** 23 + 27 **b)** 34 + 56 **c)** 67 + 53 **d)** 45 + 78 **e)** 65 + 23
f) 45 – 17 **g)** 76 – 34 **h)** 87 – 34 **i)** 77 – 56 **j)** 87 – 69

5 **a)** 35 + 52 **b)** 35 + 35 **c)** 57 + 31 **d)** 12 + 23 **e)** 76 + 33
f) 34 – 22 **g)** 35 – 34 **h)** 68 – 15 **i)** 74 – 48 **j)** 91 – 52

6 **a)** 2.8 + 27 **b)** 8.4 + 36 **c)** 1.7 + 33 **d)** 5.5 + 18 **e)** 2.5 + 23
f) 45 – 3.7 **g)** 36 – 1.4 **h)** 47 – 2.4 **i)** 79 – 5.2 **j)** 81 – 6.3

Using complements

Addition and subtraction are **inverse** (opposite) operations. Suppose you are asked to work out the difference between 100 and 37. You can write this as a *subtraction*:

100 – 37 = ☐.

Another way, which is often easier, is to work out what needs to be *added* to 37 to make 100:

37 + ☐ = 100.

This can be done by adding numbers in easy steps:

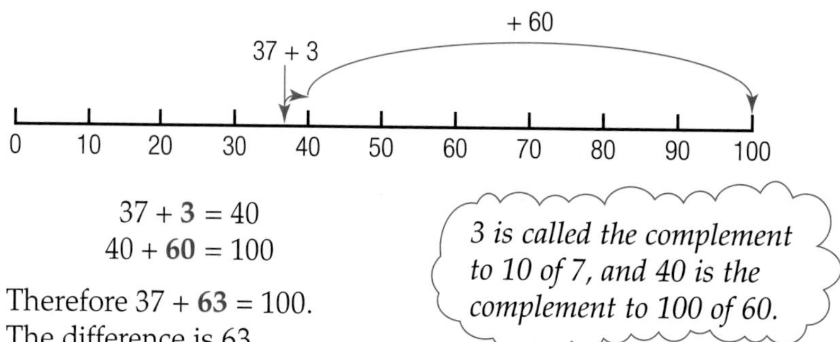

37 + **3** = 40
40 + **60** = 100

Therefore 37 + **63** = 100.
The difference is 63.

3 is called the complement to 10 of 7, and 40 is the complement to 100 of 60.

This method is called working out the **complement**. People often use this method for calculations with money, for example when handing out change in shops.

Worked example

Subtract 26 from 100.

This can be written as:

100 – 26 = ☐ or 26 + ☐ = 100.

Using complements:

26 + **4** = 30
30 + **70** = 100

Therefore 26 + **74** = 100.

EXERCISE 6.1B

Use complements to 100 to calculate each of the following.

1 **a)** 100 – 85 **b)** 100 – 46
c) 32 + ☐ = 100 **d)** ☐ + 13 = 100
e) 71 + ☐ = 100

2 **a)** \$100 – \$39 **b)** \$100 – \$16
c) \$24 + \$☐ = \$100 **d)** \$☐ + \$52 = \$100
e) \$☐ + \$17 = \$100

Written methods

To add or subtract larger numbers or numbers involving decimals, we usually use a written method rather than trying to do the calculation mentally.

Worked examples

a) Add the following amounts of money.

$6.83 $27 $0.04 $142.30

First write the four numbers so that the decimal points line up.

$$
\begin{array}{rrrcrr}
 & {}^{1} & {}^{1} & & & \\
 & & 6 & . & 8 & 3 \\
 & 2 & 7 & . & 0 & 0 \\
 & & 0 & . & 0 & 4 \\
+\,1 & 4 & 2 & . & 3 & 0 \\
\hline
1 & 7 & 6 & . & 1 & 7
\end{array}
$$

If the total of any column is 10 or more, the tens are carried over to the next column (as shown in red).

The total of the amounts is $176.17.

b) Subtract $72.87 from $200.30.

$$
\begin{array}{rrrcrr}
 & {}^{9} & {}^{9} & & & \\
{}^{1}\not{2} & {}^{1}\not{0} & {}^{1}\not{0} & . & {}^{12}\not{3} & {}^{1}0 \\
- & 7 & 2 & . & 8 & 7 \\
\hline
1 & 2 & 7 & . & 4 & 3
\end{array}
$$

If the digit on top is smaller than the digit below, a ten is carried over from the next column.

The difference between the amounts is $127.43.
The answer can be checked by addition:

$$
\begin{array}{rrrcrr}
{}^{1}1 & {}^{1}2 & {}^{1}7 & . & {}^{1}4 & 3 \\
+ & 7 & 2 & . & 8 & 7 \\
\hline
2 & 0 & 0 & . & 3 & 0
\end{array}
$$

EXERCISE 6.2

1 Work out these calculations.

a) $27.43 + $89.29

b) $100 – $57.57

c) $4.62 + $0.82 + $105.62

d) $500 – $46.30 – $3.88

e) $26.43 + $102.11 – $37.28

2 A glass with capacity 230 ml is filled from a jug containing 725 ml of water. How much water is left in the jug after:

a) one glass of water is poured

b) two glasses of water are poured

c) three glasses of water are poured?

3 A family of four people check in their suitcases at the airport. The weights of the four cases are 18.5 kg, 26.2 kg, 15.4 kg and 23.7 kg.

a) Calculate the total weight of the four cases.

b) The weight limit for the four cases is 100 kg.
Calculate how much extra weight the family could have carried.

4 A boy is 81 cm tall. He needs to be at least 1 m tall before he can go on a particular ride at a theme park. How much more does the boy need to grow before he will be allowed on the ride?

5 A bridge over a road is 3.2 m high at its lowest point. A lorry 2.65 m high passes under the bridge. Calculate the height of the gap between the bridge and the lorry, giving your answer in centimetres.

6 A pizzeria offers the following pizzas for sale.

Margherita	$6.25
La Reine	$8.15
Veneziana	$6.85
Fiorentina	$7.95

A group of friends order one Margherita pizza, two La Reine pizzas, one Veneziana pizza and three Fiorentina pizzas.

a) Calculate the total cost of the pizzas.

b) They pay for the pizzas with $60.
Calculate the amount of change they are due.

7 ICT, investigations and problem solving

1 Squeeze

'Squeeze' a number between each of the following pairs of numbers. The number you choose must be bigger than one of the numbers given, but smaller than the other one. For example,

28

28.3

29

28.3 has been squeezed between 28 and 29. Notice that the number does not need to be half way between the two given numbers.

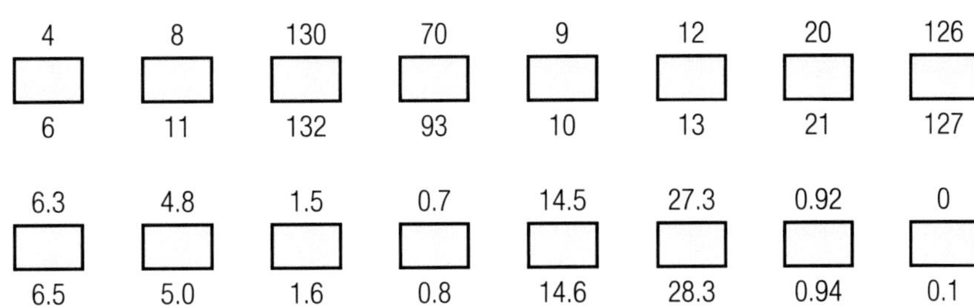

2 Triangles and shapes

These four triangles are such that triangles 1 and 2 are congruent (identical in shape and size) and triangles 3 and 4 are congruent. Triangles 1 and 2 are half the width of triangles 3 and 4. All four triangles are the same height.

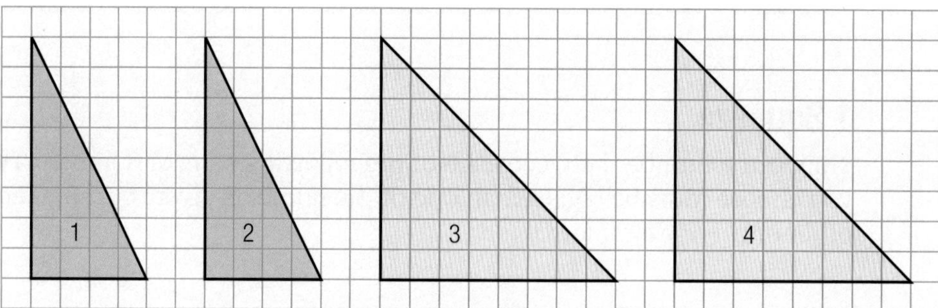

a) Investigate how many different triangles and quadrilaterals you can form by joining two or more of these triangles along an edge. You can reflect or rotate the triangles if necessary. An example is shown (right).

b) Write down the name of each new shape.

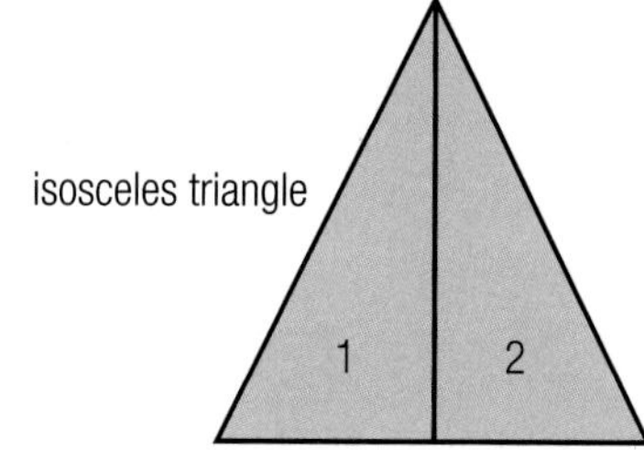

3 Euler's rule

Euler (1707–1783) was a Swiss mathematician who made many important discoveries in mathematics. One of his discoveries was about polyhedra. You met some basic polyhedra in Chapter 3, including the four below.

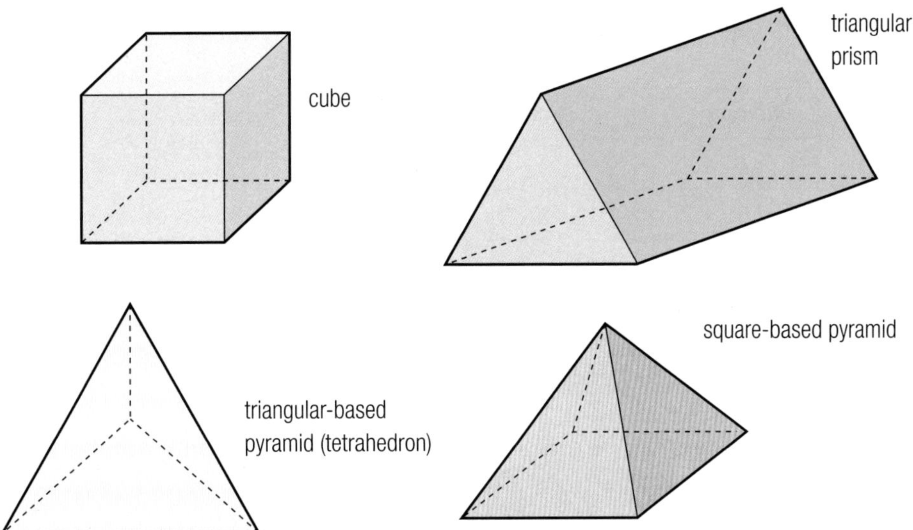

a) Count the number of faces, vertices and edges in each of these shapes. Record your results in a table like this.

3-D shape	Faces	Vertices	Edges
cube			
triangular prism			
triangular-based pyramid (tetrahedron)			
square-based pyramid			

b) Using books or the internet, find at least four more polyhedra. Enter their properties in your table.

c) Look at your results and find a rule linking the numbers of faces, vertices and edges. Describe your rule in words.

d) Using F for the number of faces, V for the number of vertices and E for the number of edges, write your rule using algebra.

4 Prime sum

A **prime number** is one which can only be divided exactly by itself and by 1. The prime numbers less than 20 are:

2 3 5 7 11 13 17 19

Some numbers can be made by adding two or more different prime numbers together. The table shows some examples.

Number	Prime sum
4	
5	2 + 3
6	
7	2 + 5
8	3 + 5

Some numbers can be written as a sum of different prime numbers in more than one way. For example,

$16 = 13 + 3$ and $16 = 11 + 5$

a) Investigate which numbers can be written as the sum of two different prime numbers.

b) Which numbers can be written as the sum of three different prime numbers?

Review 1A

1 Round the following numbers to one decimal place.
a) 0.872 **b)** 4.89 **c)** 19.38

2 Re-write this calculation using brackets to make it true.
$7 + 3 \times 2 - 6 = 14$

3 Simplify the following expressions using the correct order of operations.
a) $2x + 4(x - 7) - 5x$
b) $-3r + 4 - (2r - 3) + 8r$

4 Write an expression for the area of a rectangle 7 units long and $(x - 3)$ units wide.

5 Write an expression for the perimeter of the rectangle in question 4.

6 A square has side length $(t - 7)$ units. Write an expression for its perimeter.

7 Draw a trapezium with one line of symmetry.

8 Draw a regular octagon.
a) Write down how many lines of symmetry it has.
b) Write down its order of rotational symmetry.

9 Convert each of these measures to the units shown in brackets.
a) 7.142 kg (g) **b)** 12 568 m (km) **c)** 4.12 litres (m*l*)

10 A fitness club carries out a survey to find out the ages of its members. Here are the results.

28	18	33	17	49	42	50	19	21	23	21	16
38	55	62	41	17	19	23	46	38	42	35	65
18	42	63	48	19	67	17	23	36	48	54	60

a) Make a grouped tally and frequency table using the age groups 1–10, 11–20, 21–30, etc.
b) Draw a frequency diagram of the data.
c) Draw some conclusions from your frequency diagram.
d) The club wishes to know what are the best times for social events, competitions, club nights, etc. Design a questionnaire to be given to the members.

Review 1B

1 Round the following numbers to one decimal place.
a) 0.84 **b)** 4.99 **c)** 29.88

2 Re-write this calculation using brackets to make it true.
$3 \times 2 \times 6 + 2 = 48$

3 Simplify the following expressions using the correct order of operations.
a) $3x + 2(x - 7) - x$
b) $-8r + 4 - (5r - 3) + r$

4 Write an expression for the area of a rectangle 9 units long and $(2x - 7)$ units wide.

5 Write an expression for the perimeter of the rectangle in question 4.

6 A square has side length $(p - 1)$ units. Write an expression for its perimeter.

7 Draw a triangle with one line of symmetry.

8 Draw a regular hexagon.
a) Write down how many lines of symmetry it has.
b) Write down its order of rotational symmetry.

9 Convert each of these measures to the units shown in brackets.
a) 2.3 kg (g) **b)** 5568 m (km) **c)** 0.42 litre (m*l*)

10 A golf club carries out a survey to find out the ages of its members. Here are the results.

28	68	57	79	42	50	19	21	23	21	56	16
38	55	62	71	27	49	63	46	68	42	35	65
18	72	63	48	69	67	17	43	36	48	54	60

a) Make a grouped tally and frequency table using the age groups 1–10, 11–20, 21–30, etc.
b) Draw a frequency diagram of the data.
c) Draw some conclusions from your frequency diagram.
d) The club wishes to know if fees should be raised to make improvements to the golf course, and to find out why the club restaurant is not used much at certain times of the week and in certain months of the year. Design a questionnaire to be given to the members.

SECTION 2

8 Integers, powers and roots

- Recognise negative numbers as positions on a number line, and order, add and subtract positive and negative integers in context.
- Recognise multiples, factors, common factors and primes (all less than 100), making use of simple tests of divisibility; find the lowest common multiple in simple cases; use the 'sieve' for generating primes developed by Eratosthenes.
- Recognise squares of whole numbers to at least 20 × 20, and the corresponding square roots; use the notation 7^2 and $\sqrt{49}$.

The Chinese have studied mathematics for many hundreds of years. Some of the world's oldest surviving books on mathematics come from China. One Chinese mathematician, Wang Xiaotong, wrote a book called *The Continuation of Ancient Mathematics* around 600 CE. In one of its chapters he wrote about calculations involving squares, square roots, cubes and cube roots.

This book was a continuation of an earlier work. It is therefore possible that the work you will be doing in this chapter has echoes of work done in China nearly 2000 years ago.

Integers

Whole numbers such as 1, 2, 3, 4, etc. are called **natural numbers**.

Integers are whole numbers but can be positive, negative or zero. Examples of integers are 7, 12, –3 and –5.

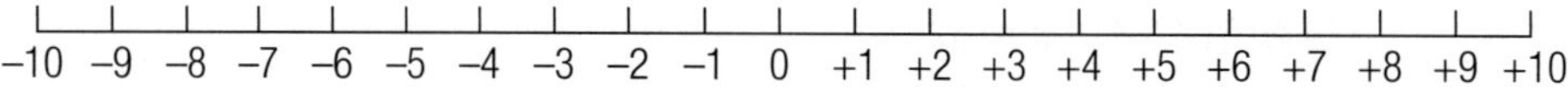

Integers are shown on this number line. Left to right is the positive direction. Right to left is the negative direction.

By looking at the number line we can see that the integers +10, –6, +7, –4, –1, +5 can be arranged into order as –6, –4, –1, +5, +7, +10.

Adding integers

Worked examples

a) Use a number line to add (+4) and (–2).

Start at (+4) and move 2 in the negative direction.

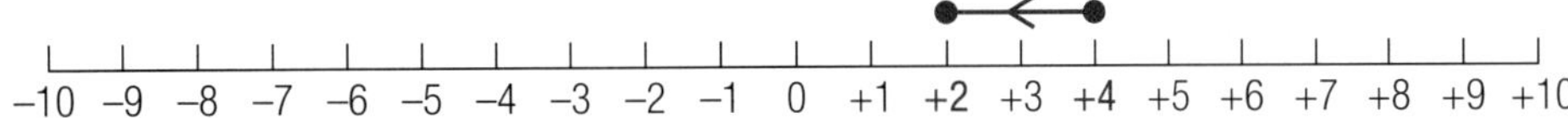

So

(+4) + (–2) = (+2) or 2

b) Use the number line to add (–5) and (+7).

Start at (–5) and move 7 in the positive direction.

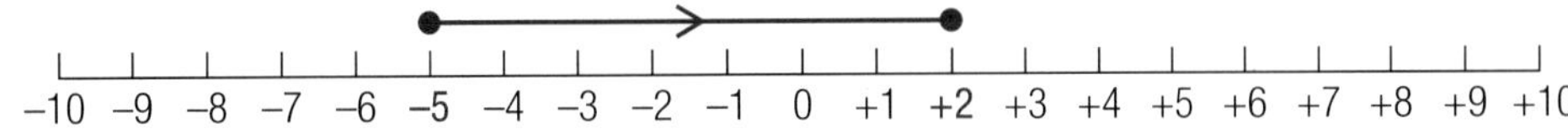

So

(–5) + (+7) = (+2) or 2

c) Use the number line to add (–1) and (–3).

Start at –1 and move 3 in the negative direction.

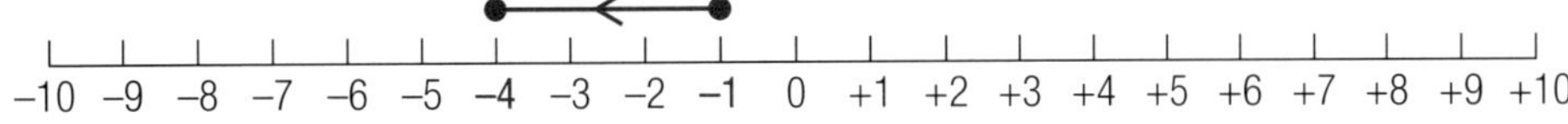

So

(–1) + (–3) = (–4) or –4

EXERCISE 8.1A

Draw a number line in your book from –10 to +10. Use it to answer these questions.

1 **a)** (+6) + (–3) **b)** (+4) + (–4) **c)** (+9) + (–6)

2 **a)** (–7) + (+5) **b)** (–6) + (+5) **c)** (–1) + (–7)

3 **a)** (–2) + (–4) **b)** (–4) + (–1) **c)** (–7) + (–1)

4 **a)** (–4) + (+4) + (–1) **b)** (–3) + (–5) + (+6) **c)** (+3) + (–6) + (–3)

5 Write each of these sets of integers in order, lowest first.

a) (+6) (–3) (+9) (–5) (–1)
b) (+9) (–8) (–2) (+6) (–3)
c) (+5) (–5) (+2) (+4) (–9)
d) (+7) (–8) (+5) (+4) (–6) (–3)
e) (+12) (+43) (–21) (+65) (–43) (–26)

Subtracting integers

Worked examples

a) Use a number line to calculate (+6) – (+2).

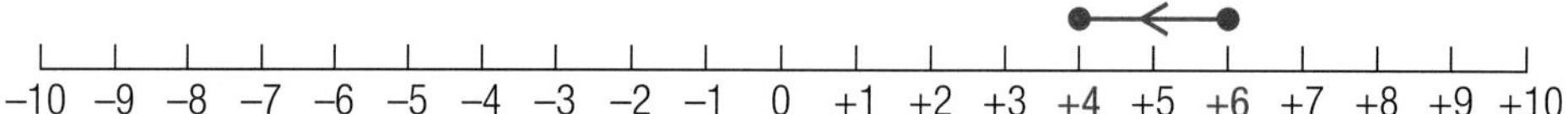

Start at (+6) and move 2 in the negative direction.
So

(+6) – (+2) = (+4) or 4

b) Use a number line to calculate (–2) – (+3).

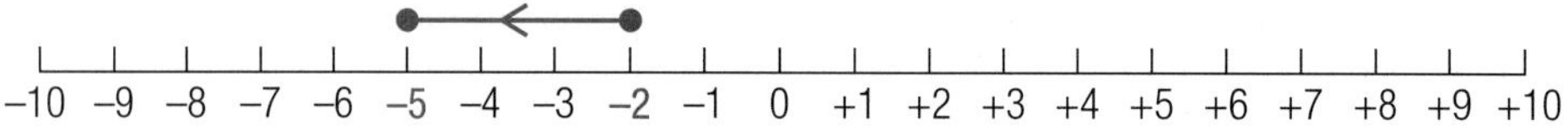

Start at (–2) and move 3 in the negative direction.
So

(–2) – (+3) = (–5) or –5

c) Use a number line to calculate (–3) – (–6).

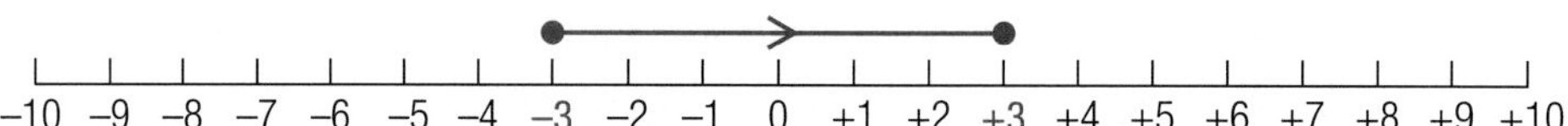

Start at (–3) and move 6 in the positive direction.
So

(–3) – (–6) = (+3) or 3

d) We can use the addition and subtraction of integers in real-life problems.

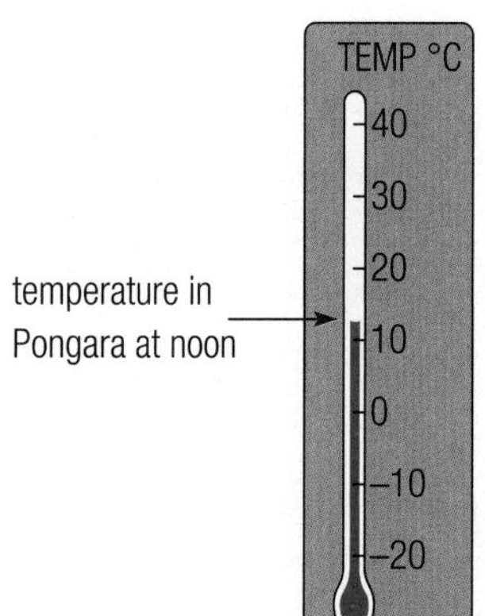

This thermometer shows the temperature in degrees Celsius (°C).

On a winter's day in Pongara the temperature at noon is 12 °C.

The lowest temperature that night is 20 °C lower.

What is the lowest temperature that night?

12 °C – 20 °C = –8 °C

The fall in temperature is represented by the minus sign before the 20.

Therefore the lowest temperature that night is –8 °C.

e) The coldest temperature during the night in a village outside Athens is –4 °C. During the day the temperature rises by 25 °C.
What is the temperature during the day?

–4 °C + 25 °C = 21 °C

Therefore the temperature during the day is 21 °C.

The rise in temperature is represented by the plus sign before the 25.

EXERCISE 8.1B

Work out the answers to the following calculations. You may need to use a number line.

1 **a)** (+5) – (+4) **b)** (+6) – (+3) **c)** (+6) – (+4)
d) (+5) – (+2) **e)** (+7) – (+1) **f)** (+8) – (+5)

2 **a)** (+3) – (+4) **b)** (+5) – (+6) **c)** (+2) – (+5)
d) (+1) – (+6) **e)** (+2) – (+3) **f)** (+8) – (+9)

3 **a)** (–3) – (+3) **b)** (–4) – (+4) **c)** (–2) – (+12)
d) (–3) – (+4) **e)** (–1) – (+5) **f)** (–6) – (+6)

4 **a)** (–9) – (–5) **b)** (–3) – (–2) **c)** (–4) – (–1)
d) (–8) – (–7) **e)** (–4) – (–4) **f)** (–9) – (–7)

5 **a)** (–3) – (–4) **b)** (–2) – (–5) **c)** (–2) – (–6)
d) (–4) – (–5) **e)** (–3) – (–7) **f)** (–2) – (–4)

6 Find the new temperature for each of the following. You may need to draw a number line.

a) The temperature is –5 °C and rises by 15 °C.
b) The temperature is –8 °C and rises by 12 °C.
c) The temperature is –20 °C and rises by 10 °C.
d) The temperature is –3 °C and rises by 8 °C.
e) The temperature is 3 °C and rises by 15 °C.
f) The temperature is 3 °C and falls by 15 °C.
g) The temperature is 8 °C and falls by 12 °C.
h) The temperature is –4 °C and falls by 5 °C.
i) The temperature is –9 °C and falls by 11 °C.
j) The temperature is 5 °C below zero and falls by 16 °C.

→

7 My bank account shows a balance of $620 in credit.
Write down my new balance as a positive or negative number after each of these amounts has been paid or received.

Transactions

Date	Details	Money out	Money in	Balance
				620.00
17 Aug	Car insurance	360.00		**a)**
19 Aug	Rent	550.00		**b)**
22 Aug	Salary		1320.00	**c)**
23 Aug	Credit card	840.00		**d)**
29 Aug	Air tickets refund		280.00	**e)**

8 A lift in an office block has stopped at a restaurant on one of the floors. Call this floor zero. What floors does it stop at on the following sequence of journeys? Write each answer as either a positive or a negative number.

a) up 8 floors
b) then down 17 floors
c) then down 12 floors
d) then up 20 floors
e) then down 14 floors

9 A plane is flying at 8200 metres above the sea. It drops a sonar beacon to the ocean floor. The beacon falls 9650 metres. How deep is the ocean at this point?

10 A man is standing at the top of a vertical cliff. He is at a height of 123 metres above sea level. 59 metres below the top of the cliff, there is a small ledge. What is the height of the ledge above sea level?

Factors and primes

Prime numbers have fascinated mathematicians for centuries.

Eratosthenes (276–194 BCE) identified primes with a 'sieve'.

Mersenne, a French monk (1588–1648 CE), thought he had a clever theory about primes, which proved partly correct.

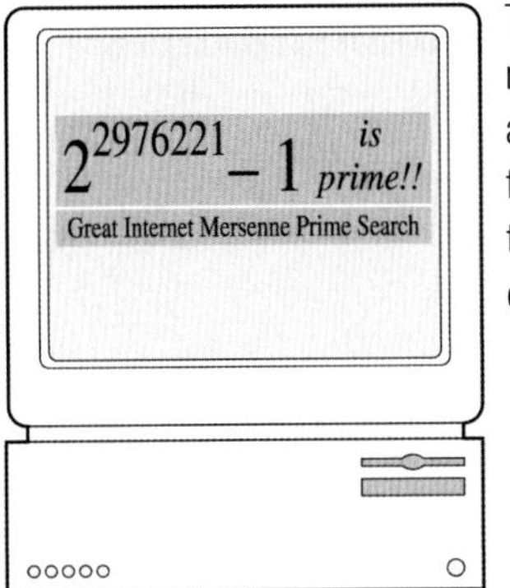

Teams of mathematicians are now searching for primes using the GIMPS database.

There is a big cash prize for finding new prime numbers.

Factors

Factors of a number are all the whole numbers (positive integers) which divide exactly into that number. For example, the factors of 12 are all the numbers which divide into 12 exactly. They are 1, 2, 3, 4, 6, 12.

Prime numbers

A **prime number** is a number which has only two factors, 1 and itself.

By definition, 1 is not a prime number.

Prime factors

A **prime factor** is a factor of a number which is also a prime number. Therefore, the prime factors of 12 are 2 and 3.

EXERCISE 8.2A

This question is a method of finding prime numbers. It was first used by the Greek mathematician Eratosthenes. A short poem goes:
'Cross out twos and cross out threes.
The sieve of Eratosthenes.
Cross out all multiples. In time,
The numbers you have left are prime.'

1 Draw a 10 × 10 grid and write the numbers 1 to 100.

Cross out number 1.

Cross out all the even numbers after 2 (these have 2 as a factor).

Cross out every third number after 3 (these have 3 as a factor).

Continue with 5, 7, 11 and 13, then list all the prime numbers less than 100.

2 Use the internet or an encyclopaedia to answer the following questions.
a) What is a Mersenne prime number?
b) What is the biggest prime number known to date?

3 List all the factors of the following numbers and circle the prime factors.

a) 6	**b)** 9	**c)** 7	**d)** 15	**e)** 24
f) 36	**g)** 35	**h)** 25	**i)** 42	**j)** 100

Highest common factor and lowest common multiple

The factors of 12 are 1, 2, 3, 4, 6 and 12.

The factors of 18 are 1, 2, 3, 6, 9 and 18.

The largest factor to appear in both groups is 6, so 6 is the **highest common factor** of 12 and 18.

The multiples of 6 are those numbers in the 6 × table, i.e. 6, 12, 18, 24, 30, etc.

The multiples of 8 are those numbers in the 8 × table, i.e. 8, 16, 24, 32, 40, etc.

The smallest multiple to appear in both groups is 24, so 24 is the **lowest common multiple** of 6 and 8.

EXERCISE 8.2B

1 Find the common factors of the following numbers.

a) 6, 12 **b)** 35, 42 **c)** 9, 15
✪ **d)** 10, 20, 30 ✪ **e)** 24, 30, 36

2 Find the common factors of the following numbers.

a) 8, 12 **b)** 10, 25 ✪ **c)** 12, 18, 24
✪ **d)** 15, 21, 27 ✪ **e)** 36, 63, 108

In questions 3–5 find the lowest common multiple of each set of numbers.

3 **a)** 2, 5 **b)** 3, 4 **c)** 3, 5
d) 4, 6 **e)** 10, 15

4 **a)** 6, 12 **b)** 9, 6 **c)** 14, 21
d) 22, 33 ✪ **e)** 8, 5, 10

5 **a)** 6, 14 **b)** 4, 15 ✪ **c)** 2, 7, 10
✪ **d)** 3, 9, 10 ✪ **e)** 3, 7, 11

Lowest common multiples and highest common factors will be covered in more detail in Student's Book 2.

Squares

This pattern sequence is made up of 1 cm squares.

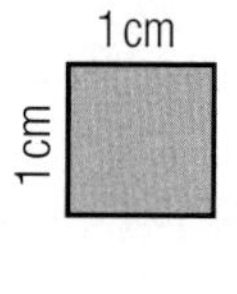

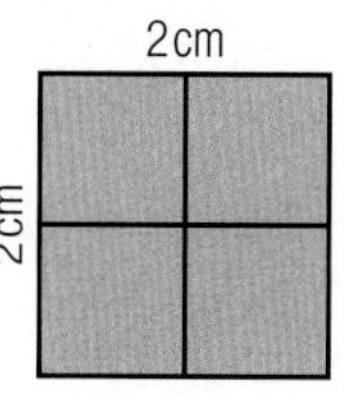

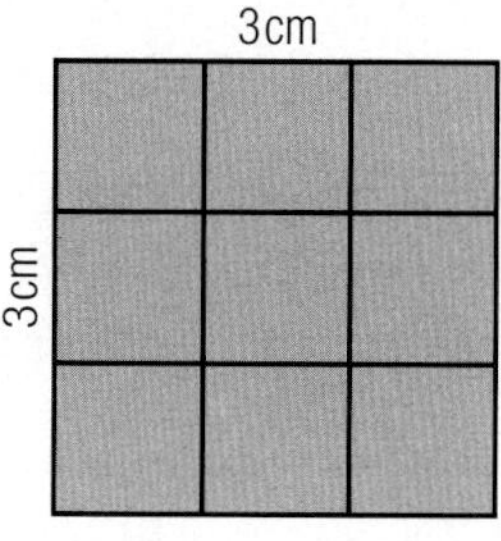

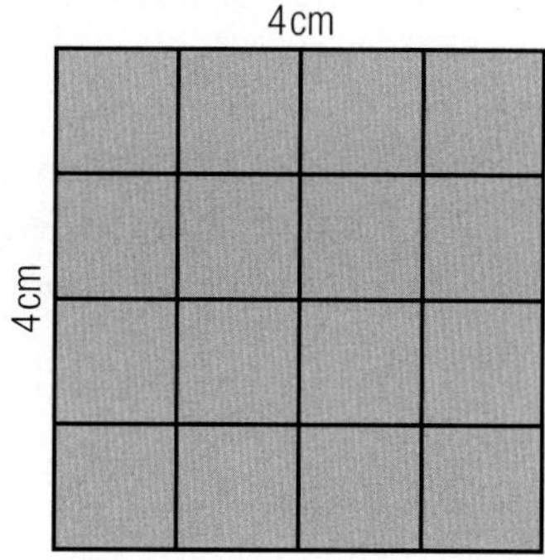

The 1 cm × 1 cm square contains *one* 1 cm × 1 cm square.
The 2 cm × 2 cm square contains *four* 1 cm × 1 cm squares.
The 3 cm × 3 cm square contains *nine* 1 cm × 1 cm squares.
The 4 cm × 4 cm square contains *sixteen* 1 cm × 1 cm squares.

The numbers 1, 4, 9, 16 are **square numbers**, and are made by multiplying an integer (whole number) by itself. For example,

$$8 \times 8 = 64$$

therefore 64 is a square number.

But

$$2.3 \times 2.3 = 5.29$$

5.29 is *not* a square number as 2.3 is not an integer.

Squaring a number is multiplying a number by itself. For example,

8 squared is 8 × 8
2.3 squared is 2.3 × 2.3

There is a short way to write a number squared. It involves using **indices**. For example,

$$8 \times 8 = 8^2$$
$$2.3 \times 2.3 = 2.3^2$$

Using a calculator

The squared button on the calculator usually looks like this: 

Worked example

Use the calculator to evaluate 17^2.

[1] [7] [x^2] [=] 289

Square roots

The **inverse** (opposite) operation to addition is subtraction, and the inverse operation to multiplication is division. Squaring also has an inverse operation.

Using a calculator

All scientific calculators can work out the **square root** of a number by using the [√] key.

Worked example

Use a calculator to work out $\sqrt{729}$.

These instructions are for calculators that use direct algebraic logic. For some calculators, particularly older ones, the calculation needs to be entered differently. Check how yours works.

Calculations without a calculator

Worked examples

a) Without using a calculator evaluate $\sqrt{0.36}$.

0.36 can be written as a fraction.

$$0.36 = \frac{36}{100}$$

$$\sqrt{0.36} = \frac{\sqrt{36}}{\sqrt{100}} = \frac{6}{10}$$

$$\frac{6}{10} = 0.6$$

Therefore $\sqrt{0.36} = 0.6$.

b) Without using a calculator evaluate $\sqrt{0.81}$.

0.81 can be written as a fraction.

$$0.81 = \frac{81}{100}$$

$$\sqrt{0.81} = \frac{\sqrt{81}}{\sqrt{100}} = \frac{9}{10}$$

$$\frac{9}{10} = 0.9$$

Therefore $\sqrt{0.81} = 0.9$.

EXERCISE 8.3

1 How many 1 cm × 1 cm would make up squares with the following side lengths?

a) 3 cm **b)** 5 cm **c)** 8 cm **d)** 10 cm
e) 11 cm **f)** 12 cm **g)** 15 cm **h)** 20 cm

2 Evaluate the following without using a calculator.

a) $\sqrt{25}$ **b)** $\sqrt{9}$ **c)** $\sqrt{121}$ **d)** $\sqrt{169}$
e) $\sqrt{0.01}$ **f)** $\sqrt{0.09}$

3 Use the $\sqrt{\ }$ key on your calculator to check your answers to question 2.

4 Evaluate the following without using a calculator.

a) $\sqrt{\frac{1}{9}}$ **b)** $\sqrt{\frac{1}{49}}$ **c)** $\sqrt{\frac{4}{9}}$ **d)** $\sqrt{\frac{9}{100}}$
e) $\sqrt{\frac{25}{36}}$ **f)** $\sqrt{\frac{49}{81}}$

9 Equations and simple functions

- Construct and solve simple linear equations with integer coefficients (unknown on one side only), e.g. $2x = 8$, $3x + 5 = 14$, $9 - 2x = 7$.
- Represent simple functions using words, symbols and mappings.
- Generate coordinate pairs that satisfy a linear equation, where y is given explicitly in terms of x; plot the corresponding graphs; recognise straight-line graphs parallel to the x or y axis.

Equations

An equation represents two quantities which are equal to each other. To see what an equation is and how it can be used it is useful to look at it as a pair of scales.

Worked examples

a) Look at these scales.

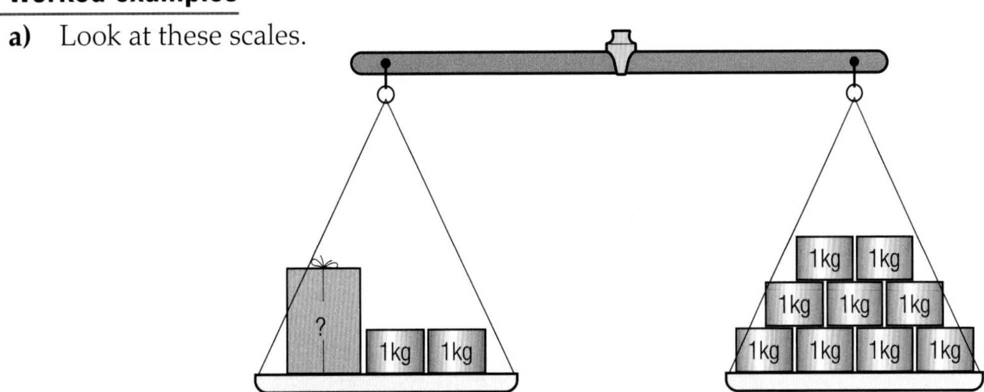

The mass of each of the small boxes is 1 kg. Calculate the mass of the large box.

Because the scales are balanced, the left-hand side of the scales must weigh the same as the right-hand side. In order to keep the scales balanced, whatever we do to the left-hand side of the scales we must also do to the right-hand side.

Take 1kg 1kg from both sides. This leaves:

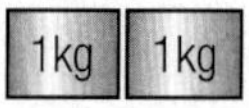

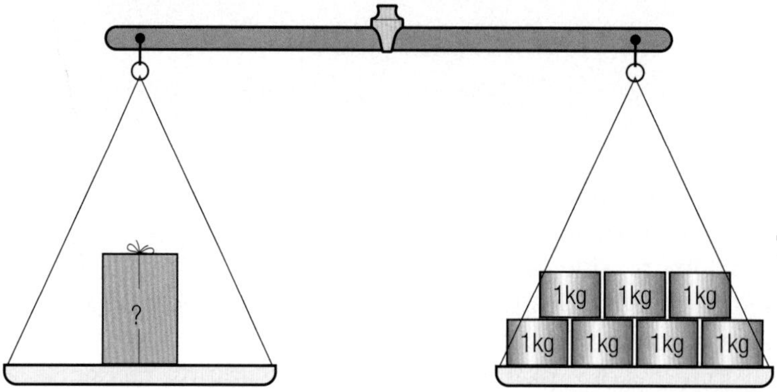

Therefore  ? = 7 kg

b) Look at these scales.

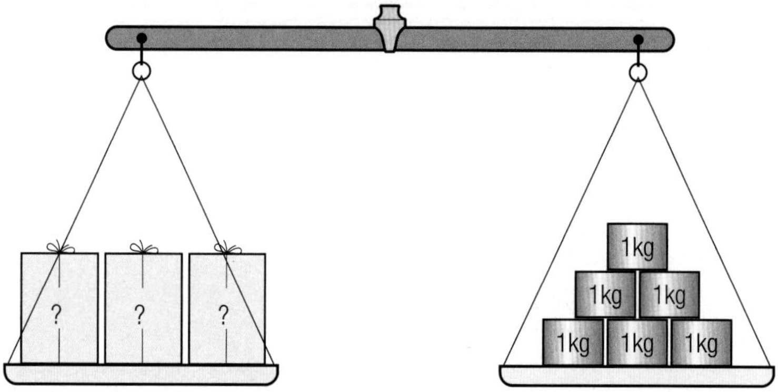

The mass of each of the small boxes is 1 kg. Calculate the mass of each of the large boxes.

We want to find something that we can do to both sides which will leave just one large box on the left-hand side. We can't take two large boxes from both sides as there aren't two to take from the right-hand side. We can divide both sides by 3. This leaves:

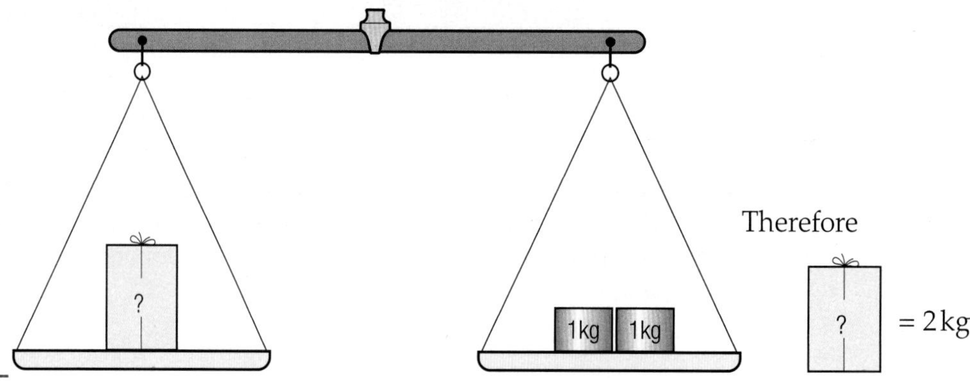

Algebra is a simple way of writing equations like the ones in the examples above.
We can use x to represent the mass of a large box.
Then Example **a)** becomes

$$x + 2\text{kg} = 9\text{kg}$$
$$x + 2\text{kg} - 2\text{kg} = 9\text{kg} - 2\text{kg} \quad \text{(take 2kg from each side)}$$
$$x = 7\text{kg}$$

We write 1x as just x.

Example **b)** becomes:

$$3x = 6\text{kg}$$
$$3x \div 3 = 6\text{kg} \div 3 \quad \text{(divide both sides by 3)}$$
$$x = 2\text{kg}$$

EXERCISE 9.1A

Solve these equations.

1 $a + 3 = 5$	**2** $b + 4 = 9$	**3** $c + 8 = 15$
4 $d + 7 = 8$	**5** $e + 12 = 20$	**6** $f + 8 = 11$
7 $g + 4 = 12$	**8** $h + 9 = 11$	**9** $8 + i = 10$
10 $4 + j = 9$	**11** $15 + k = 20$	**12** $l + 5 = 6$
13 $m + 7 = 9$	**14** $n + 8 = 10$	**15** $13 = e + 2$
16 $17 = p + 8$	**17** $20 = q + 18$	**18** $21 = r + 4$
19 $15 = s + 12$	**20** $20 = t + 1$	**21** $3u = 12$
22 $5v = 20$	**23** $6w = 42$	**24** $4x = 48$
25 $6y = 60$	**26** $7z = 49$	**27** $14 = 7a$
28 $24 = 8b$	**29** $54 = 9c$	**30** $144 = 12d$

Worked example

Solve this equation.

$$3t - 4 = 8$$

In this case, in order to get $3t$ on its own on the left-hand side of the equation, we need to add 4 to each side.

$$3t - 4 + 4 = 8 + 4$$
$$3t = 12$$
$$t = 4 \quad \text{(divide both sides by 3)}$$

EXERCISE 9.1B

Solve these equations.

1 $a - 1 = 4$
2 $b - 6 = 5$
3 $c - 7 = 2$
4 $d - 9 = 8$
5 $e - 3 = 1$
6 $f - 9 = 9$
7 $2g - 3 = 7$
8 $3h - 1 = 2$
9 $7i - 15 = 6$
10 $3j - 18 = 3$
11 $5k + 7 = 32$
12 $9m + 11 = 74$
13 $6n + 12 = 72$
14 $7r - 8 = 41$
15 $6q - 12 = 84$
16 $3k + 7 = 46$
17 $5m + 12 = 72$
18 $9n + 9 = 72$
19 $6r - 8 = 40$
20 $11q - 10 = 89$

Worked example

Solve this equation.

$$\frac{t}{4} = 3$$

$\frac{t}{4}$ means t ÷ 4. To get t on its own on the left-hand side of the equation, multiply both sides of the equation by 4.

$$\frac{t}{4} \times 4 = 3 \times 4$$

Therefore

$$t = 12$$

EXERCISE 9.1C

Solve these equations.

1 $\frac{a}{3} = 4$
2 $\frac{b}{5} = 2$
3 $\frac{c}{4} = 1$
4 $\frac{d}{8} = 3$
5 $\frac{e}{9} = 5$
6 $4 = \frac{f}{3}$
7 $3 = \frac{g}{9}$
8 $2 = \frac{h}{6}$
9 $5 = \frac{i}{4}$
10 $8 = \frac{j}{3}$

EXERCISE 9.1D

Solve these equations.

1 $11a + 2 = 35$

2 $5b - 7 = 3$

3 $6c = 42$

4 $\frac{d}{3} = 4$

5 $e - 4 = 11$

6 $3f - 9 = 12$

7 $4g = 24$

8 $\frac{h}{5} = 3$

9 $55 = 11i - 22$

10 $6 = 3j + 3$

11 $14 = 2k$

12 $3 = \frac{l}{5}$

13 $3m - 9 = 3$

14 $2n - 4 = 8$

15 $3p = 15$

16 $\frac{q}{5} = 4$

17 $20 = 4 + 2r$

18 $8 = 3s - 1$

19 $1 = \frac{t}{3}$

20 $28 = 7r + 7$

Functions

Modern calculators can work out complex calculations, and can draw graphs and run programs. Early calculators, like this one, were used for simple arithmetic.

You enter the number (the *input*), and the calculator does the arithmetic and produces the answer (the *output*).

A **function machine** works in a similar way to a basic calculator.

A number is entered. The function machine carries out the mathematical operations according to a rule (the **function**) and produces an output (the answer). In this case, the function is 'multiply by 2 and then add 6'.

Worked example

The numbers 1, 2, 3, 4, 5, 6 are entered into the function machine shown on the previous page. Calculate the output in each case.

Input	Output
1	8
2	10
3	12
4	14
5	16
6	18

The information in the table can also be shown using a diagram known as a **mapping diagram**.

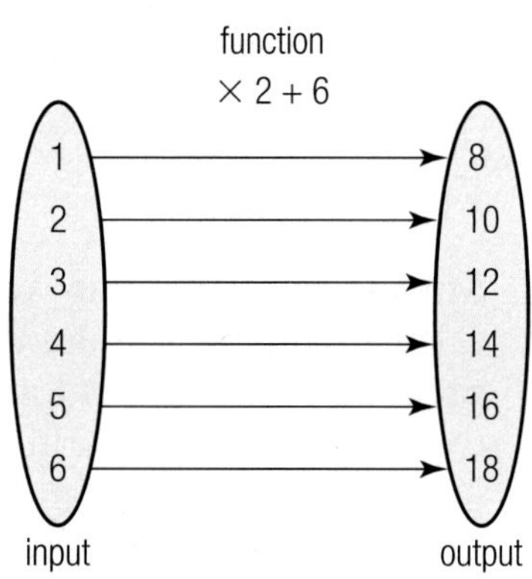

EXERCISE 9.2

In the following questions a number machine is given. The input numbers are listed in the table. Calculate the output values.

1

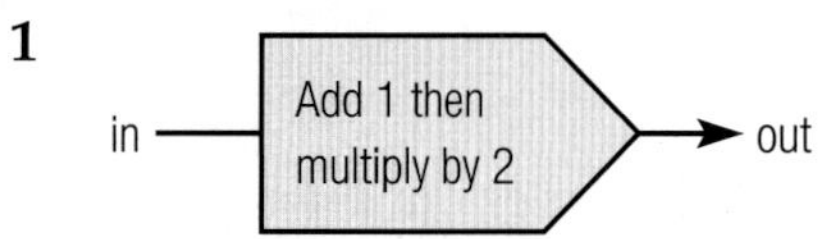

Input	Output
0	
1	
2	
3	

2

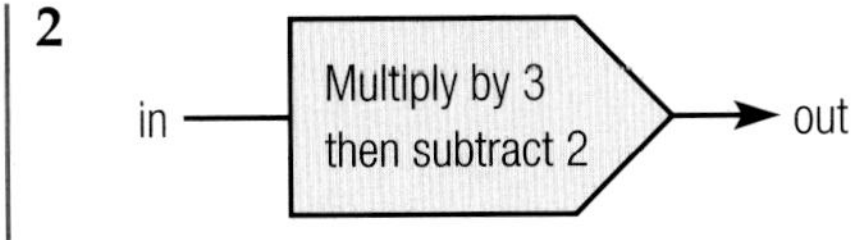

Input	Output
2	
4	
6	
8	

3

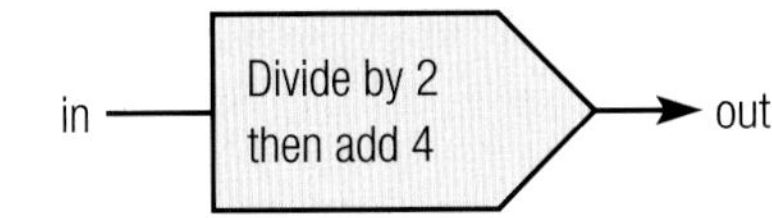

Input	Output
2	
4	
6	
8	

4

in — Subtract 3 then multiply by 2 → out

Input	Output
5	
10	
15	
20	

Graphs of linear functions

A line is made up of an infinite number of points. The coordinates of every point on a straight line all have a common relationship. In other words the x and y values follow a pattern. It is this pattern that gives the equation of the line.

The line below is plotted on a coordinate grid.

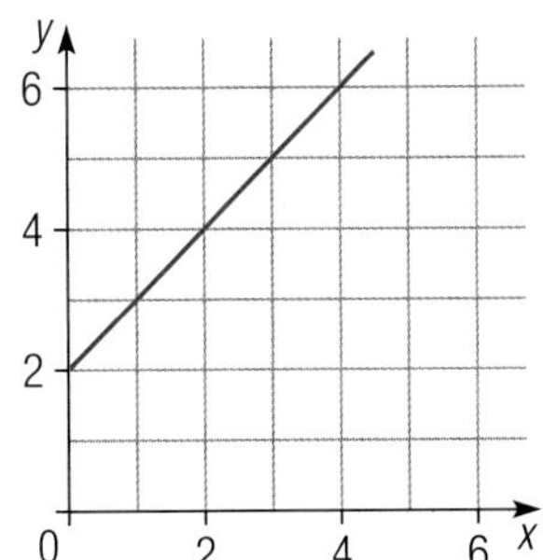

By looking at the coordinates of some of the points on the line we can see a pattern.

In words, the pattern linking the x and y coordinates can be described as follows.
The y coordinates are 2 more than the x coordinates.
Written algebraically, this is

$$y = x + 2.$$

This is an **equation of a straight line**.

x	y
0	2
1	3
2	4
3	5
4	6

Worked example

a) By looking at the coordinates of some of the points on the line below, establish the equation of the straight line.

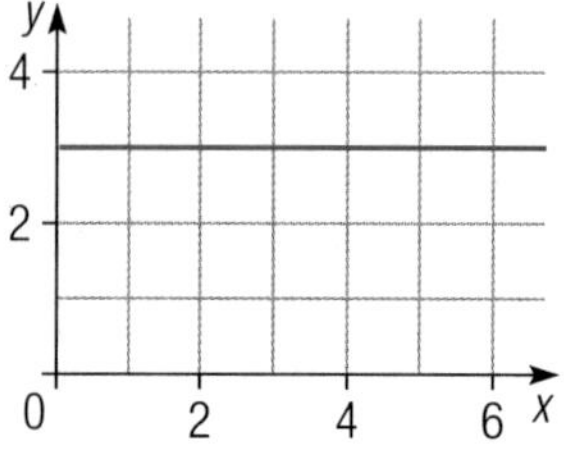

x	y
0	3
2	3
4	3
6	3

By looking at the table we can see that the only rule which all the points have in common is that the y values are always equal to 3. Therefore the equation of the straight line is $y = 3$.

b) By looking at the coordinates of some of the points on the line below, establish the equation of the straight line.

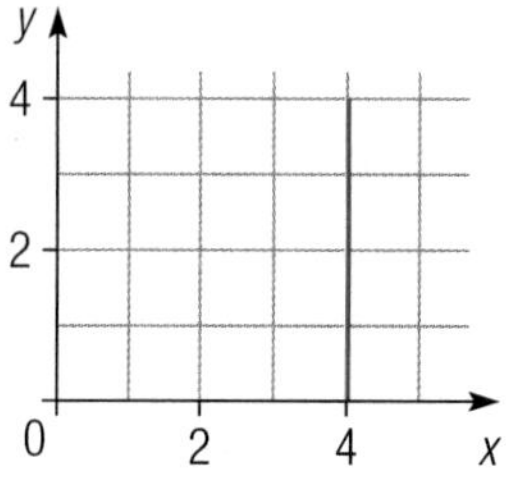

x	y
4	0
4	1
4	2
4	3

By looking at the table we can see that the only rule which all the points have in common is that the x values are always equal to 4. Therefore the equation of the straight line is $x = 4$.

EXERCISE 9.3A

For each of the straight lines in questions 1–8, identify the coordinates of some of the points on the line and use these to find the equation of the straight line.

1

2

3

4

5

6

7

8

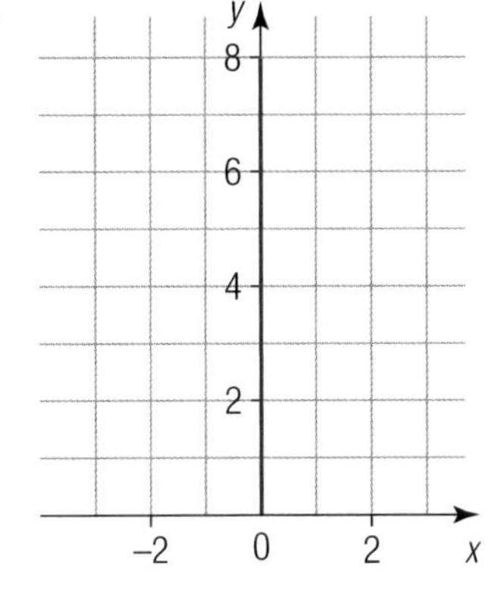

In questions 9–15 work out, simply by looking at the equation, whether if plotted it would produce a horizontal or a vertical line.

9 $y = 6$ **10** $x = 3$ **11** $x = -3$ **12** $y = -2$

13 $x = 6$ **14** $y = -3$ **15** $x = 0$

16 Plot each of the straight lines in questions 9–15 to check your answers.

Points on a straight line

So far we have been looking at the equations of horizontal and vertical lines. Lines which are neither horizontal nor vertical have equations that involve both x and y. For example,

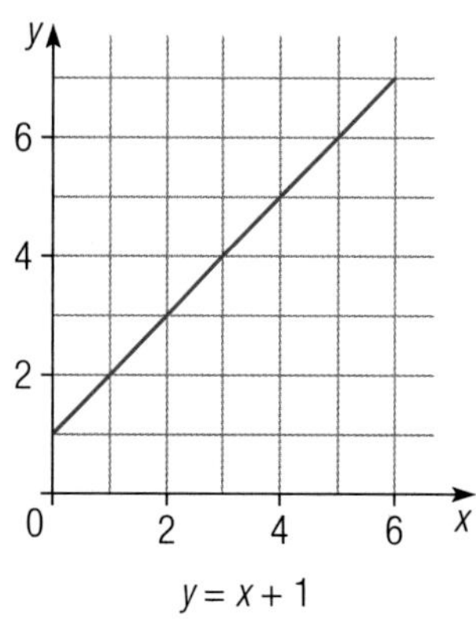

$y = x + 1$

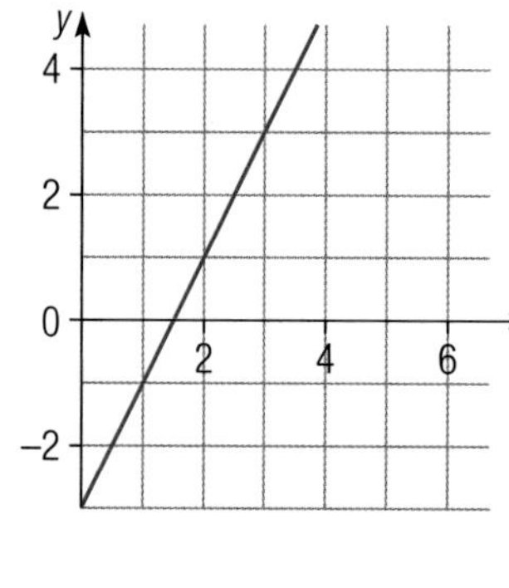

$y = 2x - 3$

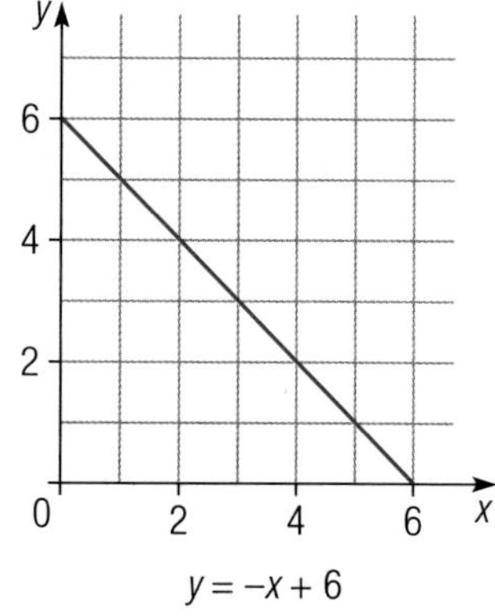

$y = -x + 6$

But these graphs show only a part of each line. The lines can be extended at both ends.

By looking at the equation of a line, it is possible to work out what points lie on it. The x and y coordinates of *any* point on the line must satisfy its equation. We can substitute the x and y values of the coordinates of a point into the equation to see whether the point is on the line.

Worked example

This graph shows a straight line.
Its equation is $y = 3 - x$.
The line is of infinite length.
Work out which of the following points are on the line.

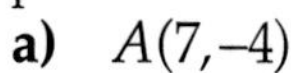

a) $A(7,-4)$
b) $B(-1,4)$
c) $C(10,-6)$

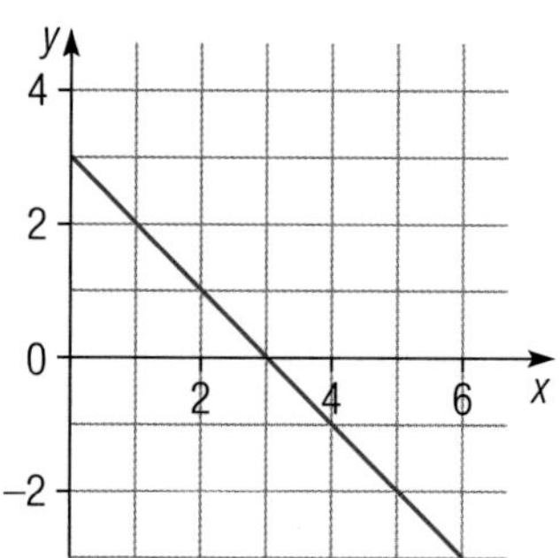

a) Substituting $x = 7$ and $y = -4$ into the equation $y = 3 - x$ gives:

$-4 = 3 - 7$

$-4 = -4$

This is true, so $A(7,-4)$ lies on the line $y = 3 - x$.

b) Substituting $x = -1$ and $y = 4$ into the equation $y = 3 - x$ gives:

$4 = 3 - (-1)$

$4 = 4$

This is true, so $B(-1,4)$ lies on the line $y = 3 - x$.

c) Substituting $x = 10$ and $y = -6$ into the equation $y = 3 - x$ gives:

$-6 = 3 - 10$

$-6 = -7$

This is *not* true, so $C(10,-6)$ does not lie on the line $y = 3 - x$.

EXERCISE 9.3B

In questions 1–6 decide which of the points listed lie on the line given.

1	$y = x$	$A(3,3)$	$B(12,12)$	$C(3,-3)$	$D(-5,-5)$
2	$y = 2x$	$P(0,0)$	$Q(3,5)$	$R(-5,10)$	$S(-4,-8)$
3	$y = 2x - 1$	$F(1,0)$	$G(6,11)$	$H(-3,-7)$	$I(0,-1)$
4	$y = \frac{1}{2}x + 3$	$W(2,4)$	$X(12,9)$	$Y(-6,0)$	$Z(-20,-7)$
5	$y = 4 - x$	$K(4,0)$	$L(0,4)$	$M(-5,-1)$	$N(-5,9)$
6	$y = -2x + 4$	$T(0,2)$	$U(7,-10)$	$V(-3,-2)$	$W(\frac{1}{2},3)$

In questions 7–10, the equation of a straight line is given. In each case the x coordinate of three points on the line are also given. Calculate the y coordinate of each point on the line.

7	$y = x + 5$	**a)** (3,)	**b)** (8,)	**c)** (–4,)
8	$y = 2x - 3$	**a)** (0,)	**b)** (4,)	**c)** (–1,)
9	$y = \frac{1}{2}x + 1$	**a)** (2,)	**b)** (0,)	**c)** (–4,)
10	$y = -x + 3$	**a)** (3,)	**b)** (6,)	**c)** (–2,)

10 Measurement and construction

- Use a ruler, set square and protractor to:
  - measure and draw straight lines to the nearest millimetre
  - measure and draw acute, obtuse and reflex angles to the nearest degree
  - draw parallel and perpendicular lines
  - construct a triangle given two sides and the included angle (SAS) or two angles and the included side (ASA)
  - construct squares and rectangles
  - construct regular polygons, given a side and the internal angle.
- Estimate the size of acute, obtuse and reflex angles to the nearest 10°.

Look at these pyramids. The engineers who planned their construction must have had a good knowledge of two-dimensional (flat) shapes. Constructing triangles and rectangles accurately was central to the construction methods used by ancient civilisations.

Lines and angles

Lines

EXERCISE 10.1A

1 Measure these lines with a ruler. Be as accurate as you can.

a) ____

b) ____________________________

c) ____________

d) ____________

e) ____________

f) ____________

g) ____________

h) —

i) ____________

j) ____________

2 Draw lines of the following lengths using a ruler.

a) 3 cm b) 40 mm c) 4.7 cm

d) 53 mm e) 68 mm f) 7.4 cm

Angles

An **angle** is a measure of turn. Angles can be drawn using a protractor or an angle measurer. The units of turn are **degrees** (°).

Worked examples

a) Measure this angle.

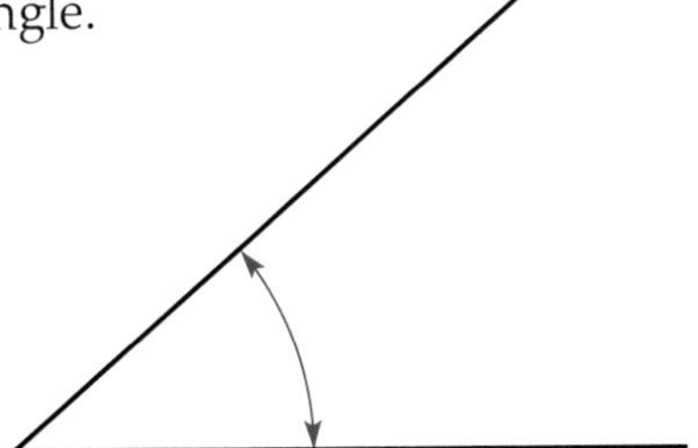

- Place the protractor over the angle as shown.

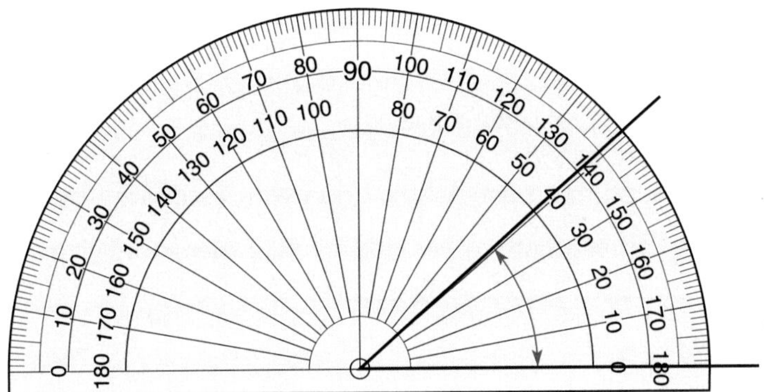

- Align one of the lines of the angle with 0° on the protractor.
- Decide which scale to use. In this case, the inner scale starts at 0°. The angle is 41°.

b) Draw an angle of 120°.

- First draw a straight line about 6 cm long.
- Place the protractor on the line so that the central cross hair is on one of the end points of the line. Make sure that the line lines up with 0° on the protractor.

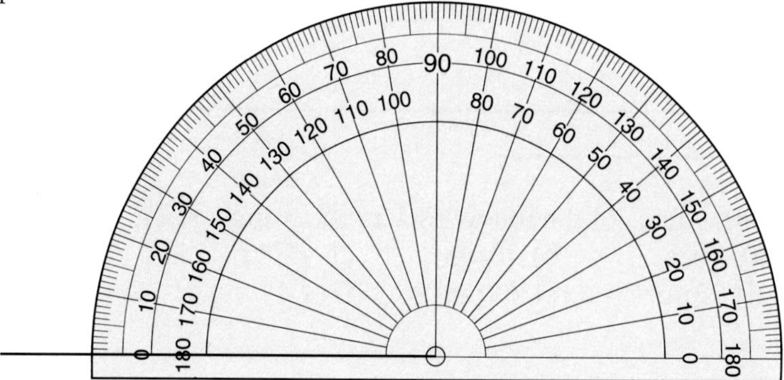

- Decide which scale to use. In this case, the outer scale starts at 0°.
- Mark where the protractor reads 120°.
- Join the mark to the end of the line.

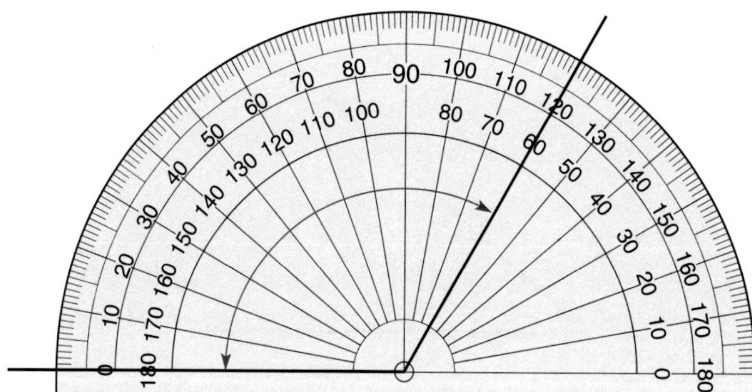

EXERCISE 10.1B

1 For each of the following angles:

(i) estimate its size

(ii) measure it and check how good your estimate was.

Aim for your estimate to be within 10° of the actual size.

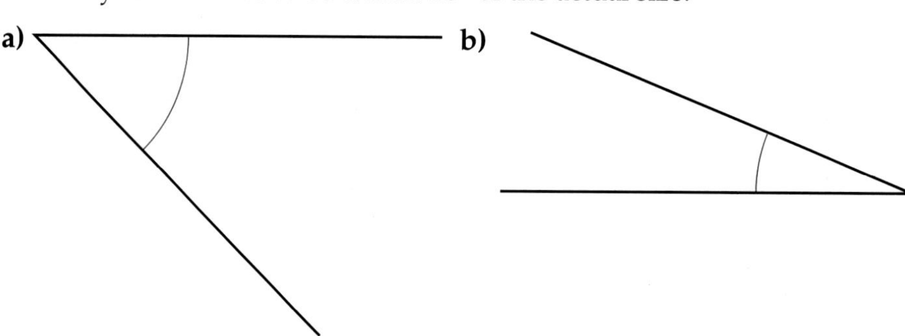

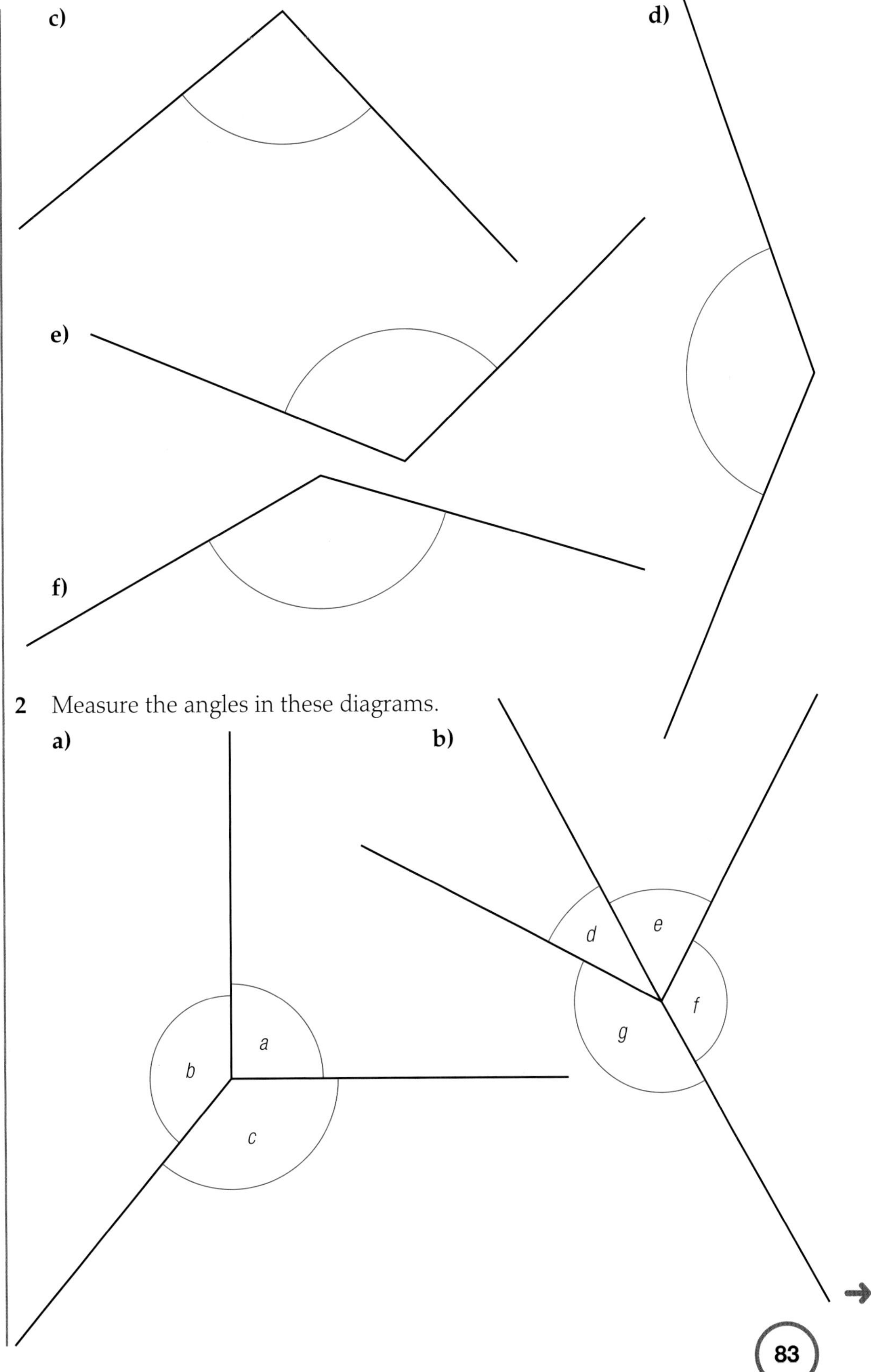

2 Measure the angles in these diagrams.

a) **b)**

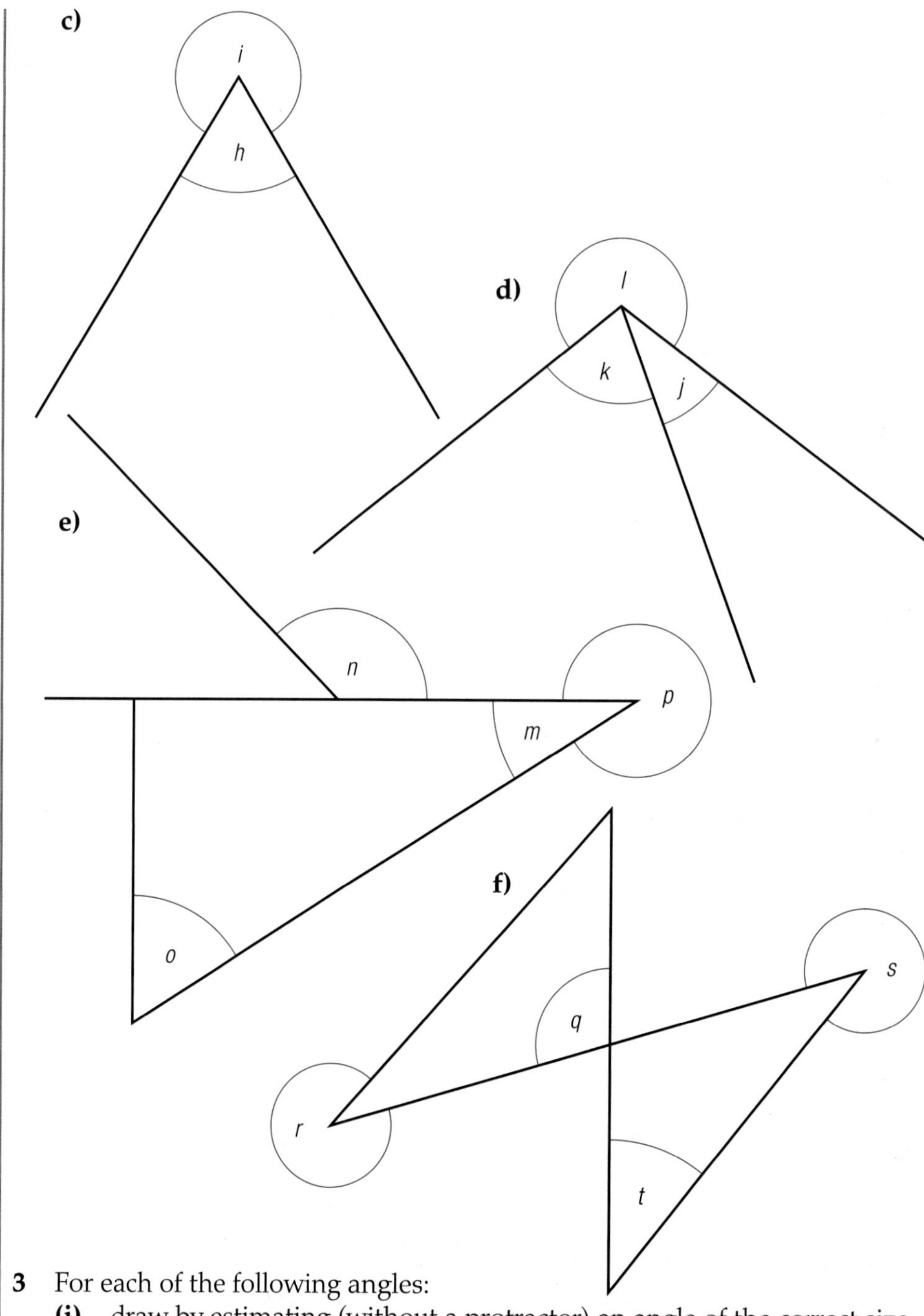

3 For each of the following angles:

(i) draw by estimating (without a protractor) an angle of the correct size

(ii) alongside your first diagram, draw the same angle with a protractor.

Compare your results. How good were your estimates?

a) 20°	**b)** 45°	**c)** 90°	**d)** 120°
e) 157°	**f)** 172°	**g)** 14°	**h)** 205°
i) 311°	**j)** 283°	**k)** 198°	**l)** 352°

Constructing triangles

To construct triangles accurately, a range of mathematical equipment is needed. This includes:

- a ruler
- a protractor/angle measurer.

This next section will show how to construct triangles accurately depending on the type of information given.

Given the length of the base of the triangle and the sizes of the two base angles

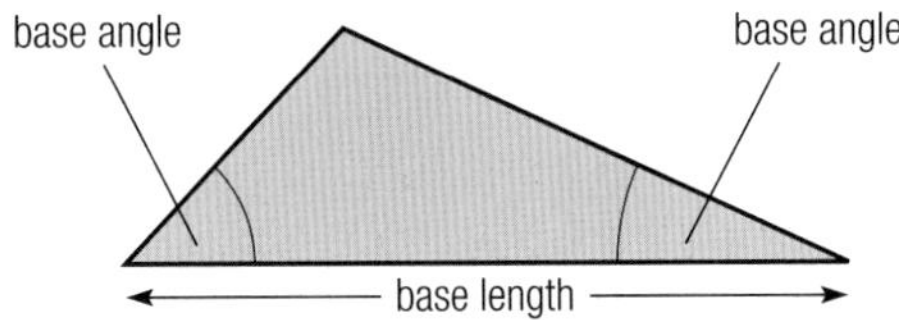

Worked example

Draw a triangle ABC where the length of side AB is 8.2 cm, $\angle A = 52°$ and $\angle B = 40°$. Use a ruler and protractor.

Make sure to leave enough room above the line for the rest of the triangle.

- First draw a line 8.2 cm long and label its ends A and B.

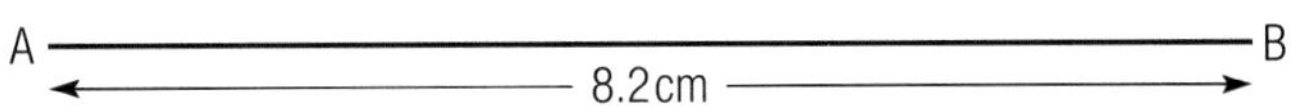

- Then use your protractor as shown to mark angles A and B.

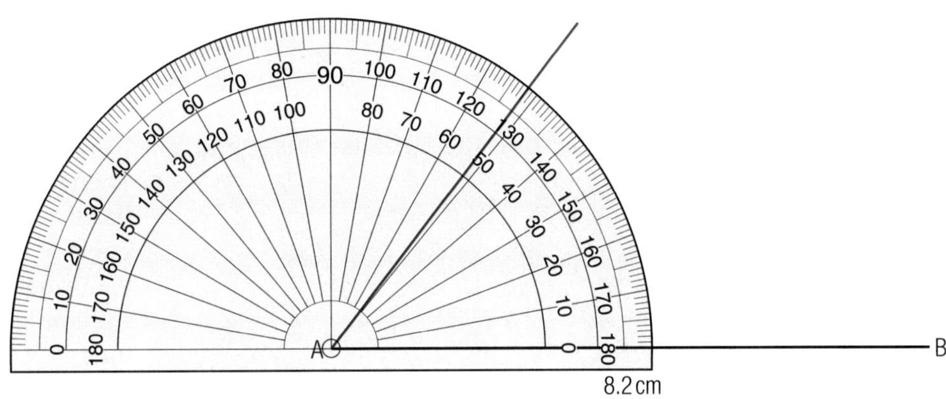

- Extend each of the lines drawn so that they intersect. Label the point of intersection C.

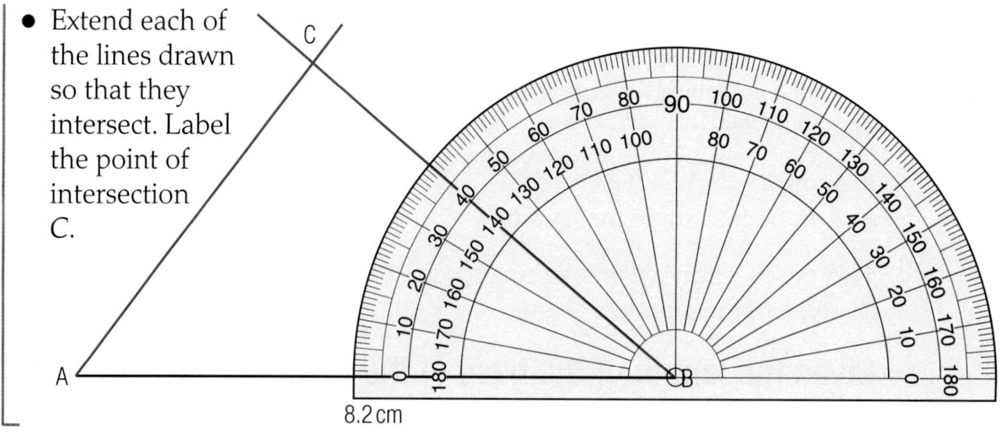

EXERCISE 10.2A

Draw the following triangles *ABC*. After each construction measure the sides *AC* and *BC* and angle *C*. You will need a ruler and a protractor.

1 $AB = 7\,\text{cm}$ $\quad\angle A = 50°$ $\quad\angle B = 40°$

2 $AB = 8.5\,\text{cm}$ $\quad\angle A = 30°$ $\quad\angle B = 60°$

3 $AB = 9.0\,\text{cm}$ $\quad\angle A = 45°$ $\quad\angle B = 45°$

4 $AB = 8.3\,\text{cm}$ $\quad\angle A = 100°$ $\quad\angle B = 30°$

5 $AB = 7.6\,\text{cm}$ $\quad\angle A = 112°$ $\quad\angle B = 41°$

Given the lengths of two sides and the size of one angle

Worked example

Construct the triangle *ABC*, where the length $AB = 8\,\text{cm}$, $AC = 7\,\text{cm}$ and $\angle A = 60°$. You will need a ruler and a protractor.

- First draw a line 8 cm long and label its ends *A* and *B*.
- Then use your protractor to mark an angle of 60° at *A*. Use your ruler to draw a straight line from *A* to the mark, and extend the line.

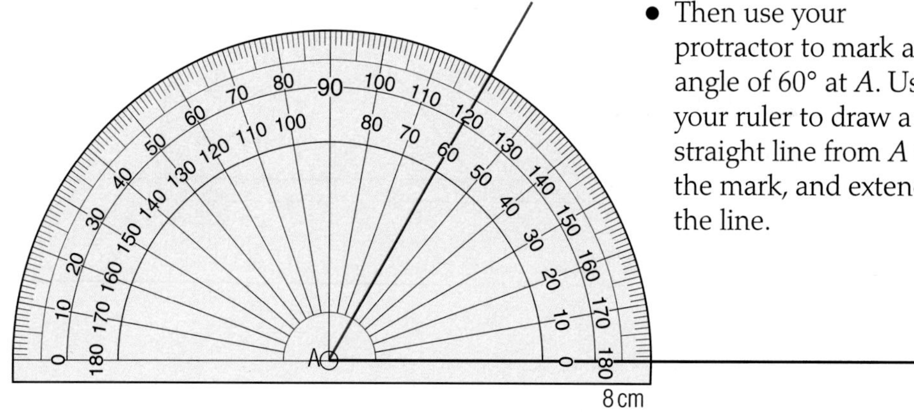

- Measure 7 cm from *A* along this line. Label this point *C*.

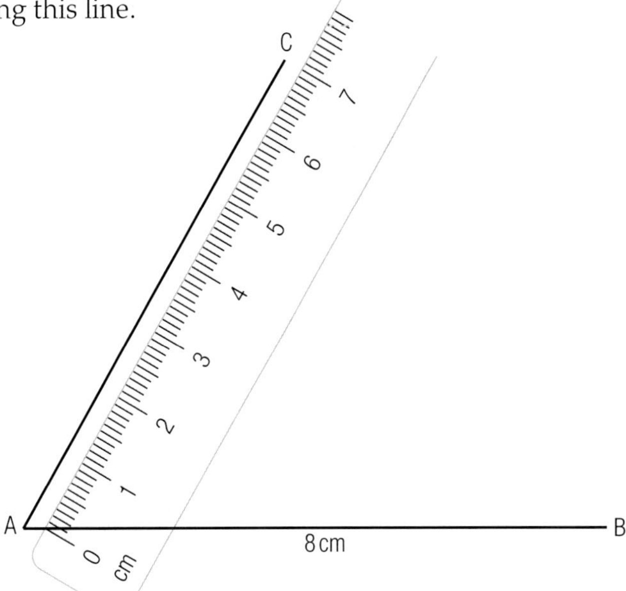

- Now draw a straight line from *B* to *C*. This completes the triangle *ABC*.

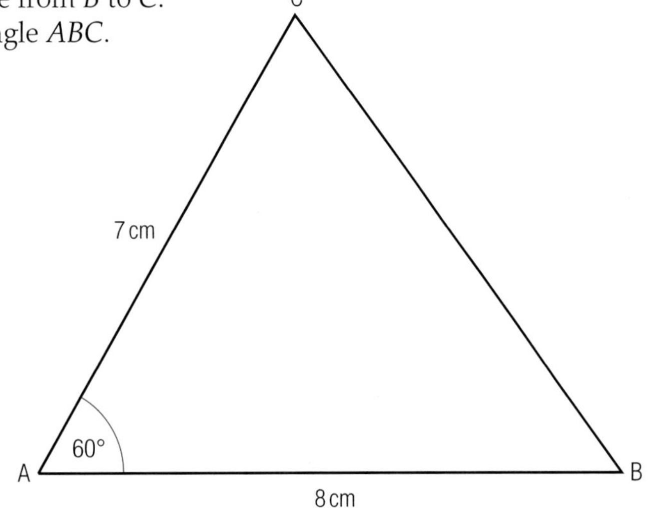

EXERCISE 10.2B

Construct the following triangles *ABC*.

1 $AB = 10\text{ cm}$ $AC = 8\text{ cm}$ $\angle A = 45°$

2 $AB = 13\text{ cm}$ $AC = 12\text{ cm}$ $\angle A = 35°$

3 $AB = 8\text{ cm}$ $AC = 10\text{ cm}$ $\angle A = 100°$

4 $AB = 6.8\text{ cm}$ $AC = 6.8\text{ cm}$ $\angle A = 72°$

Constructing simple geometric figures

Constructing a polygon accurately requires careful use of a ruler and a protractor.

Worked example

Construct a regular polygon of side length 4 cm and internal angles of size 108°. You will need a ruler and a protractor. Describe the polygon you have constructed.

- Draw a line *AB*, 4 cm long.

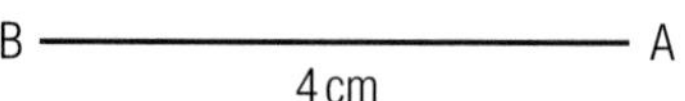

- Place your protractor on *B* and mark an internal angle of 108°.

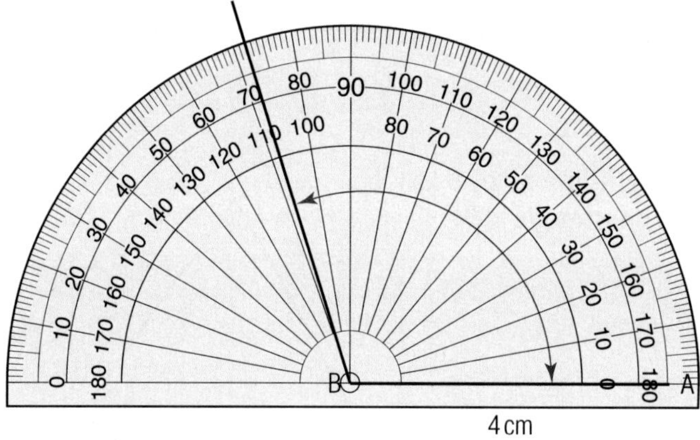

- Draw a line from *B* through the mark and measure off 4 cm. Label this new point *C*.

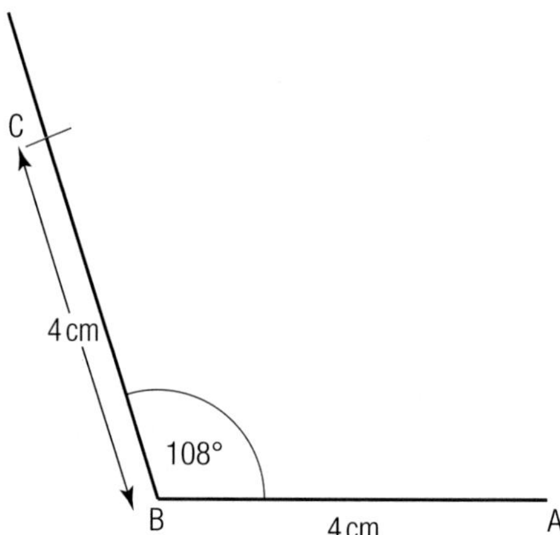

- Place the protractor on *C* and repeat the procedure until the polygon is complete.

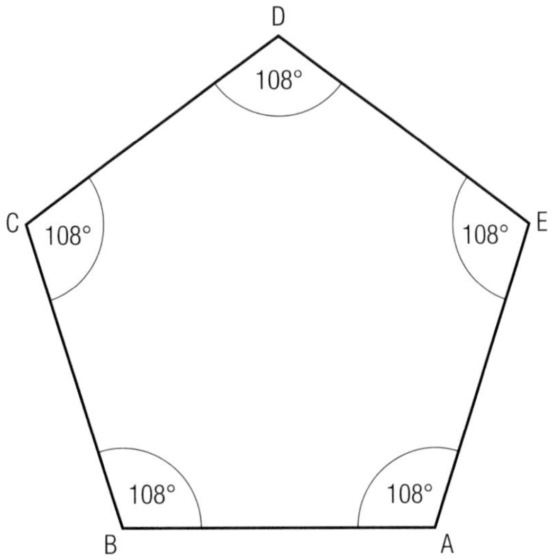

The polygon is a regular pentagon.

EXERCISE 10.3A

1 Construct the following shapes using a ruler and protractor.

a)

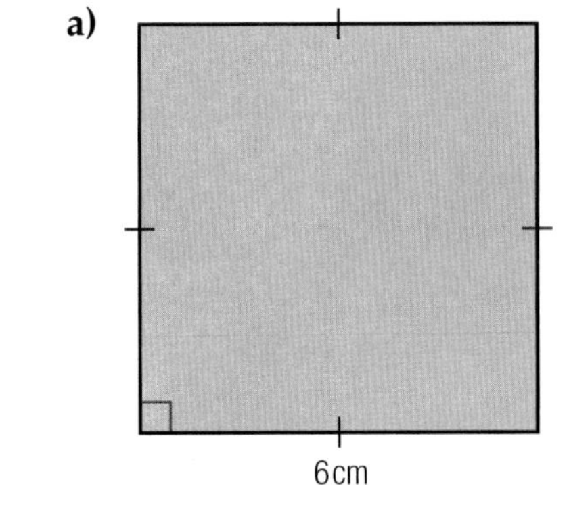

b)

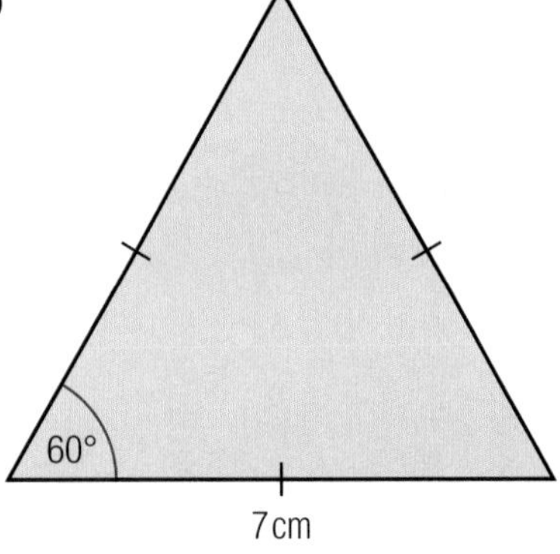

c)

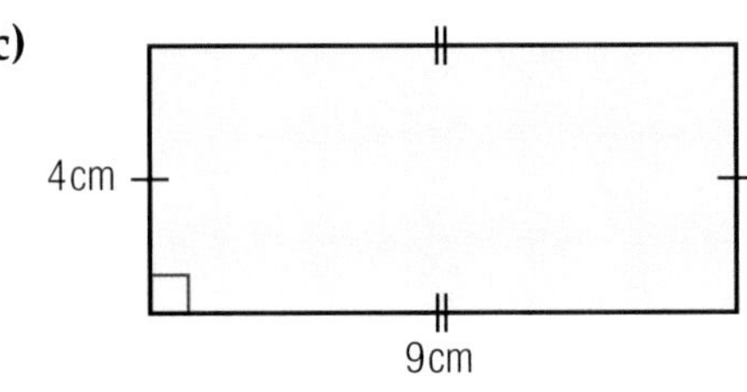

2 **a)** Construct a regular polygon with side length 5 cm and internal angles of size 120°.
b) Name the regular polygon you have drawn.

3 **a)** Construct a regular polygon with side length 4 cm and internal angles of size 135°.
b) Name the regular polygon you have drawn.

Exercise 10.3A question 2 involved constructing a regular hexagon. Although construction using a pair of compasses are not covered until later in the series, the worked example below provides a quick alternative method.

Worked example

Construct a regular hexagon using a pair of compasses and a ruler.

- Open up a pair of compasses to about 3 cm and draw a circle.
- Keep the compasses open by the same amount. Put the compass point on the circumference of the circle and draw an arc. Make sure that the arc intersects the circumference.
- Place the compass point on the point of intersection of the arc and the circumference and draw another arc. Repeat this procedure until you have drawn six arcs.

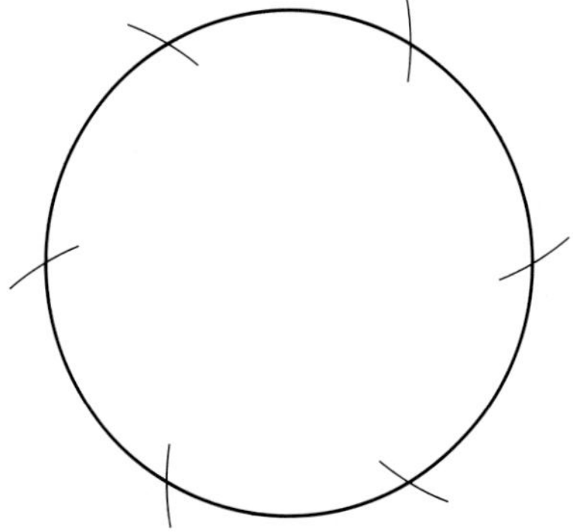

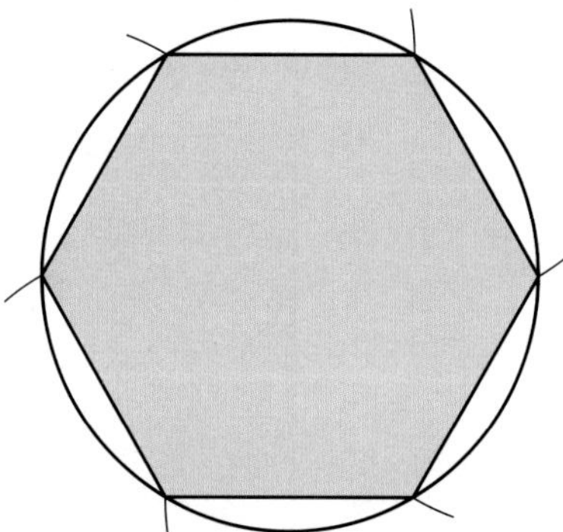

- Join up the six arcs to form a regular hexagon.

You can also construct shapes using a ruler and a set square. The set square provides a right angle, which you use to draw lines perpendicular (at right angles) to each other. Set squares in the shape of an isosceles triangle also provide angles of 45°.

Worked example

Construct a square of side length 6 cm.

- Draw a line 6 cm long.
- Place a set square at the end of the line. Make sure that one of the perpendicular sides rests on your line. Draw another line 6 cm long, perpendicular to your first line.
- Repeat this for the remaining two sides.

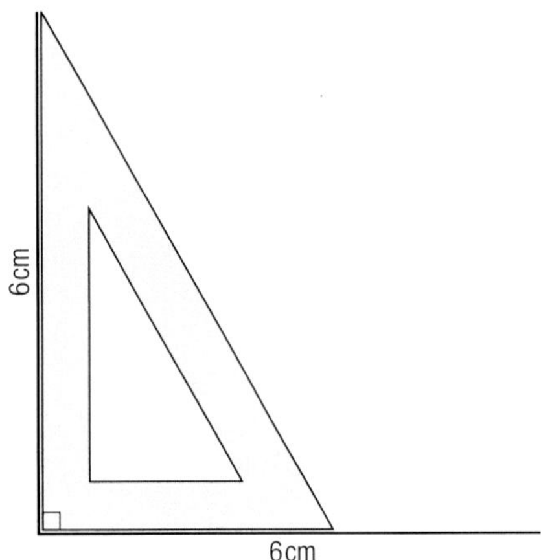

EXERCISE 10.3B

Using a ruler and set square only, construct the following shapes.

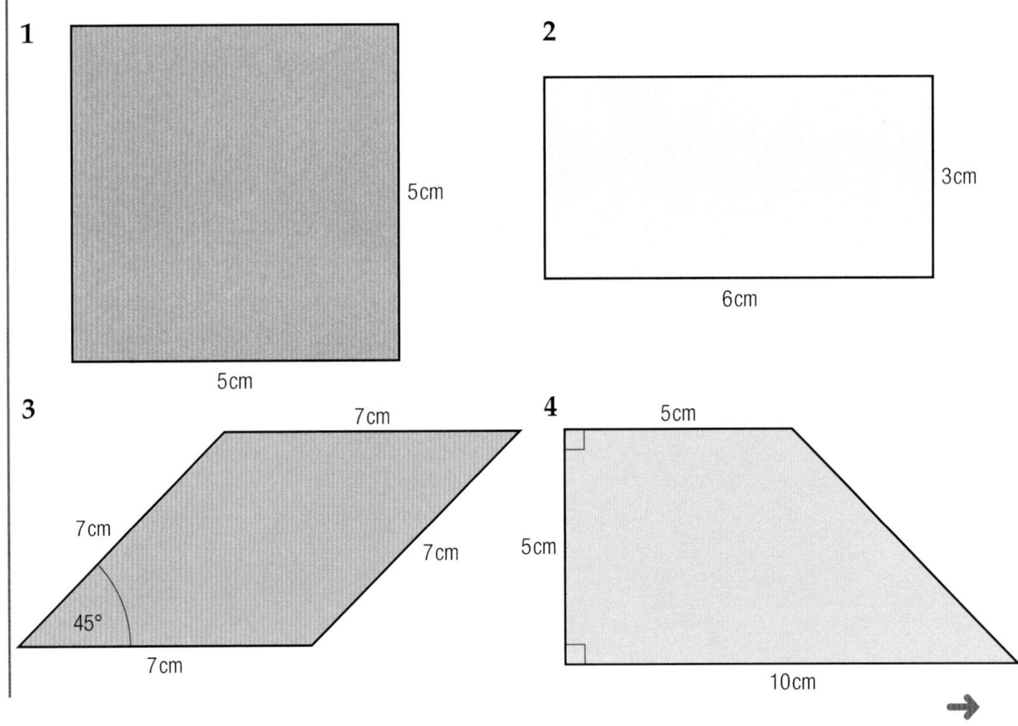

Using appropriate mathematical equipment, construct the following shapes.

5

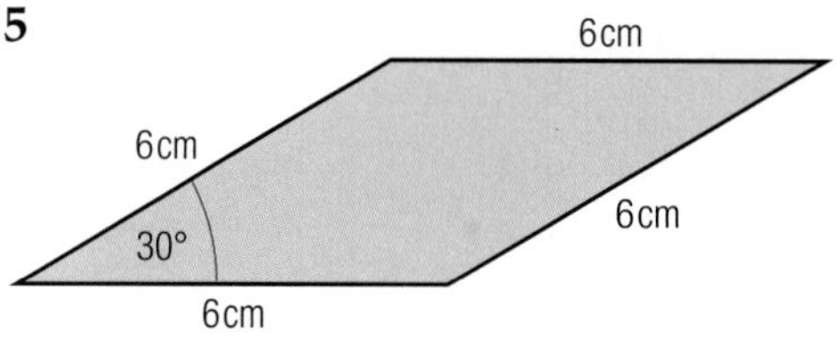

6cm
6cm
30°
6cm
6cm

6

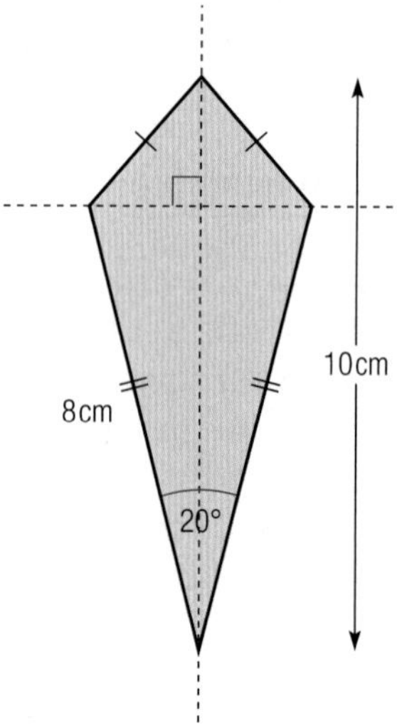

8cm
20°
10cm

7

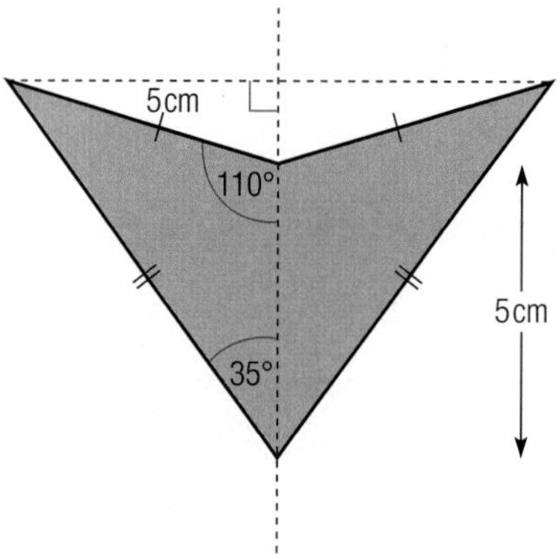

5cm
110°
35°
5cm

8

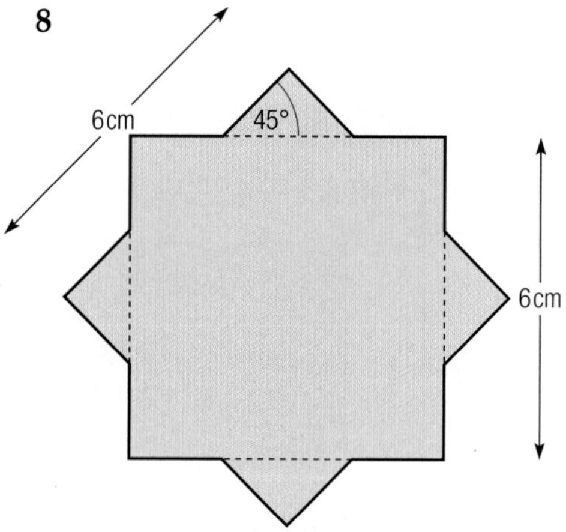

6cm
45°
6cm

11 Time

- Draw and interpret graphs in real life contexts involving more than one stage, e.g. travel graphs.
- Know the relationships between units of time; understand and use the 12-hour and 24-hour clock systems; interpret timetables; calculate time intervals.

The 12-hour and 24-hour clocks

The system of time keeping we use today is extremely precise. It is based on the Earth's movement around the Sun, and it is so accurate that it will take 44 000 years before it falls out of step with the Sun by as much as a single day.

Although all countries use the same units for measuring the passage of time (seconds, minutes, hours, days, years), they do not all use the same reference point (year 0). The Christian world is in its third millennium because Christians take their reference point as the birth of Christ. Orthodox Jews take their reference point as the day they believe the Earth was created, 6 October 3761 BCE. Muslims calculate the date from the year after Mohammed's flight to Mecca in 622 CE. Hindus calculate from the birth of Brahma.

The units of time are now the same all over the world but this was not always true. You may like to look on the internet or in books to find out about the ways that passage of time was measured in earlier cultures.

The system used in the modern world is as follows:

60 seconds is one minute,
60 minutes is one hour,
24 hours is one day.

There are two common ways of describing the time of day: the 12-hour clock and the 24-hour clock. The 12-hour clock uses a.m. and p.m. to distinguish between morning and afternoon. With the 24-hour clock, times from 00 00 to 12 00 refer to the morning, and times from 12 00 up to 24 00 refer to the afternoon or evening.

Worked examples

a) Write these times as 24-hour clock times.

(i) 5a.m. **(ii)** 9p.m. **(iii)** 8.35p.m.

To change a.m. times to 24-hour clock times, simply write them using four digits, adding a leading zero if necessary.
To change p.m. times to 24-hour clock times, add 12 hours and write them using four digits.

(i) 5a.m. is written as 0500.
(ii) 9p.m. is written as 2100.
(iii) 8.35p.m. is written as 2035.

b) Write these times as 12-hour clock times.

(i) 0730 **(ii)** 1620 **(iii)** 2345

To change 24-hour clock times which are before 1200 to 12-hour clock times, simply write them using a.m.
To change 24-hour clock times which are after 1200 to 12-hour clock times, subtract 12 hours and write them using p.m.

(i) 0730 is written as 7.30a.m.
(ii) 1620 is written as 4.20p.m.
(iii) 2345 is written as 11.45p.m.

EXERCISE 11.1A

Write each time in questions 1–4 as a 24-hour clock time.

1 **a)** 8.30a.m. **b)** 5.35a.m. **c)** 9.55a.m.

2 **a)** 6.45p.m. **b)** 11.30p.m. **c)** 4.50p.m.

3 Seven o'clock in the evening.

4 Noon.

5 How long is it:
a) from twenty past ten in the evening to five past midnight?
b) from ten past ten at night until midnight?
c) from a quarter past eight in the morning until noon?
d) from noon until a quarter past eight at night?
e) from a quarter past eight in the morning until ten past nine at night?
f) from a quarter to eight at night until ten past nine the next morning?

6 How long is it:
a) from 0800 until 0945? **b)** from 1800 until 2045?
c) from 0400 until 2235? **d)** from 0830 until 1945?
e) from 0745 until 0900? **f)** from 0655 until 1445?

7 How long is it:
a) from 1800 until 0945 the next day?
b) from 0730 until 0145 the next day?
c) from 1850 until 0920 the next day?
d) from 0810 until 0035 the next day?

EXERCISE 11.1B

1 A boy cycles from home to school and his journey takes 25 minutes. What time will he arrive when he leaves home at the following times?
a) 0815 **b)** 0755 **c)** 0735

2 A girl walks home from school and her journey takes 18 minutes. What time will she arrive when she leaves school at the following times?
a) 1612 **b)** 1548 **c)** 1745

3 The train journey from a town to a city takes 1 hour 8 minutes. Copy and complete the timetable below.

Depart	Arrive
0523	
0715	
	1012
	1136
1445	
1622	
	1917
	2125

4 A plane flies between four airports in Turkey. They are Istanbul, Ankara, Bursa and Izmir. The time taken for each journey remains constant. Copy and complete the timetable below for the journeys.

Istanbul	0500	0715			
Ankara	0630		1045		
Bursa	0805				1620
Izmir	0850			1430	

→

5 British Airways planes fly twice a day from London to Dubai. Dubai is 2 hours ahead of London. The flight time is 6 hours 12 minutes. Copy and complete the timetable below.

	London	Dubai (local time)	London	Dubai (local time)
Sunday	0200		1400	
Monday		1012		2200
Tuesday	0310		1510	
Wednesday		1148		2133
Thursday	0255		1515	
Friday		0909		2248
Saturday	0638		1648	

6 Try to obtain a coach or train timetable for a city or town near where you live. Write five questions based on the timetable. Exchange your questions with those of another student in your class, and answer each other's questions.

Travel graphs

When an object moves, there are several variables that can be measured. These include the distance it travels and the speed it is travelling at. Often an object's movement can be best visualised using a distance–time graph.

An object travelling at a constant speed can be shown as a straight line on a graph.

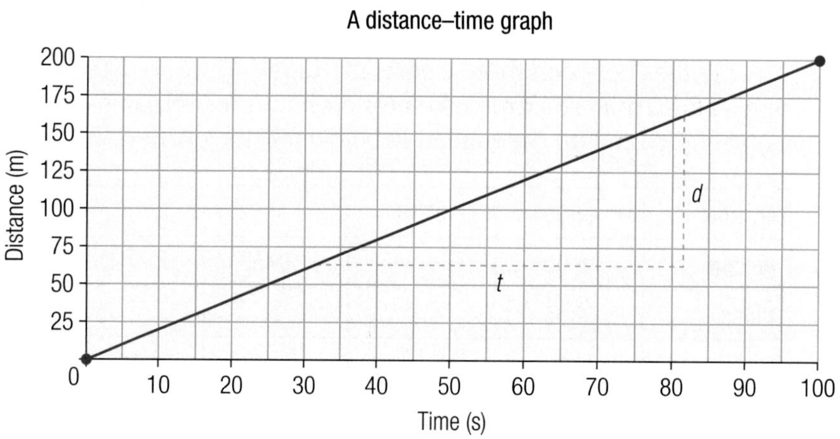

The gradient of the graph is found by the formula:

$$\text{gradient} = \frac{d}{t}$$

This gradient represents the speed of the object. If the distance is in metres and the time in seconds, the units of the gradient are m/s.

EXERCISE 11.2A

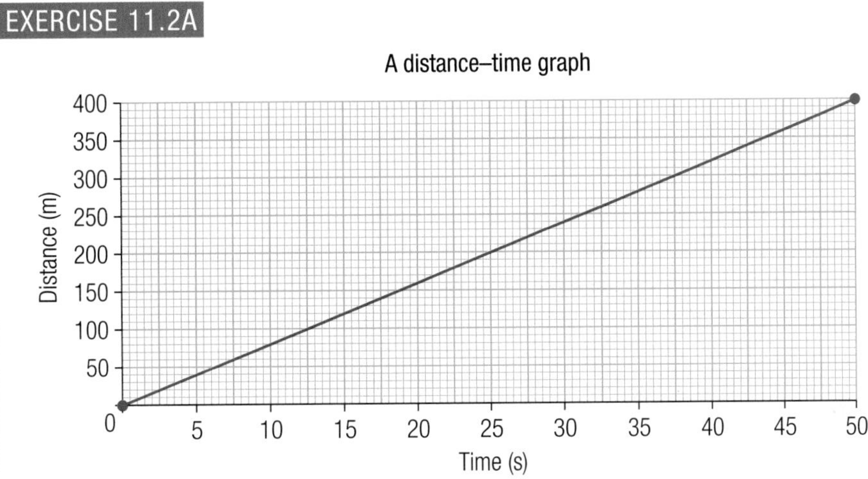

The graph above shows an object travelling at 8 m/s (a distance of 80 m in 10 seconds).

Using the graph or by any other method, find:

1 how long the object takes to travel 50 m

2 how far the object travels in 5 seconds

3 how long the object takes to travel 70 m

4 how far the object travels in 8 seconds

5 how long the object takes to travel 650 m

6 how far the object travels in 1 minute

7 how long the object takes to travel 1 km

8 how far the object travels in 5 minutes

9 how long the object takes to travel 550 m

10 how many metres the object travels in 1 hour.

EXERCISE 11.2B

A second object travels at 12 m/s.

Draw a graph and use it to answer the questions in Exercise 11.2A for this object.

EXERCISE 11.2C

The graph below shows a family car journey. Copy the graph and use it to answer the questions below.

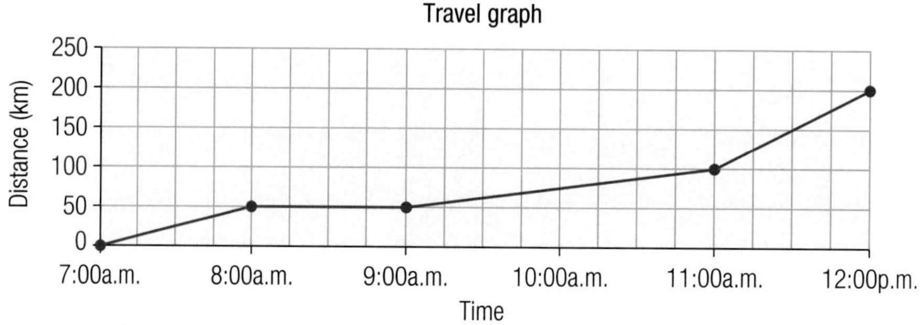

1 What time did the family set out?

2 **a)** How far did they travel in the first hour?
b) What was their average speed?

3 What time did they stop for breakfast?

4 How long did they stop for breakfast?

5 How far did they travel between 9.00a.m. and 11.00a.m?

6 The average speed is calculated by dividing the total distance travelled, by the total time taken. Calculate their average speed during those two hours.

7 The family reached a motorway at 11.00a.m. What was their average speed for the next hour?

8 How long did the whole journey take?

9 How far did they travel in total?

10 What was the average speed for the whole journey?

11 A second family sets out on the same journey by train. They leave at 9.00a.m. and arrive at noon. Show this journey on your graph.

12 What was the average speed of the train?

EXERCISE 11.2D

1 A salesman leaves home at 08 00 and travels for $1\frac{1}{2}$ hours at an average speed of 60 km/h. He then stops for 30 minutes. He continues for 2 more hours at 50 km/h and stops for 1 hour. He then returns home and arrives home at 16 00.

a) Show this in a travel graph.

b) Calculate his average speed for his return journey.

2 A train leaves a station at 07 30. It travels for 1 hour 30 minutes at 100 km/h and then stops for 15 minutes. It travels a further 200 km at 100 km/h and then stops for 30 minutes. It then does the return journey non-stop at 100 km/h.

a) Draw a graph of the journey.

b) When does the train arrive back at the station?

3 The graph below shows a cycle journey for a boy. Use it to answer the questions below.

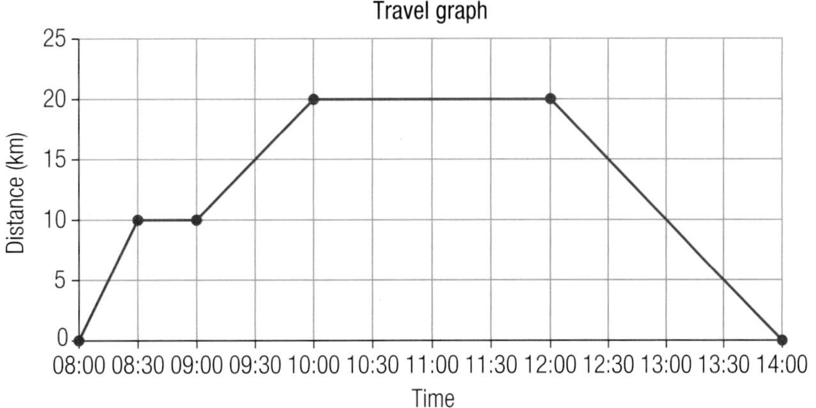

a) At what time did he leave?

b) **(i)** How long did he cycle for before first stopping?

(ii) What was his average speed before he first stopped?

(iii) How long was his first stop for?

c) **(i)** How long did he travel before stopping again?

(ii) How far had he travelled during this time?

(iii) What was his average speed for this part of the journey?

d) What does the graph show from noon to 14 00 hours?

e) What was his average speed for his return journey?

f) What was his average speed for the day's ride?

12 Averages

- Find the mode (or modal class for grouped data), median and range.
- Calculate the mean, including from a simple frequency table.
- Draw conclusions based on the shape of graphs and simple statistics.
- Compare two simple distributions using the range and the mode, median or mean.

Averages

When asked if she was good at maths, a student said she was average. A boy thought he was of average height for his class. What they were saying was that, in the group being discussed, they were somewhere in the middle.

This is useful in general conversation, but may not be specific enough for all purposes. 'Average earnings', 'average speed' and 'average throw' may mean different things depending on how the data is considered.

Mathematicians have realised that there are three useful ways of looking at the average of a set of data. They are called the *mean*, the *median* and the *mode* of the data.

Mean

You will probably be familiar with this measure of average. Look at this diagram showing strips of squares.

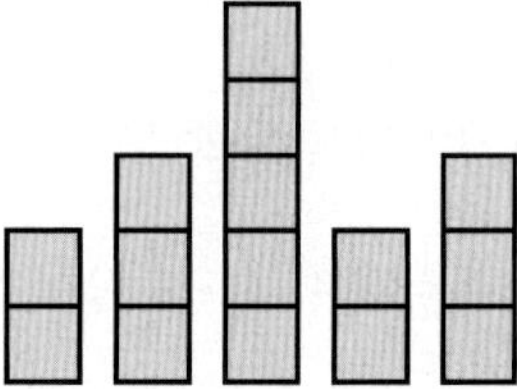

If the strips are rearranged so that there are the same number of squares in each strip, how many will there be in each? These squares have been rearranged to show this.

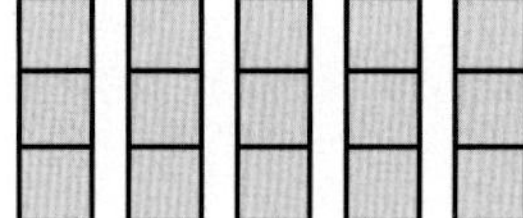

This problem can be solved by moving the squares around, as shown on the previous page, but there is another way. We can count the number of squares, 15, and divide by the number of strips, 5, giving a **mean** of 3.
In general,

$$\text{mean} = \frac{\text{sum of all the values}}{\text{number of values}}$$

Worked example

A football team scores these numbers of goals in its matches.

1 3 2 4 4 2 2 5 2 3

Calculate the mean number of goals scored per match.
The mean number of goals scored per match is:

$$\text{mean} = \frac{\text{sum of all the goals}}{\text{number of matches}}$$

$$\text{mean} = \frac{28}{10} = 2.8 \text{ goals per match}$$

Notice that the mean can include parts of a goal.

Median

Another way of looking at the average number of goals is to put the scores in order of size as shown here.

1 2 2 2 2 ⁞ 3 3 4 4 5

Since there are ten scores, the middle would be between the fifth and sixth values, which are 2 and 3. So 2.5 is the **median**.

Mode

A third way to look at the scores is to see which value occurred *most often*.

This is called the **mode** (or the **modal value**). In the example above it is 2 because the team scored 2 goals more often than any other number.

Range

A further value, which is often useful, is the **range** of the values. This gives a measure of how *spread out* the data is.

This table shows the times taken, in minutes, by two runners over a set distance.

Runner 1	10	10	10	12	12	12	12	12	13	13
Runner 2	8	8	9	10	12	12	12	12	15	18

A summary of the mean, median and mode for each runner gives us little information with which to distinguish between the two.

	Mean	Median	Mode
Runner 1	11.6	12	12
Runner 2	11.6	12	12

The range of each runner's results, however, does give us some more information.

Range = highest value – smallest value
Range for Runner 1 = 13 – 10 = 3 minutes
Range for Runner 2 = 18 – 8 = 10 minutes

The first runner is *consistent*. This means his or her times are all quite close together. The second runner is *less consistent* as his or her times are more widely spread.

Q Which runner might a coach choose in:
a) an individual event
b) a team event?
Give reasons for your answers.

Q Sometimes inconsistent sportswomen and sportsmen are chosen because they are described as 'match winners'. What do you think this means?

$$\text{Mean} = \frac{\text{sum of all the values}}{\text{number of values}}$$

Median = middle value when they are in order of size
Mode = value which occurs most often
Range = difference between the greatest and the smallest values

EXERCISE 12.1

Find the mean, median, mode and range of each set of data in questions 1–5.

1 1 1 2 3 3 4 4 4 4 5 5

2 3.2 4.8 5.6 5.6 7.3 8.9 9.1

3 1 2 3 4 4 3 2 4 2 3 6 4 0

4 17 23 36 112 18 23 40 23

5 1 2 0 2 1 0 2 3 4 1 5 0 3 2 1

6 Two discus throwers keep a record of their best throws (in metres) in the last ten competitions.

Discus thrower A	32	34	32	33	35	35	32	36	36	35
Discus thrower B	32	30	38	38	33	34	36	38	34	32

As a coach, you can only choose one of them for the next competition. Which would you choose? Justify your choice mathematically.

7 The mean mass of the 15 players in a rugby team is 85.2 kg. The mean mass of the team plus a substitute is 85.4 kg. What is the mass of the substitute?

8 After eight matches a basketball player has a mean of 27 points. After ten matches his mean was 31 points. How many points in total did he score in his last two matches?

9 A factory makes tins of tomatoes. On average, a full can should weigh 410 g. A sample of 20 cans is tested. The weights are shown below.

410 410 411 412 408 411 409 414 416 410
410 412 413 415 410 415 409 410 412 411

Does the canning machine need to be adjusted? Give reasons for your answer.

10 Measure the height of the students in your class.
a) Find the mean, median, mode and range of heights of the students.
b) As one of the group, are you average or not?
c) Give mathematical reasons to describe your position in the group.

Calculations using frequency tables

In Chapter 5 you saw that data is often presented in a frequency table or as grouped data. This makes some of the calculations of average more complicated.

Worked examples

a) A class carries out a survey to find out how many pets the students have. The results are shown in the frequency table.

Number of pets	Frequency
0	5
1	8
2	4
3	2
8	1

Calculate the mean, mode and range of the number of pets for the class.

The mean number of pets is:

$$\text{mean} = \frac{\text{total number of pets}}{\text{total number of students}}$$

There are 5 students with no pets, 8 students with 1 pet, 4 students with 2 pets, etc. So the total number of pets is:

$$(5 \times 0) + (8 \times 1) + (4 \times 2) + (2 \times 3) + (1 \times 8) = 30$$

The total number of students is the sum of the frequencies, i.e. 20. So

$$\text{mean} = \frac{30}{20} = 1.5$$

Therefore the mean number of pets per student is 1.5.
The mode is the number of pets with the highest frequency. So the modal number of pets is 1.
The range is the difference between the highest number of pets and the smallest number of pets.

The highest number of pets is 8.
The smallest number of pets is 0.

Therefore the range is 8 – 0 = 8 pets.

b) A station manager records how many minutes late trains arrive at the station over a period of time. The results are shown in this grouped frequency table.

Number of minutes late	Frequency
0–4	22
5–9	12
10–14	4
15–19	2
20–24	1

Deduce the modal class from these results.

The modal class is the group with the highest frequency (the mode). It is clear that the group 0–4 minutes has the highest frequency.
Therefore the modal class is 0–4 minutes.

The mean and median of grouped data will be covered in Student's Book 2.

EXERCISE 12.2

1 This grouped frequency table shows the ages of people attending a music festival.

Age	Frequency
0–14	2200
15–29	18600
30–44	10300
45–59	3200
60–74	1100
75–99	40

Deduce the modal class.

2 This frequency table shows the numbers of fish caught by the competitors in a fishing competition over a two-hour period.

Calculate:

a) the mean number of fish caught per competitor

b) the modal number of fish caught.

Number of fish	Frequency
0	6
1	20
2	45
3	70
4	35
5	10
6	2

3 A DVD rental store keeps a record of the number of DVDs each customer rents over a one-week period. The results are shown in the table below.

Calculate:

a) the mean number of DVDs rented per person

b) the modal number of DVDs rented.

Number of DVDs	Frequency
1	20
2	65
3	110
4	30
5	4

4 The numbers of *passengers* in cars and minibuses driving past a school gate one morning were recorded. The results of the survey are shown in the table.

Number of passengers	Frequency
0	6
1	4
2	8
3	10
4	x
y	2

The total number of vehicles surveyed was 40.

a) Calculate the frequency of the vehicles with four passengers.

b) The mean number of passengers carried in the vehicles was 2.75. Calculate the number of passengers represented by y in the table.

c) Deduce the modal number of passengers carried.

13 Multiplication and division I

- Consolidate the rapid recall of number facts, including positive integer complements to 100, multiplication facts to 10 × 10 and associated division facts.
- Use the laws of arithmetic and inverse operations to simplify calculations with whole numbers and decimals.
- Know and apply tests of divisibility by 2, 3, 5, 6, 8, 9, 10 and 100.
- Use known facts and place value to multiply simple decimals by one-digit numbers, e.g. 0.8 × 6.

Basic multiplication facts

To be able to multiply two numbers together or divide them, it is important to be able to remember the basic multiplication facts up to 10 × 10. These are shown in this multiplication grid.

×	**1**	**2**	**3**	**4**	**5**	**6**	**7**	**8**	**9**	**10**
1	1	2	3	4	5	6	7	8	9	10
2	2	4	6	8	10	12	14	16	18	20
3	3	6	9	12	15	18	21	24	27	30
4	4	8	12	16	20	24	28	32	36	40
5	5	10	15	20	25	30	35	40	45	50
6	6	12	18	24	30	36	42	48	54	60
7	7	14	21	28	35	42	49	56	63	70
8	8	16	24	32	40	48	56	64	72	80
9	9	18	27	36	45	54	63	72	81	90
10	10	20	30	40	50	60	70	80	90	100

Remembering these facts is not as difficult as it may seem. The following tips can help.

This reduces the number of facts to remember by nearly a half!

- When multiplying two numbers together, the order does not matter. For example, 6×8 is the same as 8×6.
- Multiplying a number by 1 gives the same number. For example, $8 \times 1 = 8$.
- Multiplying a number by 2 is the same as doubling the number. For example, 7×2 is the same as doubling 7.
- Multiplying a number by 4 is the same as doubling and doubling again.
- When multiplying by 9, the first digit in the answer is 1 less than the number being multiplied by 9, and the two digits in the answer add up to 9. For example, $\mathbf{8} \times 9 = \mathbf{7}2$ and $7 + 2 = 9$.
- When multiplying a number by 10, a zero is written after the number. For example, $3 \times 10 = 3\mathbf{0}$.
- Multiplying a number by 5 is the same as multiplying the same number by 10 and halving the result. For example, $7 \times 5 = \frac{1}{2} \times 7 \times 10 = \frac{1}{2} \times 70 = 35$.

These tips have been highlighted in red on this copy of the multiplication grid.

×	1	2	3	4	5	6	7	8	9	10
1	1	2	3	4	5	6	7	8	9	10
2	2	4	6	8	10	12	14	16	18	20
3	3	6	9	12	15	18	21	24	27	30
4	4	8	12	16	20	24	28	32	36	40
5	5	10	15	20	25	30	35	40	45	50
6	6	12	18	24	30	36	42	48	54	60
7	7	14	21	28	35	42	49	56	63	70
8	8	16	24	32	40	48	56	64	72	80
9	9	18	27	36	45	54	63	72	81	90
10	10	20	30	40	50	60	70	80	90	100

You can see that this leaves very few multiplication facts to be memorised. Knowing the multiplication facts well also helps with divisions. For example, knowing that $7 \times 9 = 63$ will help you to remember that $63 \div 9 = 7$.

Multiplying a number by 10 is straightforward, and so is multiplying by any number which is a multiple of 10 or 100.

Worked examples

a) Multiply 50 × 7.

We know that 5 × 7 = 35.
50 is ten times bigger than 5, so 50 × 7 must be ten times bigger than 5 × 7.
50 × 7 = 35 × 10 = 350

b) Multiply 70 × 80.

We know that 7 × 8 = 56.
70 is ten times bigger than 7 and 80 is ten times bigger than 8, so 70 × 80 must be *one hundred* times bigger than 7 × 8.
70 × 80 = 56 × 100 = 5600

c) Multiply 600 × 40.

We know that 6 × 4 = 24.
600 is one hundred times bigger than 6 and 40 is ten times bigger than 4, so 600 × 40 must be *one thousand* times bigger than 6 × 4.
600 × 40 = 24 × 1000 = 24 000

You can use multiplication facts in a similar way when multiplying simple decimals by single-digit numbers.

Worked examples

a) Multiply 0.8 × 6.

We know that 8 × 6 = 48.
0.8 is ten times smaller than 8, so 0.8 × 6 must be ten times smaller than 8 × 6.
0.8 × 6 = 48 ÷ 10 = 4.8

b) Multiply 0.03 × 9.

We know that 3 × 9 is 27.
0.03 is one hundred times smaller than 3, so 0.03 × 9 must be one hundred times smaller than 3 × 9.
0.03 × 9 = 27 ÷ 100 = 0.27

EXERCISE 13.1

Do these questions in your head, without looking at the multiplication grid or using a calculator. Write down your answers.

1 Multiply the following pairs of numbers.

a) 3 × 7 **b)** 2 × 6 **c)** 4 × 3 **d)** 5 × 8
e) 1 × 10 **f)** 6 × 10 **g)** 5 × 9 **h)** 6 × 7
i) 8 × 6 **j)** 9 × 7 **k)** 9 × 9 **l)** 8 × 8

2 Work out the following divisions.

a) $16 \div 4$	**b)** $20 \div 10$	**c)** $30 \div 3$	**d)** $24 \div 6$
e) $25 \div 5$	**f)** $18 \div 3$	**g)** $49 \div 7$	**h)** $56 \div 8$
i) $63 \div 9$	**j)** $64 \div 8$	**k)** $72 \div 8$	**l)** $81 \div 9$

3 Multiply the following pairs of numbers.

a) 20×5	**b)** 30×6	**c)** 200×8	**d)** 60×9
e) 20×30	**f)** 40×60	**g)** 600×5	**h)** 70×80
i) 200×10	**j)** 90×300	**k)** 70×800	**l)** 600×70

4 Multiply the following decimals.

a) 0.3×2	**b)** 0.7×4	**c)** 0.9×5	**d)** 0.6×8
e) 0.04×5	**f)** 0.03×8	**g)** 0.08×7	**h)** 0.06×9
i) 8×0.07			

Divisibility tests

Is 411 divisible by 3? Is 81 945 divisible by 9? The answer to both of these questions is 'yes', as there is no remainder when each of these divisions is done. It is sometimes relatively easy to tell, simply by looking at a number, whether it is divisible by another number.

Here are some helpful tests of divisibility.

- A number is divisible by 2 if it ends in 0, 2, 4, 6 or 8.
- A number is divisible by 3 if the sum of its digits is divisible by 3.
  For example, 411 is divisible by 3 as $4 + 1 + 1 = 6$ and 6 is divisible by 3.
- A number is divisible by 5 if it ends in 0 or 5.
- A number is divisible by 6 if it is divisible by 2 *and* by 3.
  For example, 714 ends in 4, so it is divisible by 2.
  Also, $7 + 1 + 4 = 12$ and 12 is divisible by 3, so 714 is divisible by 3.
  As 714 is divisible by 2 *and* by 3, it is divisible by 6.
- A number is divisible by 8 if the last three digits are divisible by 8.
  For example, 1024 is divisible by 8 as 024 is divisible by 8.
- A number is divisible by 9 if the sum of its digits is divisible by 9.
  For example, 8028 is divisible by 9 as $8 + 0 + 2 + 8 = 18$ and 18 is divisible by 9.
- A number is divisible by 10 if it ends in 0.
- A number is divisible by 100 if it ends in 00.

EXERCISE 13.2

Type this formula into cell A1 in a spreadsheet:

=RANDBETWEEN(0,500).

This will generate a random integer (whole number) between 0 and 500.
Copy the formula down to cell A20 to generate 20 random numbers in the first column of the spreadsheet, for example as shown here.

	A	B
1	85	
2	139	
3	9	
4	245	
5	439	
6	246	
7	478	
8	34	
9	161	
10	134	
11	492	
12	89	
13	392	
14	493	
15	195	
16	150	
17	391	
18	80	
19	17	
20	485	
21		

1 Use divisibility tests to find out which of your random numbers are divisible by either 2, 3 or 6.

2 Which of your random numbers are divisible by either 5, 10 or 100?

3 Which of your random numbers are divisible by 9?

4 Is it true that any number which is divisible by 9 is also divisible by 3? Explain your answer.

5 Is it true that any number which is divisible by 10 is also divisible by 5? Explain your answer.

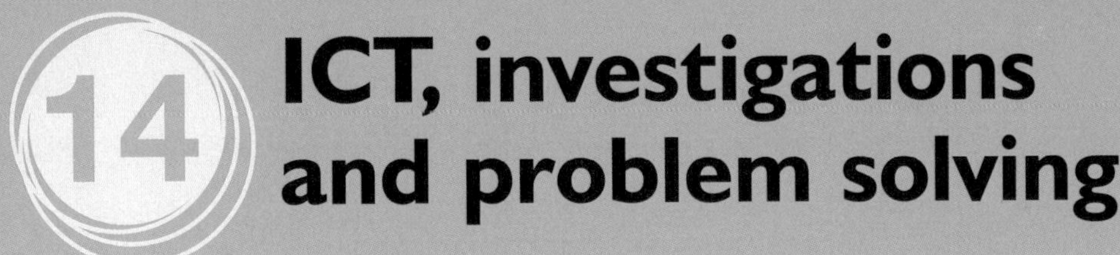

1 Four fours

Using four 4s each time and any mathematical operation(s), carry out calculations to make each of the numbers 0 to 20. For example,

$$\frac{4 \times 4 + 4}{4} = 5 \text{ and } \frac{44}{4} - 4 = 7$$

Remember to take account of the correct order of operations.

2 Grains of rice

There is a legend that when the inventor of the game of chess showed it to the ruler of India, the ruler was so impressed that he told the man,'Name your reward'.

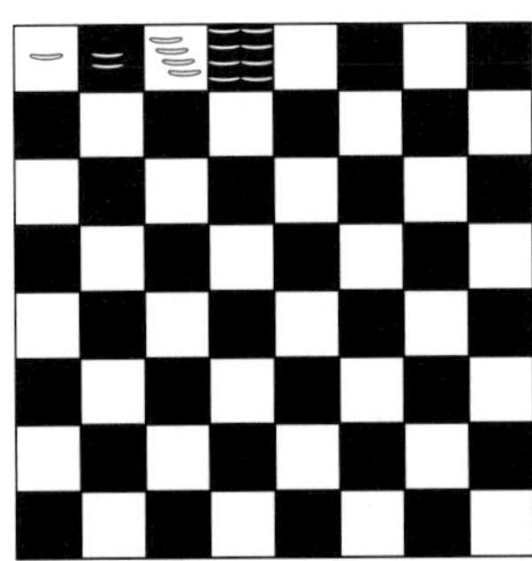

The inventor said that all he asked for was that one grain of rice be placed on the first square of the chess board, two grains on the second square, four grains on the third, eight grains on the fourth, and so on. Each square would have two times as many grains of rice as the previous one.

a) *Guess* how many grains of rice the ruler would need to cover all 64 squares of the chess board.

b) Copy and complete the table on page 112, showing how many grains of rice are placed on the first 16 squares of the chess board.

→

Square	Number of grains of rice	Total
1	1	1
2	2	3
3	4	7
4	8	15
5		
6		
7		
8		
9		
10		
11		
12		
13		
14		
15		
16		

c) Use a spreadsheet to calculate the number of grains of rice needed for all 64 squares.

d) How does your answer to part **c)** compare with your guess in part **a)**?

e) The volume of one grain of rice is about 5 mm^3. Calculate the total volume of rice needed for all 64 squares of the chess board.

f) Estimate how much the rice would weigh.

3 Clocks

A clock face has twelve numbers, equally spaced around its outside edge.

a) What is the angle between two consecutive numbers on the clock face?

b) Calculate the size of the acute angle between the hour and minute hands of each of these clocks.

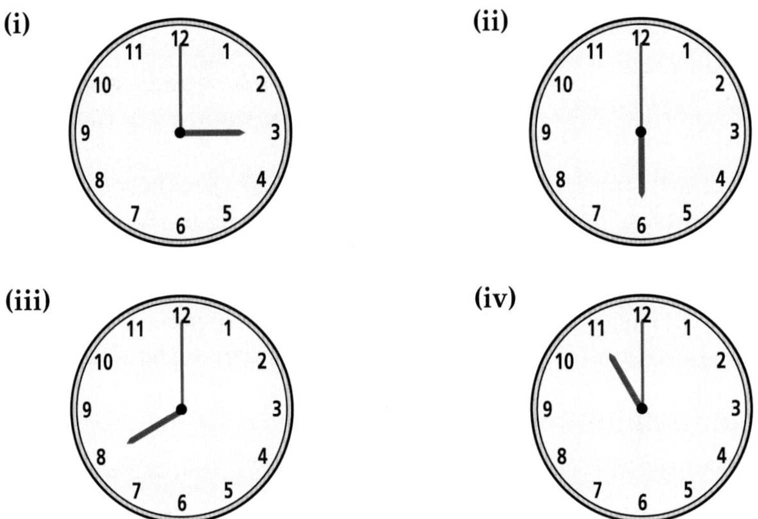

c) How many degrees does the minute hand turn through in one minute?

d) How many degrees does the hour hand turn through in one minute?

e) Calculate the size of the acute angle between the hour and minute hands on each of these clocks.

(i)

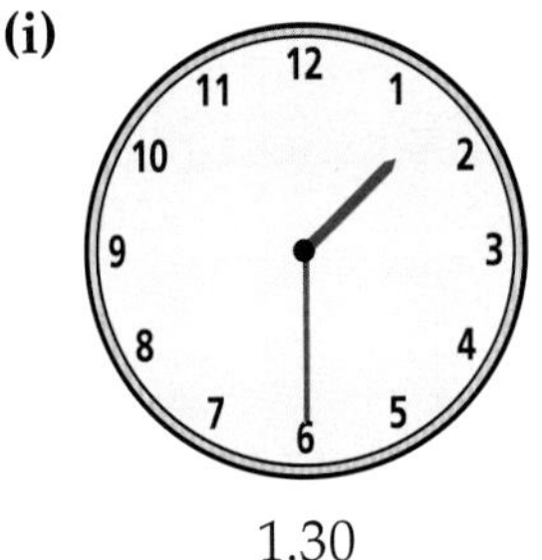

1.30

(ii)

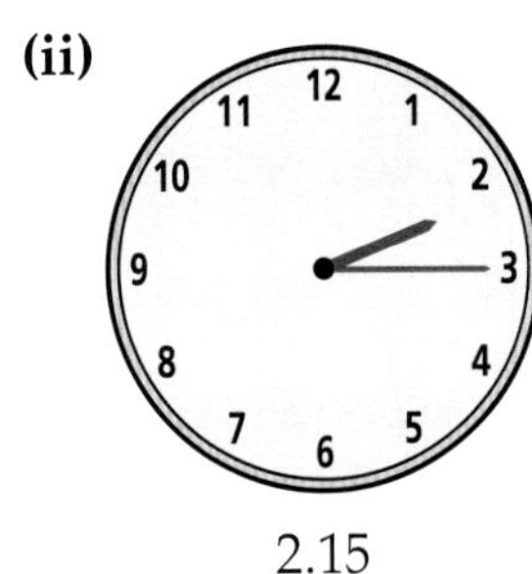

2.15

(iii)

5.40

4 Travel plans

To travel by train between two towns, you often need to catch more than one train. If the towns are small, you may need to catch a train and a bus.

a) Select two large towns near where you live, which are not directly linked by train (i.e. it is not possible to catch one train to get from one town to the other). Collect the necessary train timetables, and work out a schedule which will enable someone to travel by train from one town to the other.

Make sure to include all arrival and departure times at any station where they will need to change trains.

b) Select two small towns or villages near where you live. Collect the necessary train and bus timetables for a journey from one to the other. Work out a schedule to show how someone can travel between the two places.

c) Repeat one of parts **a)** and **b)**, but for places in two different countries.

This time you may need to investigate air or coach travel as well.

5 Visitor numbers

A new tourist attraction opened to the public on 1 January 2011. Here is a list of the numbers of people who visited the attraction in January 2011.

Saturday	1 Jan	11 190
Sunday	2 Jan	22 252
Monday	3 Jan	21 718
Tuesday	4 Jan	17 535
Wednesday	5 Jan	9414
Thursday	6 Jan	7506
Friday	7 Jan	9838
Saturday	8 Jan	20 541
Sunday	9 Jan	16 325
Monday	10 Jan	6670
Tuesday	11 Jan	5990
Wednesday	12 Jan	6243
Thursday	13 Jan	5084
Friday	14 Jan	7650
Saturday	15 Jan	17 619
Sunday	16 Jan	15 090

Monday	17 Jan	7406
Tuesday	18 Jan	7145
Wednesday	19 Jan	6918
Thursday	20 Jan	6794
Friday	21 Jan	9079
Saturday	22 Jan	18 040
Sunday	23 Jan	16 262
Monday	24 Jan	6746
Tuesday	25 Jan	8437
Wednesday	26 Jan	7696
Thursday	27 Jan	8208
Friday	28 Jan	13 247
Saturday	29 Jan	23 304
Sunday	30 Jan	19 486
Monday	31 Jan	6987

Use a spreadsheet and appropriate formulae to answer the following questions.

a) What was the total number of visitors to the attraction during January?
b) What was the mean daily number of visitors?
c) What was the mean number of visitors for each of the different days of the week?
d) Give an explanation for the differences in mean attendance in part **c)**.
e) Suggest reasons why this information may have been useful to the managers of the attraction.

A possible way of setting out your spreadsheet is given below.

	A	B	C	D	E	F	G	H	I	J	K
1											
2		**Date**	**Day**	**Attendance**				**Day**	**Mean attendance**		
3		01-Jan	Saturday	11 190				Sunday			
4		02-Jan	Sunday	22 252				Monday			
5		03-Jan	Monday	21 718				Tuesday			
6		04-Jan	Tuesday	17 535				Wednesday			
7		05-Jan	Wednesday	9 414				Thursday			
8		06-Jan	Thursday	7 506				Friday			
9			etc...					Saturday			
10											
11									Enter the formulae		
12		**Total attendance**							here to calculate the		
13									mean attendance for		
14			Enter a formula here to calculate the total						each day of the week		
15											
16		**Mean attendance**									
17											
18			Enter a formula here to calculate the mean								
19											
20											

Review 2A

1 A boy has climbed 210 m up a 350 m vertical cliff, and is trapped there. A rescue helicopter is hovering 65 m above the top of the cliff. Calculate how far a rescuer must be lowered to reach the boy. You may draw a sketch to help you.

2 *Without using a calculator,* evaluate the following.

a) $\sqrt{225}$ **b)** $\sqrt{625}$

3 Sketch the graph of:

a) $x = -3$ **b)** $y = +5$

4 Draw lines of the following lengths using a ruler.

a) 3.5 cm **b)** 47 mm **c)** 4.9 cm

5 Draw a triangle ABC where the length $AB = 8.8$ cm, $AC = 6.5$ cm and $\angle A = 59°$.

6 Write these times as 24-hour clock times.

a) 8.30a.m. **b)** 11.30p.m. **c)** 4.50p.m.

7 A bus journey from a town to a city takes 2 hour 38 minutes. Copy and complete the timetable opposite.

Depart	Arrive
05 00	
07 20	
	11 18
	13 36
15 45	
18 22	
	21 17
	23 25

8 The mean mass of the 11 players in a football team is 80.7 kg. The mean mass of the team plus a substitute is 81.4 kg. What is the mass of the substitute to one decimal place?

9 *Without using a calculator,* work out:

a) 90×600 **b)** 80×800 **c)** 600×50

Review 2B

1 List all the factors of each of these numbers and circle the prime factors.
   a) 18 **b)** 38 **c)** 36 **d)** 44

2 Solve these equations.
   a) $a + 9 = 5$ **b)** $b - 3 = 3$ **c)** $7c = 42$ **d)** $\frac{d}{3} = 14$

3 The numbers 12, 13, 14, 15 and 16 are entered into the function machine 'multiply by 6, subtract 10 and then divide by 2'. Calculate the output in each case.

4 For each of the following angles:
   (i) estimate its size
   (ii) measure it and check how good your estimate was.

   Aim for your estimate to be within 10° of the actual size.

   a)

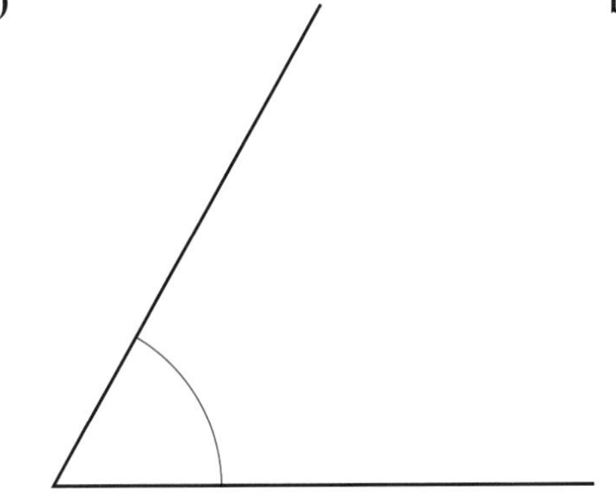

   b)

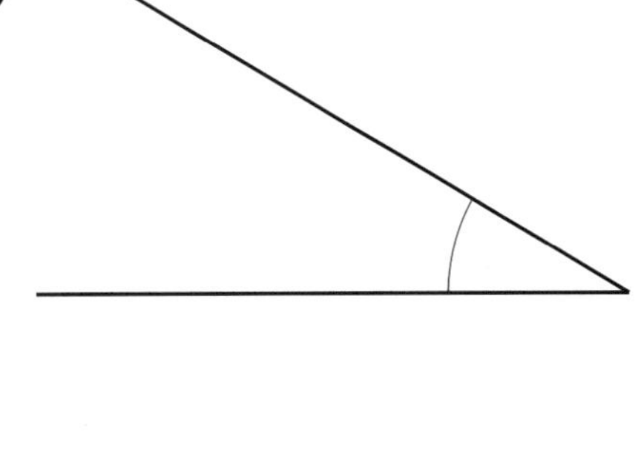

5 Construct a rhombus of side 5.7 cm and base angles 45° and 135°.

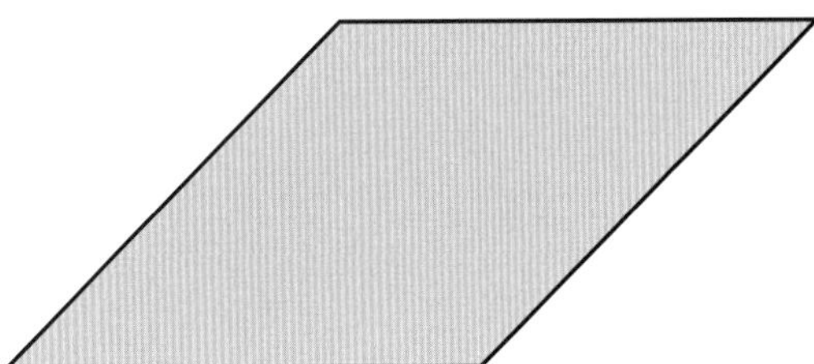

6 Write these times as 24-hour clock times.

a) 9 o'clock in the evening

b) noon

c) half past midnight

7 Find the mean, median, mode and range of this set of data.

1 1 1 1 2 2 3 4 4 4 4 4 5 5 6

8 *Without using a calculator,* work out:

a) 0.6×7 **b)** 0.008×9 **c)** 0.09×8

9 **a)** *Without dividing,* write down which of these numbers are divisible by 9.

(i) 639 **(ii)** 7651

(iii) 87 642 **(iv)** 12 345

(v) 969 345

b) Which number in part **a)** is divisible by 45? Give reasons for your answer.

SECTION 3

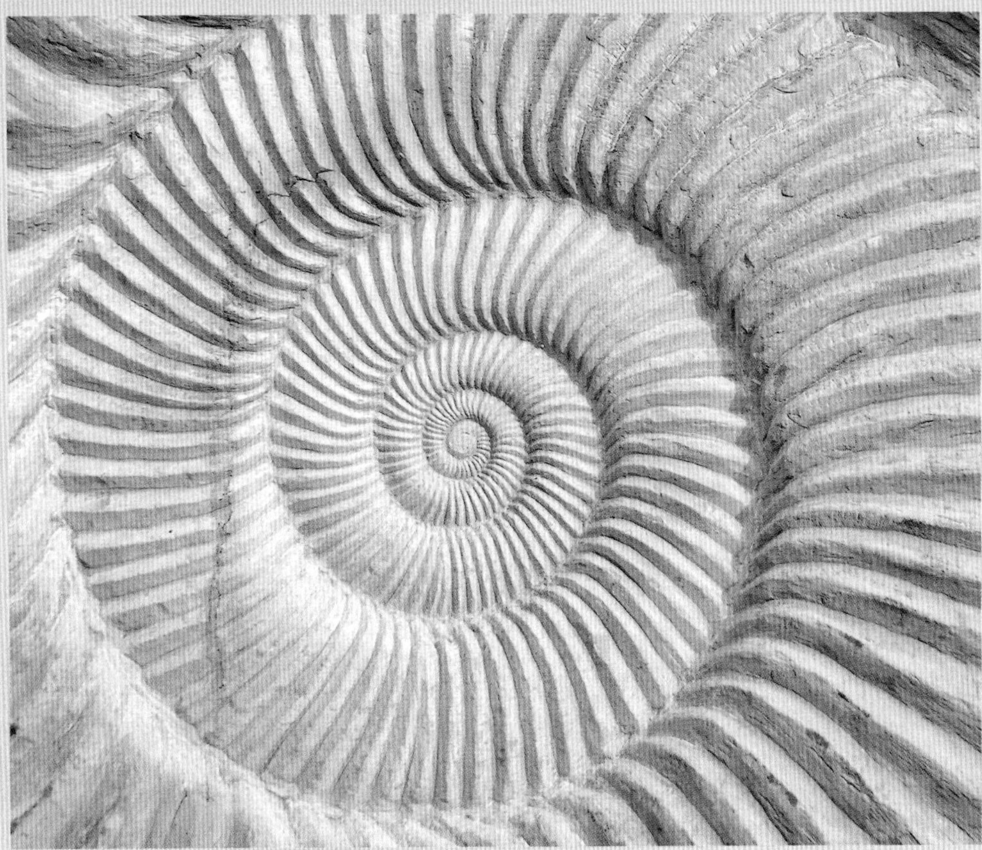

15 Fractions, decimals and percentages

- Understand percentage as the number of parts in every 100; use fractions and percentages to describe parts of shapes, quantities and measures.
- Recognise the equivalence of simple fractions, decimals and percentages.
- Simplify fractions by cancelling common factors and identify equivalent fractions; change an improper fraction to a mixed number, and vice versa; convert terminating decimals to fractions, e.g. $0.23 = \frac{23}{100}$.
- Compare two fractions by using diagrams, or by using a calculator to convert the fractions to decimals, e.g. $\frac{3}{5}$ and $\frac{13}{20}$.
- Add and subtract two simple fractions, e.g. $\frac{1}{8} + \frac{3}{8}$, $\frac{11}{12} - \frac{5}{6}$; find fractions of quantities (whole number answers); multiply a fraction by an integer.
- Multiply and divide decimals with one and/or two places by single-digit numbers, e.g. 13.7×8, $4.35 \div 5$.
- Calculate simple percentages of quantities (whole number answers) and express a smaller quantity as a fraction or percentage of a larger one.

The first written records of the use of money were found in the city of Eridu in Mesopotamia (modern Iraq). The records were on tablets like this.

The Sumerians lived in this region five thousand years ago. They used a system of recording value called Cuneiform. This system is now believed to be simply accounts of grain surpluses. This may sound insignificant now, but the change from a hunter-gatherer society to a farming-based society led directly to the sophisticated way of life we have today.

The Cuneiform tablets do not record a mathematical system based upon fractions, decimals or percentages, but almost certainly led to the system we use today.

Fractions

Fractions deal with a part of a whole. A fraction has two parts: the **numerator** and the **denominator**.

The numerator is the number above the line, whilst the denominator is the number below the line, i.e.

$$\frac{\textbf{numerator}}{\textbf{denominator}}$$

Both the numerator and denominator must be **integers** (whole numbers).

Fractions of a quantity

To work out a fraction of an amount, look at the fraction itself for help. The denominator tells us how many equal parts the amount is split into, whilst the numerator indicates how many of these parts are being used.

Worked examples

a) A teenager spends on average $\frac{2}{5}$ of his pocket money on clothes. His pocket money is \$20 a week. Calculate how much he spends on clothes.

$\frac{1}{5}$ of \$20 a week is worked out like this: \$20 ÷ 5 = \$4

$\frac{2}{5}$ of \$20 is twice as much as $\frac{1}{5}$.

Therefore $\frac{2}{5}$ of \$20 is 2 × \$4 = \$8.

So the teenager spends on average \$8 on clothes per week.

b) A magazine has 56 pages. Of those $\frac{7}{8}$ contain pictures. Calculate the number of pages with pictures.

$\frac{1}{8}$ of 56 is 56 ÷ 8 = 7

$\frac{7}{8}$ of 56 is 7 times as much as $\frac{1}{8}$.

Therefore $\frac{7}{8}$ of 56 is 7 × 7 = 49.

The magazine has 49 pages with pictures.

EXERCISE 15.1A

1 Evaluate the following.

a) $\frac{1}{5}$ of 75 **b)** $\frac{2}{5}$ of 75 **c)** $\frac{3}{5}$ of 75

2 Evaluate the following.

a) $\frac{1}{8}$ of 72 **b)** $\frac{3}{8}$ of 72 **c)** $\frac{7}{8}$ of 72

→

3 Evaluate the following.
a) $\frac{1}{11}$ of 132 b) $\frac{5}{11}$ of 132 c) $\frac{9}{11}$ of 132

4 Evaluate the following.
a) $\frac{1}{13}$ of 169 b) $\frac{7}{13}$ of 169 c) $\frac{11}{13}$ of 169

5 Evaluate the following amounts.
a) $\frac{1}{4}$ of \$6.20 b) $\frac{1}{8}$ of \$25.68
c) $\frac{4}{9}$ of \$127.89 d) $\frac{3}{7}$ of \$2884.35

6 a) $\frac{7}{12}$ of the students in a school are girls.
The school has 1044 students. Calculate the number of girls.
b) What fraction of the number of students in the school are boys?

7 A paint mixture is made up of $\frac{3}{20}$ red paint and $\frac{9}{20}$ blue paint, and the rest is white paint.
a) What fraction of the mixture is white paint?
b) The paint is sold in 5-litre containers. How many litres of red paint are needed for each container?
c) How many litres of blue paint are needed for each container?

8 A boy earns \$240 a week as a trainee manager, and $\frac{1}{5}$ of his earnings are taken in tax. He spends $\frac{1}{4}$ on clothes and $\frac{3}{8}$ on going out with friends, and he pays his parents \$35 a week in rent. The rest he saves.
a) How much tax does he pay?
b) What fraction of his earnings does he pay in rent?
c) How much does he save per week?

Equivalent fractions

Although fractions may look different from each other, sometimes they are worth the same. If fractions are worth the same, they are **equivalent fractions**.

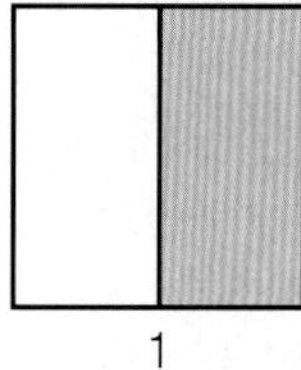

$\frac{1}{2}$

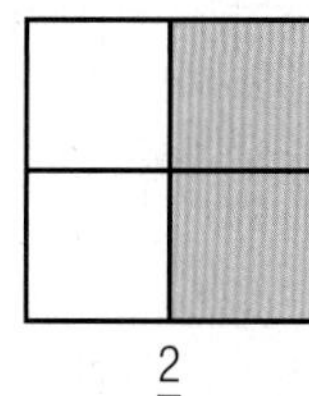

$\frac{2}{4}$

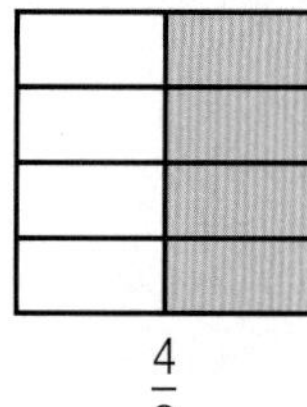

$\frac{4}{8}$

In these diagrams, the same proportion of each square is shaded. Therefore we can conclude that the three fractions $\frac{1}{2}$, $\frac{2}{4}$ and $\frac{4}{8}$ are equivalent.

In order to determine whether fractions are equivalent, they need to be *simplified*. In order to simplify fractions, divide both the numerator and denominator by their **highest common factor** (the biggest number that goes into both of them exactly).

Worked examples

a) Write $\frac{12}{42}$ as a fraction in its simplest form.

The highest common factor of 12 and 42 is 6, i.e. 6 is the largest number which goes into both 12 and 42 exactly.

$12 \div 6 = 2$

$42 \div 6 = 7$

Therefore $\frac{12}{42}$ simplifies to $\frac{2}{7}$.

b) Which of these three fractions are equivalent?

$\frac{4}{18} \quad \frac{5}{20} \quad \frac{6}{27}$

In order to find which of the three fractions are equivalent to each other, they need to be simplified.

$\frac{4}{18} = \frac{2}{9}$ (2 is the highest common factor)

$\frac{5}{20} = \frac{1}{4}$ (5 is the highest common factor)

$\frac{6}{27} = \frac{2}{9}$ (3 is the highest common factor)

From these simplifications we can see that $\frac{4}{18}$ and $\frac{6}{27}$ are equivalent.

EXERCISE 15.1B

1 Write each of the following fractions in its simplest form.

a) $\frac{2}{10}$ **b)** $\frac{3}{27}$ **c)** $\frac{9}{48}$

d) $\frac{48}{56}$ **e)** $\frac{34}{85}$ **f)** $\frac{65}{104}$

2 For each of the following, determine which of the fractions given are equivalent. Show your working clearly.

a) $\frac{3}{4} \quad \frac{5}{7} \quad \frac{15}{21}$ **b)** $\frac{5}{8} \quad \frac{20}{32} \quad \frac{18}{30}$

c) $\frac{4}{9} \quad \frac{16}{36} \quad \frac{28}{63}$ **d)** $\frac{3}{10} \quad \frac{9}{30} \quad \frac{6}{24} \quad \frac{15}{50}$

e) $\frac{6}{32} \quad \frac{4}{16} \quad \frac{3}{16} \quad \frac{15}{80}$ **f)** $\frac{3}{8} \quad \frac{2}{10} \quad \frac{6}{15} \quad \frac{4}{22}$

3 For each of the following, draw diagrams to show why the pair of fractions are equivalent.

a) $\frac{1}{3} = \frac{3}{9}$ **b)** $\frac{2}{5} = \frac{8}{20}$ **c)** $\frac{3}{4} = \frac{9}{12}$ **d)** $\frac{5}{8} = \frac{15}{24}$

Addition and subtraction of fractions

It is relatively straightforward to add or subtract fractions with the same denominator. For example,

$$\frac{1}{8} \quad + \quad \frac{3}{8} \quad = \quad \frac{4}{8} \quad = \quad \frac{1}{2}$$

Visually this can be shown like this:

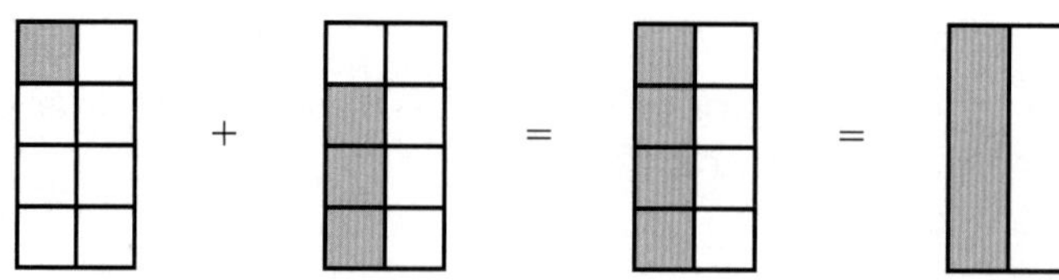

Simply add the numerators together and keep the denominator as it is.

However, adding or subtracting fractions with different denominators requires a bit more work. For example,

$$\frac{1}{4} + \frac{2}{5}$$

In order to do this, both fractions need to be converted into equivalent fractions with a common denominator. The **lowest common multiple** of both denominators is 20, i.e. 20 is the smallest number that both 4 and 5 go into. Therefore we find equivalent fractions to those given, with 20 as a denominator.

$$\frac{1}{4} = \frac{5}{20} \qquad \text{and} \qquad \frac{2}{5} = \frac{8}{20}$$

Therefore $\frac{1}{4} + \frac{2}{5}$ is the same as $\frac{5}{20} + \frac{8}{20}$.

$$\frac{1}{4} \quad + \quad \frac{2}{5} \quad = \quad \frac{13}{20}$$

Visually this can be shown like this:

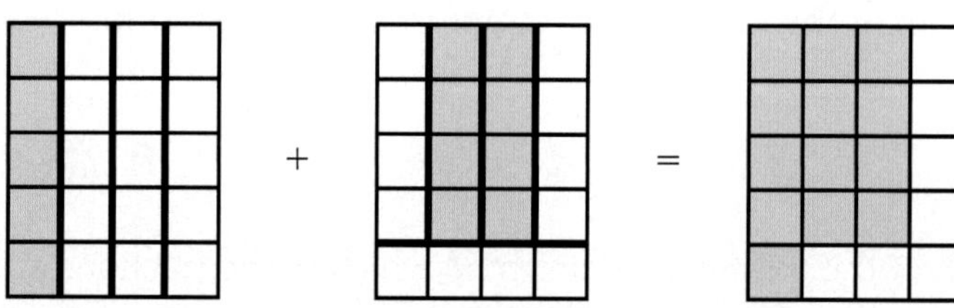

Subtraction is done in a similar way: it is also necessary to work with fractions with a common denominator.

EXERCISE 15.1C

Do not use a calculator for this exercise.

1 Add together the following fractions.

a) $\frac{1}{9} + \frac{4}{9}$ **b)** $\frac{1}{11} + \frac{4}{11}$ **c)** $\frac{4}{7} + \frac{1}{7}$

d) $\frac{2}{13} + \frac{3}{13} + \frac{5}{13}$ **e)** $\frac{6}{23} + \frac{7}{23} + \frac{9}{23}$

2 Subtract the following fractions.

a) $\frac{7}{9} - \frac{2}{9}$ **b)** $\frac{5}{7} - \frac{2}{7}$ **c)** $\frac{8}{11} - \frac{5}{11}$

d) $\frac{16}{23} - \frac{9}{23}$ **e)** $\frac{3}{5} - \frac{1}{5}$

3 Add together the following fractions. Simplify your answers where possible.

a) $\frac{1}{7} + \frac{4}{7}$ **b)** $\frac{1}{9} + \frac{5}{9}$

c) $\frac{4}{15} + \frac{6}{15}$ **d)** $\frac{5}{24} + \frac{7}{24}$

4 Do the following calculations. Show your working clearly and simplify your answers where possible.

a) $\frac{9}{14} - \frac{2}{7}$ **b)** $\frac{3}{13} - \frac{3}{26}$ **c)** $\frac{1}{8} + \frac{5}{16} - \frac{5}{24}$

d) $\frac{13}{18} - \frac{8}{9} + \frac{1}{6}$

5 Sadiq spends $\frac{1}{5}$ of his earnings on his rent and he saves $\frac{2}{7}$. What fraction of his earnings is left?

6 A farmer uses five out of seven equal strips of his land for cereal crops and $\frac{1}{8}$ of his land for root vegetables. What fraction of his land is available for other uses?

Improper fractions

This diagram shows one unit which has been split into quarters, and 3 quarters of another unit.

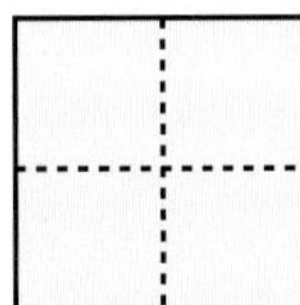
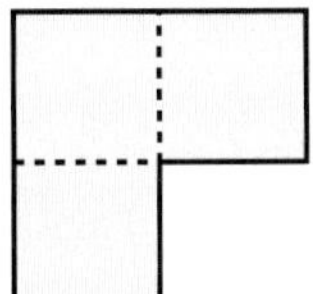

In total there are 7 quarters. As a fraction this is written as $\frac{7}{4}$. A fraction where the numerator is bigger than the denominator is called an **improper fraction**.

The same number can be written as $1\frac{3}{4}$. Then it is called a **mixed number**.

Changing between mixed numbers and improper fractions

We have seen that $1\frac{3}{4} = \frac{7}{4}$. Converting an improper fraction into a mixed number involves division.

$\frac{7}{4}$ means $7 \div 4$.

4 goes into 7 once, with a remainder of 3, i.e.

Converting a mixed number into an improper fraction involves multiplication or addition.

$1\frac{3}{4}$ represents 4 quarters added to a further 3 quarters, giving a total of 7 quarters or $\frac{7}{4}$.

We can get this result by converting 1 to $\frac{4}{4}$ then adding, i.e.

$$1\frac{3}{4} = 1 + \frac{3}{4} = \frac{4}{4} + \frac{3}{4} = \frac{7}{4}$$

Worked examples

a) Convert $2\frac{3}{5}$ into an improper fraction.

$$2\frac{3}{5} = \frac{10}{5} + \frac{3}{5} = \frac{13}{5}$$

b) Convert $\frac{21}{4}$ into a mixed number.

$$\frac{21}{4} = 5\frac{1}{4}$$

4 goes into 21 five times with a remainder of 1.

If you multiply an integer by a fraction, the answer is often an improper fraction which can then be simplified.

Worked examples

a) Work out $4 \times \frac{2}{3}$.

$$4 \times \frac{2}{3} = \frac{8}{3} = 2\frac{2}{3}$$

b) Work out $-7 \times \frac{5}{8}$.

$$-7 \times \frac{5}{8} = -\frac{35}{8} = -4\frac{3}{8}$$

EXERCISE 15.1D

In questions 1–5 convert the mixed numbers to improper fractions.

1 **a)** $2\frac{1}{3}$ **b)** $3\frac{1}{4}$

2 **a)** $5\frac{2}{5}$ **b)** $4\frac{3}{4}$

3 **a)** $6\frac{5}{6}$ **b)** $7\frac{3}{5}$

4 **a)** $9\frac{5}{11}$ **b)** $7\frac{4}{9}$

5 **a)** $6\frac{3}{25}$ **b)** $6\frac{3}{13}$

In questions 6–10 convert the improper fractions to mixed numbers.

6 **a)** $\frac{8}{3}$ **b)** $\frac{7}{2}$

7 **a)** $\frac{9}{4}$ **b)** $\frac{11}{5}$

8 **a)** $\frac{12}{5}$ **b)** $\frac{13}{7}$

9 **a)** $\frac{23}{11}$ **b)** $\frac{39}{7}$

10 **a)** $\frac{26}{13}$ **b)** $\frac{49}{12}$

In questions 11–15 work out the multiplications.

11 **a)** $5 \times \frac{3}{8}$ **b)** $4 \times \frac{6}{7}$

12 **a)** $3 \times \frac{9}{10}$ **b)** $7 \times \frac{8}{9}$

13 **a)** $6 \times \frac{4}{5}$ **b)** $9 \times \frac{8}{9}$

14 **a)** $-4 \times \frac{5}{6}$ **b)** $-7 \times \frac{7}{8}$

15 **a)** $-8 \times \frac{7}{8}$ **b)** $-5 \times \frac{3}{5}$

Using a calculator

Most scientific calculators have a fraction button. In addition to carrying out calculations with fractions, it enables the user to simplify fractions, compare magnitudes (sizes) and convert them to decimals.

The fraction button usually looks like this: $a^b/_c$

Worked examples

a) Use the fraction button on a calculator to simplify $\frac{27}{33}$.

Use this key sequence:

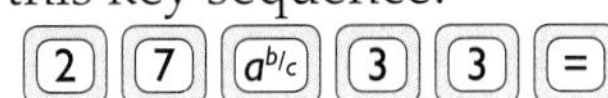

The calculator gives an answer of $\frac{9}{11}$.

b) A 5 km race takes a runner 25 minutes to complete. For $\frac{3}{5}$ of the time he is in first place and for $\frac{1}{6}$ of the time he is in second place.

(i) Calculate how long the runner spends in first place.

(ii) How long does the runner spend in second place?

(i) Use this key sequence:

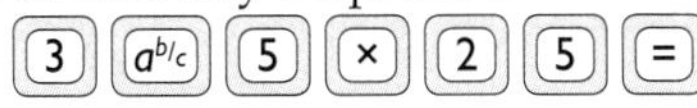

The calculator gives an answer of 15.

Therefore the runner spends 15 minutes in first place.

(ii) Use this key sequence:

Here the calculator gives an answer of $4\frac{1}{6}$.

$\frac{1}{6}$ of a minute is equivalent to 10 seconds.

Therefore the runner spends 4 minutes and 10 seconds in second place.

EXERCISE 15.1E

In each of these questions, use the fraction button on a calculator if you need to.

1 On a typical school day, a student spends 6 hours in lessons.
a) What fraction of the whole day is spent in lessons?
b) Write this fraction in its simplest form.

2 One day Maria spends $\frac{6}{20}$ of the day asleep. Calculate in hours and minutes the amount of time she spends asleep.

3 Paul sat a $2\frac{1}{2}$ hour exam. He finished $\frac{13}{15}$ of the way through the exam. Calculate the amount of time he had spare at the end, in minutes.

4 A marathon runner took 2 hours and 15 minutes to complete the race. During that time he spent 50 minutes in the lead. Write down, in its simplest form, the fraction of time he spent in the lead.

5 Michael worked out that with his mobile phone he spends 17 of every 20 minutes of the time talking to friends. He spends 3 hours and 45 minutes on the phone. Calculate how long he spends talking to friends.

6 How many minutes is represented by each of the following fractions of an hour?

a) $\frac{4}{30}$ **b)** $\frac{5}{12}$ **c)** $\frac{3}{10}$
d) $\frac{4}{5}$ **e)** $\frac{11}{15}$ **f)** $\frac{6}{45}$

7 Express each of the following numbers of minutes as a fraction of an hour in its simplest form.

a) 27 minutes **b)** 14 minutes
c) 48 minutes **d)** 35 minutes
e) $52\frac{1}{2}$ minutes **f)** 57 minutes

Decimals

Decimals are another way of writing parts of a whole number. For example, the fraction $\frac{1}{2}$ can be written as a decimal as 0.5. To convert a fraction to a decimal, simply divide the numerator by the denominator.

Worked example

Write $\frac{2}{5}$ as a decimal.

$$2 \div 5 = 0.4$$

Therefore $\frac{2}{5}$ as a decimal is 0.4.

There are different types of decimals. One of those types is called a **terminating** decimal. Another is called a **recurring** decimal.

A terminating decimal comes to an end. In a recurring decimal the digits repeat themselves and would continue to do so forever.

Worked examples

a) Convert $\frac{1}{5}$ to a decimal. Decide whether the decimal is terminating or recurring.

$$\frac{1}{5} = 0.2$$

0.2 is a terminating decimal.

b) Convert $\frac{2}{3}$ to a decimal.

$$\frac{2}{3} = 0.666\,666\,666\,666\,66\ldots$$

This is an example of a recurring decimal. This can be written as $0.\dot{6}$, where the *dot* above the 6 indicates that it repeats.

c) Convert $\frac{12}{99}$ to a decimal. Decide whether the decimal is terminating or recurring.

$$\frac{12}{99} = 0.121\,212\,121\,212\,121\,2\ldots$$

This is an example of a recurring decimal. This can be written as $0.\dot{1}\dot{2}$, where the two dots in this case indicate that both numbers repeat.

EXERCISE 15.2A

1 Using a calculator (or spreadsheet) copy and complete the table below. Divide each numerator by each denominator to convert fractions to decimals.

		Numerator											
		1	2	3	4	5	6	7	8	9	10	11	12
Denominator	1												
	2												
	3												
	4												
	5												
	6												
	7												
	8												
	9												
	10												
	11												
	12												

Using your table from question 1, answer the following questions.

2 Describe the type of fraction which gives a decimal answer greater than 1.

3 Describe the type of fraction which gives an answer of 1.

4 Name three fractions that give terminating decimals.

5 Do fractions with 7 as the denominator give recurring decimals? Explain your answer clearly.

6 Describe the different types of recurring decimals that you see.

Changing a decimal to a fraction

Just as fractions can be written as either terminating or recurring decimals, the reverse is also true. All terminating or recurring decimals can be written as a fraction. In order to do this, an understanding of place value is necessary.

Worked examples

a) Write the decimal 0.6 as a fraction in its simplest form.

By entering 0.6 into a place value table we get:

Units	•	Tenths
0	•	6

The 6 is worth 6 tenths. As a fraction, this can therefore be written as $\frac{6}{10}$.

$\frac{6}{10}$ can be simplified to $\frac{3}{5}$.

b) Write the decimal 0.325 as a fraction in its simplest form.

By entering 0.325 into a place value table we get:

Units	•	Tenths	Hundredths	Thousandths
0	•	3	2	5

3 tenths, 2 hundredths and 5 thousandths is equivalent to 325 thousandths.

As a fraction, this can therefore be written as $\frac{325}{1000}$.

$\frac{325}{1000}$ can be simplified to $\frac{13}{40}$.

Place value tables can also be used to compare two or more decimals for size.

Worked example

Which of the following two decimals is the larger?

0.2 or 0.18

Entering them both into a place value table gives:

Units	•	Tenths	Hundredths
0	•	2	0
0	•	1	8

0.2 is equivalent to 2 tenths or 20 hundredths.

0.18 is equivalent to 18 hundredths.

Therefore 0.2 is larger than 0.18.

EXERCISE 15.2B

1 **a)** Convert each of the following fractions to a decimal.

(i) $\frac{1}{20}$ **(ii)** $\frac{3}{15}$ **(iii)** $\frac{7}{28}$

(iv) $\frac{3}{14}$ **(v)** $\frac{1}{24}$ **(vi)** $\frac{17}{99}$

b) Put the fractions in part **a)** in order of size, largest first.

2 Convert each of the following decimals to a fraction in its simplest form. Show your working clearly.

a) 0.3 **b)** 0.12 **c)** 0.625 **d)** 0.37 **e)** 0.2125

3 Write each of the following sets of decimals in order of size, smallest first.

a) 0.7 0.55 **b)** 0.27 0.100

c) 0.625 0.8 0.73 **d)** 0.303 0.33 0.3003

e) 0.01 0.10 0.101 **f)** 0.32 0.43 0.403

Calculations with decimals

We carry out calculations with decimals every day when dealing with money. Although many of these calculations are now carried out using a calculator or computer, it is still important to have an understanding of how answers are obtained, at the very least to check that you are not out of pocket.

Worked examples

a) Paul went to a café and bought a sandwich costing \$1.85 and a drink costing 73 cents. Calculate the total cost of his bill.

This sum can be set out in the conventional way, ensuring that place value is taken into account.

$$\begin{array}{r} 1.85 \\ +\ 0.73 \\ \hline 2_{1}.58 \end{array}$$

b) Maggie went shopping and bought four birthday cards, each priced \$1.53. Calculate the total cost of the four cards.

$$\begin{array}{r} 1.53 \\ \times\quad\ \ 4 \\ \hline 6_{2}.1_{1}2 \end{array}$$

The total cost of the four cards was \$6.12.

c) $135.50 was shared equally between five friends. How much did they each receive?

$$\begin{array}{r|l} & 2\;7\;.\;1\;0 \\ \hline 5 & 1\;3\;{}^{3}5\;.\;5\;0 \end{array}$$

Each of the five friends received $27.10.

EXERCISE 15.2C

1 Marco goes shopping for food. A list of the items and their prices is given below.

Bread 63 cents   Soup $1.25   Coffee $2.18
Sugar 87 cents   Yoghurt 42 cents

a) Calculate the total amount Marco had to pay.
b) He paid with a $10 note. Calculate the change he received.

2 A family of two adults and two children decided to visit a museum for the day. Individual adult tickets cost $19.20, whilst an individual child ticket costs $16.70.
a) Calculate the cost of buying the two adult and two child tickets.
b) A family ticket costs $57. Calculate how much they can save by buying a family ticket instead of individual tickets.

3 A brother and sister are 1.63 m tall and 94 cm tall respectively. What is the difference in their heights:
a) in metres
b) in centimetres?

4 Isabel buys two pairs of socks costing $3.67 each and three pairs of trousers costing $34.49 each.
a) Calculate the total cost of these items.
b) Isabel only had $42 in her bank account. Work out by how much she has gone overdrawn.

5 Nine business associates share $7 365 800 from the sale of their company. Calculate, to the nearest cent, how much they each receive.

6 A table and six chairs are priced at $335 in a garden centre. The table costs $120.80. Calculate the cost of each chair.

Percentages

Percentages, fractions and decimals are all different ways of representing values. The unique feature of percentages is that they are written as values out of 100. A percentage means 'a part of 100' so 23 per cent, written 23%, means 23 parts in 100.

Here is a table showing how the same value can be written as a fraction, a decimal or a percentage.

Fraction	Decimal	Percentage
$\frac{1}{2}$	0.5	50%
$\frac{1}{4}$	0.25	25%
$\frac{3}{4}$	0.75	75%
$\frac{1}{8}$	0.125	12.5%
$\frac{3}{8}$	0.375	37.5%
$\frac{5}{8}$	0.625	62.5%
$\frac{7}{8}$	0.875	87.5%
$\frac{1}{10}$	0.1	10%
$\frac{2}{10}$ or $\frac{1}{5}$	0.2	20%
$\frac{3}{10}$	0.3	30%
$\frac{4}{10}$ or $\frac{2}{5}$	0.4	40%
$\frac{6}{10}$ or $\frac{3}{5}$	0.6	60%
$\frac{7}{10}$	0.7	70%
$\frac{8}{10}$ or $\frac{4}{5}$	0.8	80%
$\frac{9}{10}$	0.9	90%

Simple percentages of a quantity

Worked examples

a) Find 25% of 60.

From the table, 25% is $\frac{1}{4}$.

$\frac{1}{4}$ of 60 = 60 ÷ 4 = 15

b) Find 30% of 250.

From the table, 30% is $\frac{3}{10}$.

$\frac{1}{10}$ of 250 = 25

So $\frac{3}{10}$ of 250 = 3 × 25 = 75

EXERCISE 15.3A

Use the table on page 134 or another method to calculate the following.

1 50% of 300

2 75% of 400

3 40% of 600

4 25% of 360

5 80% of 250

6 37.5% of 240

7 87.5% of 880

8 12.5% of 320

9 75% of 40

What do you notice?

10 40% of 75

Simple percentages

Worked examples

a) Of 100 sheep in a field, 88 are ewes.
(i) What percentage of the sheep are ewes?
(ii) What percentage are not ewes?

(i) 88 out of 100 are ewes
= 88%

(ii) 12 out of 100 are not ewes
= 12%

b) A gymnast scored the following marks out of 10 from five judges:

8.0   8.2   7.9   8.3   7.6

Express these marks as percentages.

$\frac{8.0}{10} = \frac{80}{100} = 80\%$ $\frac{8.2}{10} = \frac{82}{100} = 82\%$

$\frac{7.9}{10} = \frac{79}{100} = 79\%$

$\frac{8.3}{10} = \frac{83}{100} = 83\%$ $\frac{7.6}{10} = \frac{76}{100} = 76\%$

c) Convert the following percentages into fractions and decimals.

(i) 27%

(ii) 5%

(i) $\frac{27}{100} = 0.27$

(ii) $\frac{5}{100} = \frac{1}{20} = 0.05$

EXERCISE 15.3B

1 In a survey of 100 cars, 47 were white, 23 were blue and 30 were red. Express each of these numbers as a percentage of the total.

2 $\frac{7}{10}$ of the surface of the Earth is water. Express this as a percentage.

3 There are 200 birds in a flock. 120 of them are female. What percentage of the flock is:

a) female   **b)** male?

4 Write these percentages as fractions of 100.

a) 73%   **b)** 28%   **c)** 10%   **d)** 25%

5 Write these fractions as percentages.

a) $\frac{27}{100}$ **b)** $\frac{3}{10}$ **c)** $\frac{7}{50}$ **d)** $\frac{1}{4}$

6 Convert the following percentages to decimals.

a) 39%   **b)** 47%   **c)** 83%

d) 7%   **e)** 2%   **f)** 20%

7 Convert the following decimals to percentages.

a) 0.31   **b)** 0.67   **c)** 0.09

d) 0.05   **e)** 0.2   **f)** 0.75

16 Sequences

- Generate terms of an integer sequence; find a term given its position in the sequence; find simple term-to-term rules.
- Generate sequences from spatial patterns and describe the general term in simple cases.

Sequences and patterns

A **sequence** is an ordered set of numbers. Each number in the sequence is called a **term**. The terms of a sequence form a pattern.

Below are examples of three different types of sequences.

- **2 4 6 8 10 12**
  In this sequence we are adding 2 to each term in order to produce the next term.
- **1 2 4 8 16 32**
  In this sequence we double each term in order to produce the next term.
- **1 4 9 16 25 36**
  Here, the difference between consecutive terms increases by 2 each time. It is also the sequence of square numbers.

Sequences in diagrams

Sequences can also be expressed as a series of diagrams. The example below shows the first four diagrams in a sequence of tile patterns.

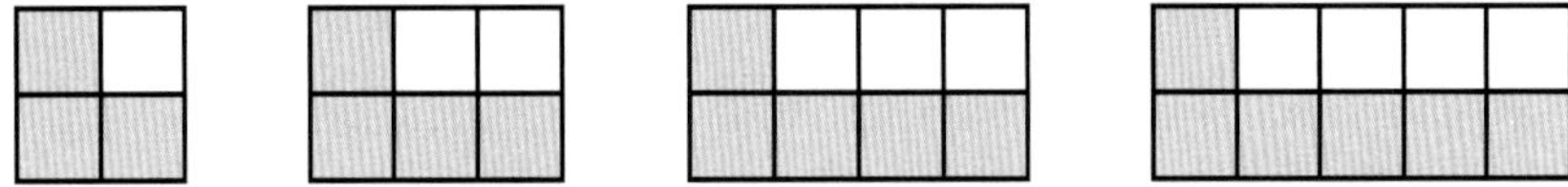

We can see that the tile patterns grow according to a rule. We can enter the numbers of white and blue tiles in each pattern into a table of results.

Number of white tiles	1	2	3	4
Number of blue tiles	3	4	5	6

There are two types of rules which describe the sequence of blue tiles:

- The number of blue tiles increases by 1 each time.
- The number of blue tiles is always 2 more than the number of white tiles.

The second rule is useful if we know the number of white tiles and want to work out the number of blue tiles. For example, if there are 100 white tiles, how many blue tiles are there?

Number of blue tiles = number of white tiles + 2
Number of blue tiles = 100 + 2 = 102

EXERCISE 16.1

These diagrams show the first three patterns in a sequence of growing tile patterns.

1  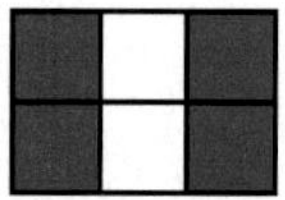 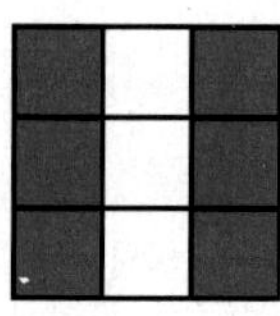

a) Draw the next two diagrams in the sequence.
b) Copy and complete this table.

Number of white tiles	1	2	3	4	5
Number of red tiles					

c) Describe the pattern linking the number of white tiles and the number of red tiles.
d) Use your rule in part **c)** to predict the number of red tiles in a pattern with 100 white tiles.

2 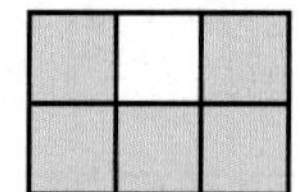 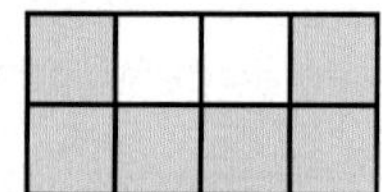 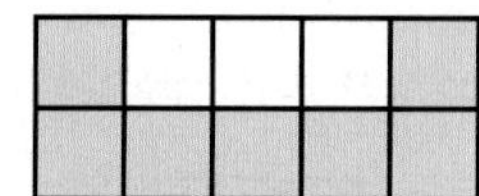

a) Draw the next two diagrams in the sequence.
b) Copy and complete this table.

Number of white tiles	1	2	3	4	5
Number of green tiles					

c) Describe the pattern linking the number of white tiles and the number of green tiles.
d) Use your rule in part **c)** to predict the number of green tiles in a pattern with 100 white tiles.

3 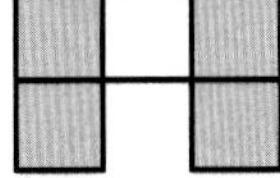 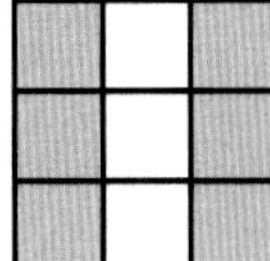 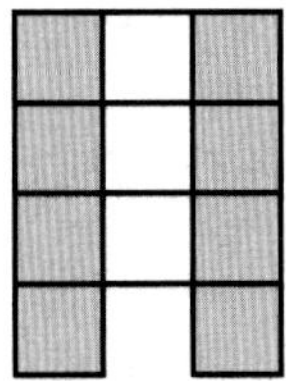

a) Draw the next two diagrams in the sequence.
b) Copy and complete this table.

Number of white tiles	1	2	3	4	5
Number of orange tiles					

c) Describe the pattern linking the number of white tiles and the number of orange tiles.
d) Use your rule in part **c)** to predict the number of orange tiles in a pattern with 100 white tiles.

4 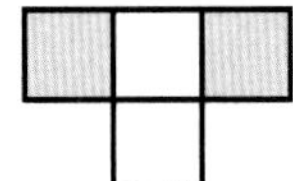 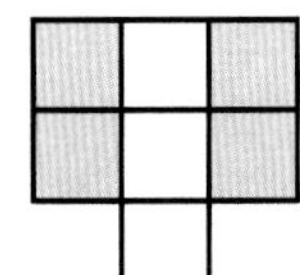

a) Draw the next two diagrams in the sequence.
b) Copy and complete this table.

Number of white tiles	1	2	3	4	5
Number of blue tiles					

c) Describe the pattern linking the number of white tiles and the number of blue tiles.
d) Use your rule in part **c)** to predict the number of blue tiles in a pattern with 100 white tiles.

5 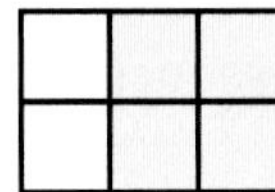 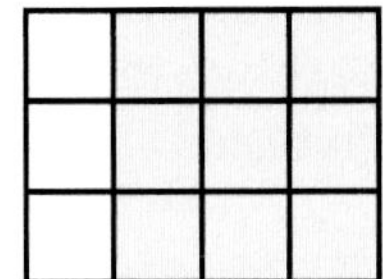

a) Draw the next two diagrams in the sequence.
b) Copy and complete this table.

Number of white tiles	1	2	3	4	5
Number of yellow tiles					

c) Describe the pattern linking the number of white tiles and the number of yellow tiles.
d) Use your rule in part **c)** to predict the number of yellow tiles in a pattern with 100 white tiles.

Term-to-term rules

A rule which describes how to get from one term to the next is called a **term-to-term** rule.

Worked examples

a) Here is a sequence of numbers.

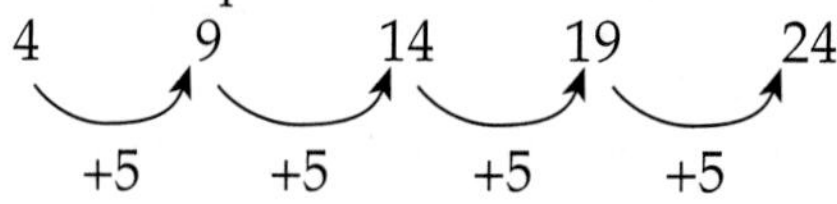

The term-to-term rule for this sequence is +5. What is the tenth term?
To calculate the tenth term in the sequence, the pattern can be continued using the term-to-term rule:

4 9 14 19 24 29 34 39 44 **49**

b) Here is a sequence of numbers.

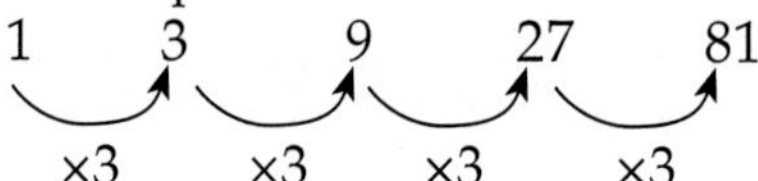

The term-to-term rule for this sequence is ×3. What is the eighth term?
To calculate the eighth term in the sequence, the pattern can be continued using the term-to-term rule:

1 3 9 27 81 243 729 **2187**

EXERCISE 16.2

For each of the sequences in questions 1–10:
a) describe the term-to-term rule
b) write down the next two terms of the sequence
c) calculate the tenth term.

1 2 4 6 8 10

2 1 3 5 7 9

3 4 7 10 13 16

4 2 6 10 14 18

5 1 8 15 22 29

6 7 14 21 28 35

7 9 18 27 36 45

8 9 7 5 3 1

9 32 28 24 20 16

10 144 132 120 108

17 Angle properties

- Start to recognise the angular connections between parallel lines, perpendicular lines and transversals.
- Calculate the sum of angles at a point, on a straight line and in a triangle, and prove that vertically opposite angles are equal; derive and use the property that the angle sum of a quadrilateral is 360°.
- Solve simple geometrical problems by using side and angle properties to identify equal lengths or calculate unknown angles, and explain reasoning.

Angle relationships

For a long period during the Middle Ages, Spain was ruled by Muslims. Evidence of their great influence on its culture remains to be seen today. The Alhambra is a walled city and fortress in Granada, Spain. It was built during the last Islamic sultanate on the Iberian Peninsula. The palace is lavishly decorated with stone and wood carvings, and tile patterns on most of the ceilings, walls and floors. Islamic art does not use representations of living beings, but heavily uses geometric patterns, especially symmetrical patterns.

The picture below is an example of one of the tilings at the Alhambra Palace and demonstrates how an understanding of angle can lead to the creation of a beautiful symmetrical pattern.

The word **angle** comes from the Latin word *angulus* meaning corner. An angle is a measure of turn. People often give instructions such as 'turn round the corner' or 'turn over a page'; these both represent an amount of turn and, as a result, an angle.

The most common unit of measurement for an angle is the **degree** (°). This chapter will look mainly at the special angle properties and relationships that exist.

In Chapter 10 you looked at ways of measuring angles and constructing triangles. The simplest way to measure an angle is with a protractor. The angle shown here is 41°, measured anticlockwise from the base line, using the inner scale.

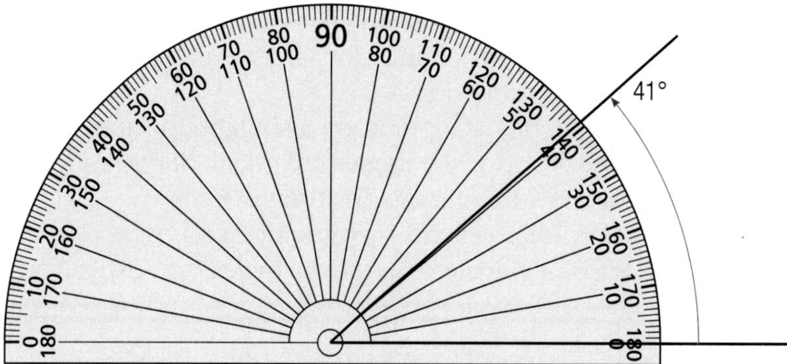

If you wished to measure the obtuse angle formed by continuing the base line you could measure clockwise from zero on the outside scale. The size of that angle is 139°.

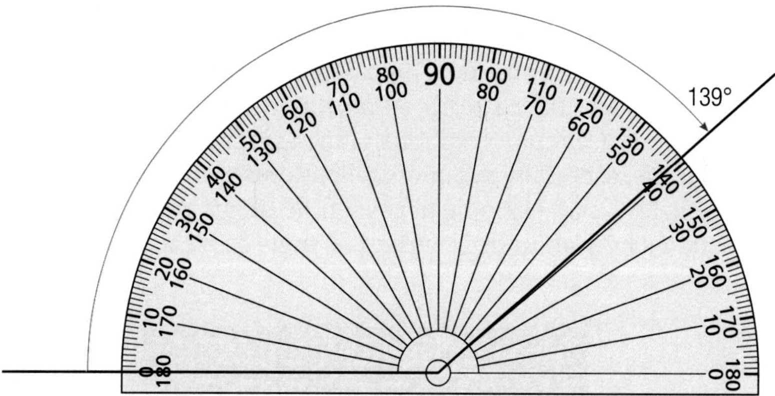

Angles on a straight line

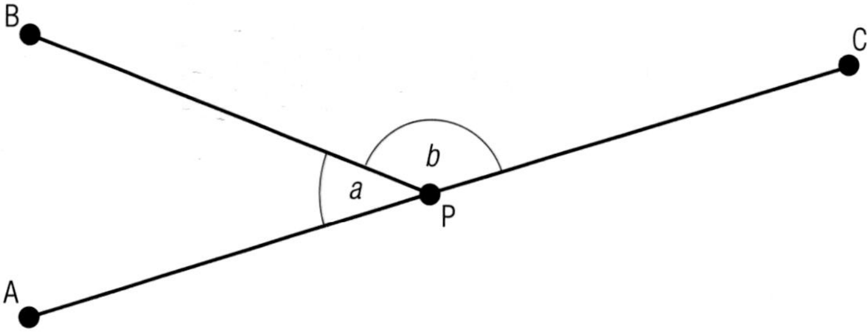

The point P lies on the straight line AC. A person standing at point P, initially facing point A, turns through an angle a (in degrees) to face point B and then turns a further angle b to face point C. The person has turned through half a complete turn and therefore rotated through 180°. Therefore $a + b = 180°$. This can be summarised like this:

Angles at a point on a straight line add up to 180°.

Worked example

Calculate the size of angle x.

$$x + 130° = 180°$$
$$x = 180° - 130°$$

Therefore $x = 50°$.

Two angles which fit together on a straight line are called **supplementary** angles. They add up to 180°.

If you know an angle on a straight line it is easy to find the supplementary angle.

Worked example

Calculate the supplementary angle.

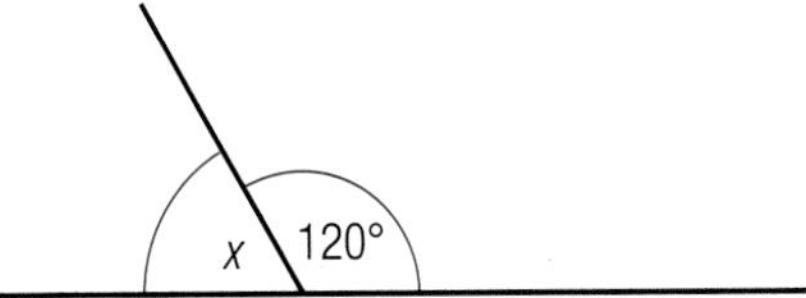

$$x + 120° = 180°$$
$$x = 180° - 120°$$
$$x = 60°$$

So the supplementary angle is 60°.

EXERCISE 17.1

Calculate these supplementary angles.

1

2

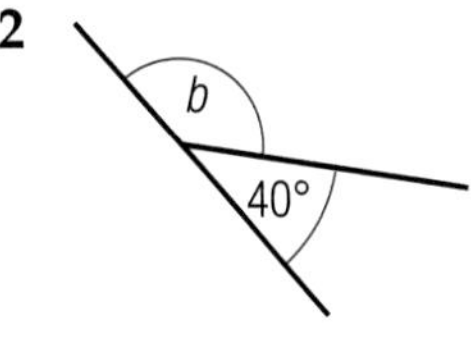

3

4

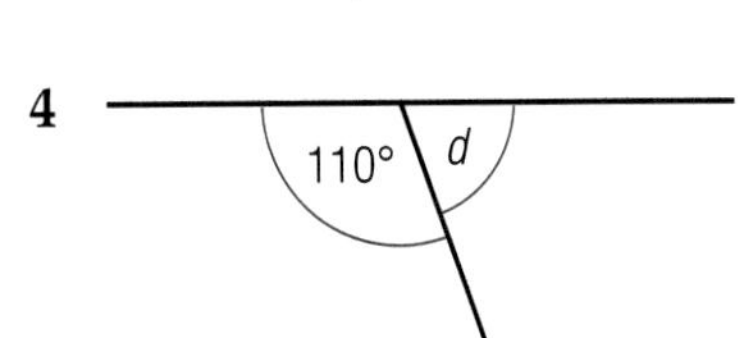

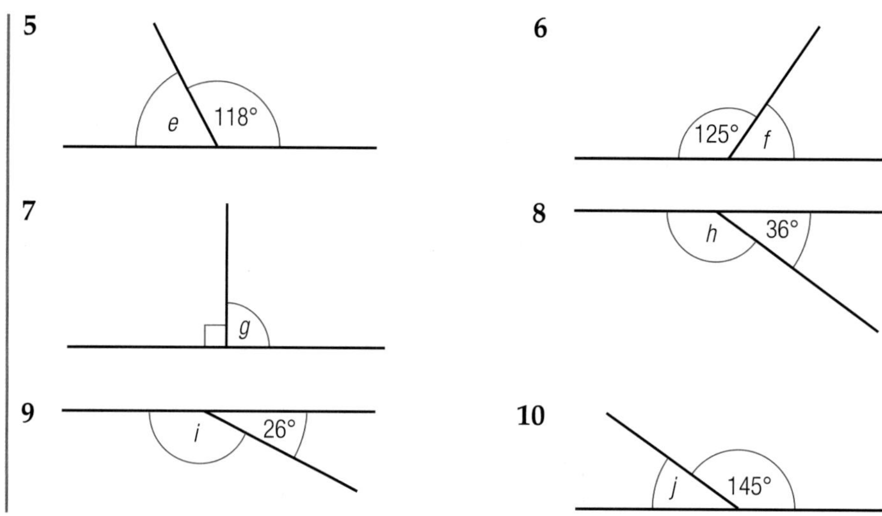

Angles around a point

In this diagram it can be seen that if a person standing at P turns through each of the angles a, b and c in turn, then the total amount turned will be 360° (a complete turn).

$$a + b + c = 360°$$

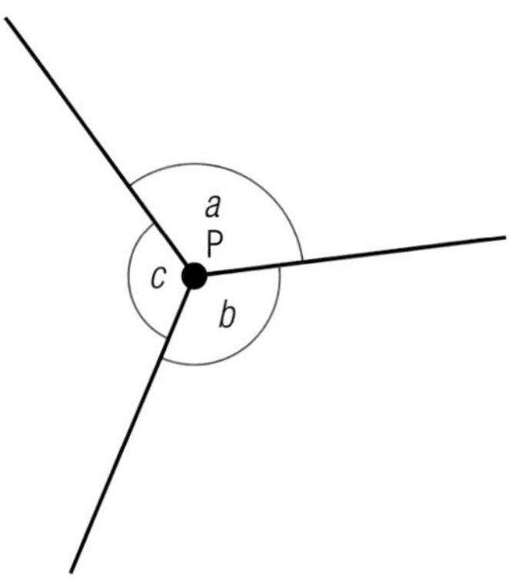

Angles about a point add up to 360°.

EXERCISE 17.2

Work out the size of the unknown angle in each of these questions.

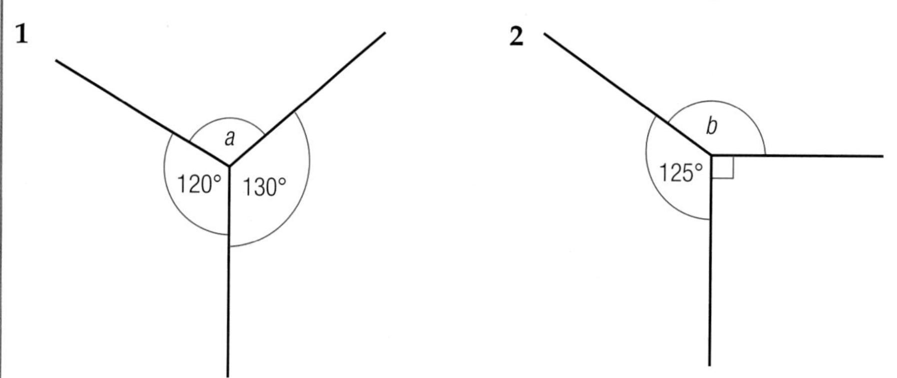

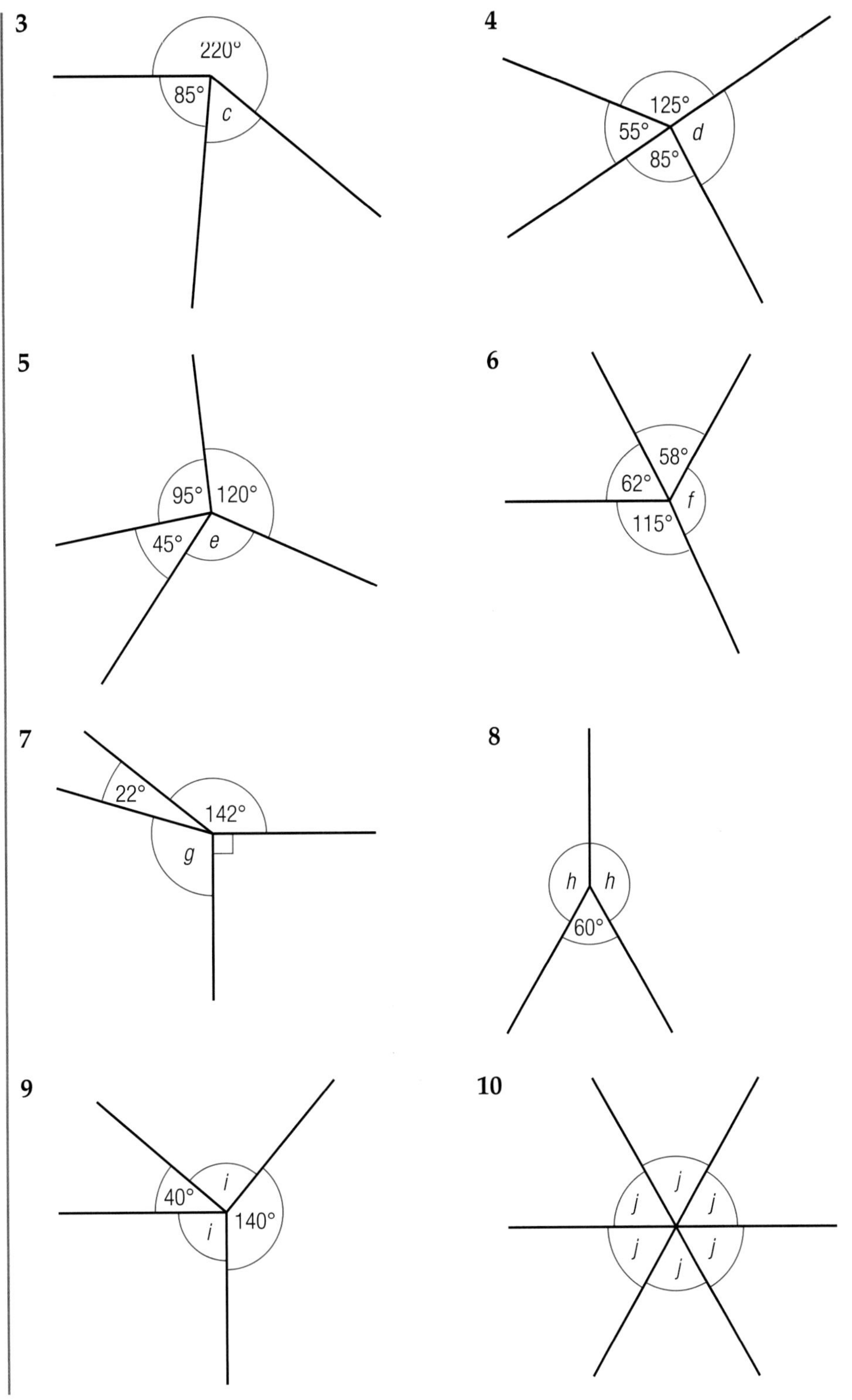
3
220°
85°
c
4
125°
55°
d
85°
5
95°
120°
45°
e
6
58°
62°
f
115°
7
22°
142°
g
8
h
h
60°
9
i
40°
i
140°
10
j
j
j
j
j
j

Angles formed within parallel lines

EXERCISE 17.3A

1 Draw a similar diagram to the one shown. Measure carefully each of the labelled angles and write down their values.

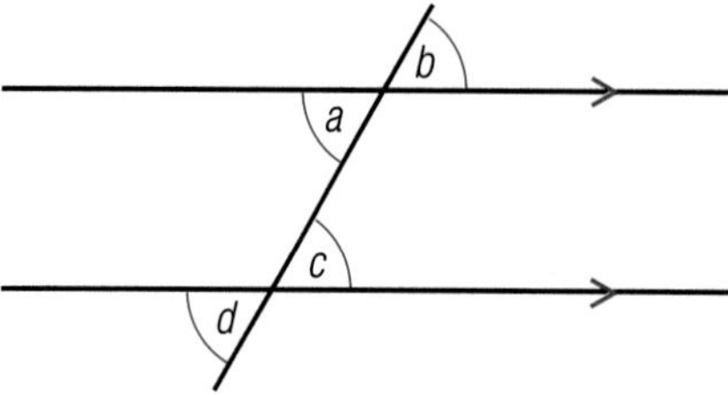

2 Draw a similar diagram to the one shown. Measure carefully each of the labelled angles and write down their values.

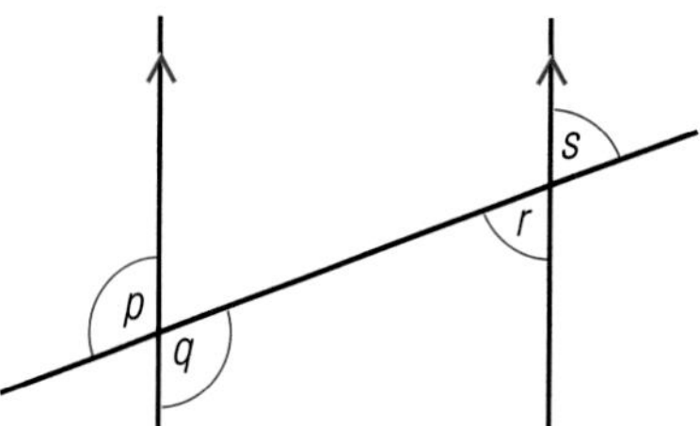

3 Draw a similar diagram to the one shown. Measure carefully each of the labelled angles and write down their values.

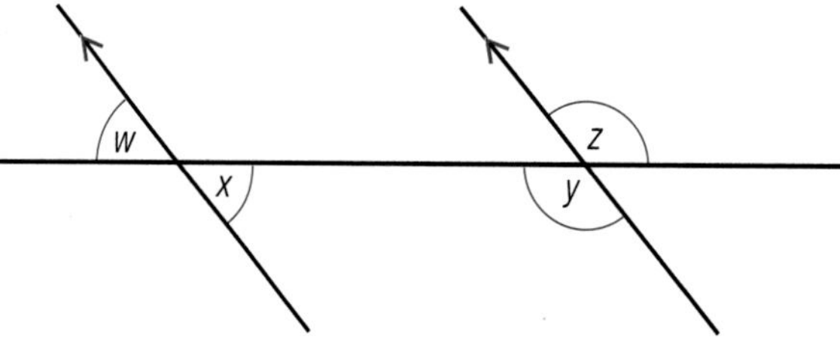

4 Write down what you have noticed about the angles that you measured in questions 1–3.

When two straight lines cross, the angles opposite each other are the same size. They are known as **vertically opposite angles**.

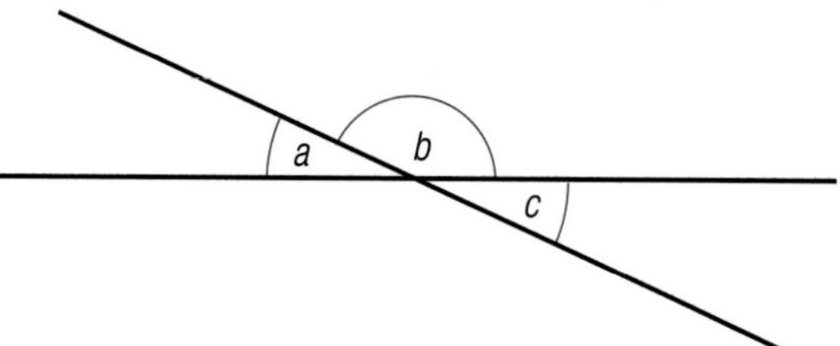

By using the fact that angles at a point on a straight line add up to 180°, we can show why vertically opposite angles must always be equal in size.

$a + b = 180°$

$c + b = 180°$

Therefore, a is equal to c.

EXERCISE 17.3B

1 Draw a similar diagram to the one shown. Measure carefully each of the labelled angles and write down their values.

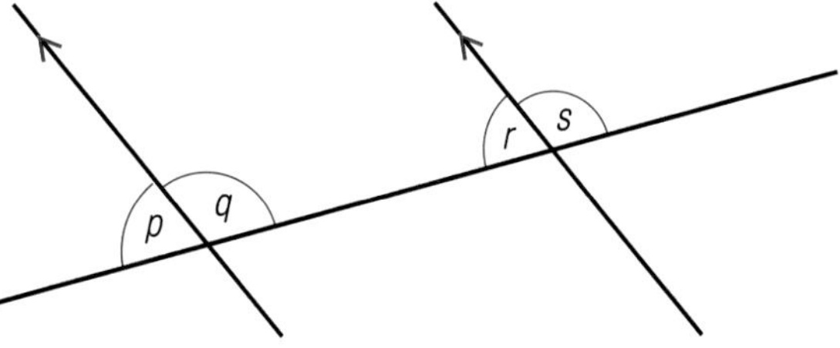

2 Draw a similar diagram to the one shown. Measure carefully each of the labelled angles and write down their values.

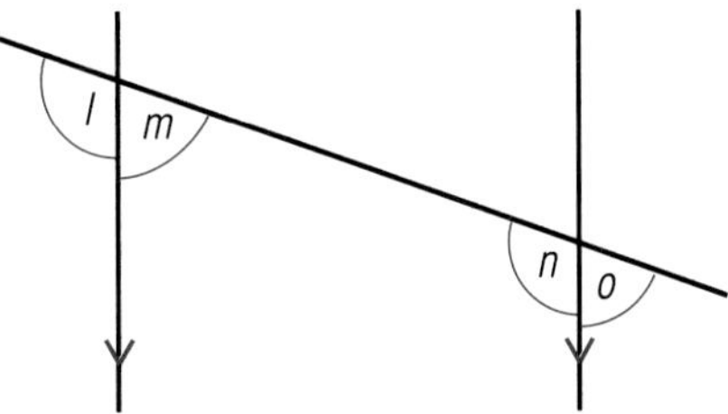

3 Draw a similar diagram to the one shown. Measure carefully each of the labelled angles and write down their values.

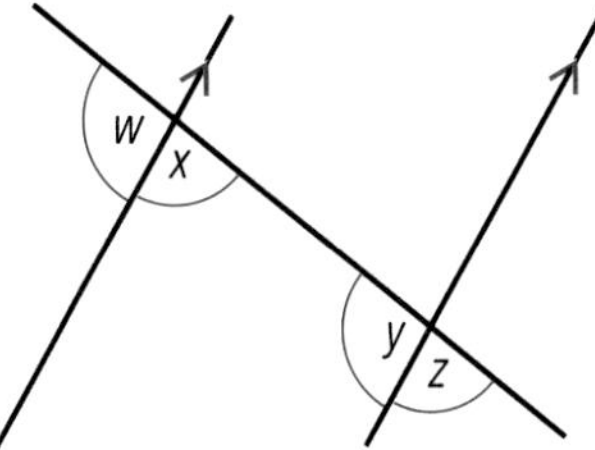

4 Write down what you have noticed about the angles that you measured in questions 1–3.

When a line intersects two parallel lines, as in the diagram below, we find that certain angles are the same size.

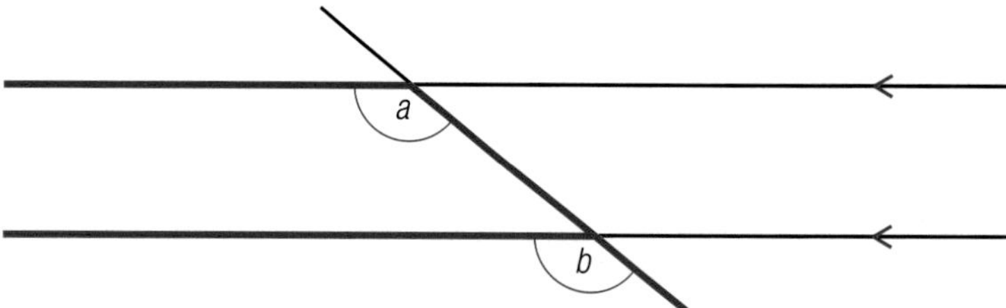

The angles a and b, in the diagram above, are equal and are known as **corresponding angles**. Corresponding angles can be found by looking for an **'F'** formation in a diagram.

A line intersecting two parallel lines also produces another pair of equal angles known as **alternate angles**. We can show these are equal by using the fact that both vertically opposite and corresponding angles are equal.

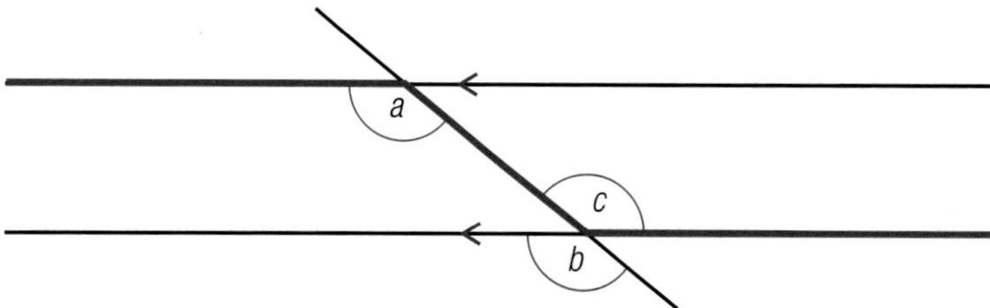

In the diagram above, $a = b$ (corresponding angles). But $b = c$ (vertically opposite). We can therefore deduce that $a = c$.

Angles a and c are alternate angles. These can be found by looking for a **'Z'** formation in a diagram.

EXERCISE 17.3C

Work out the size of each of the unknown angles in these diagrams. Give reasons for your answers.

1

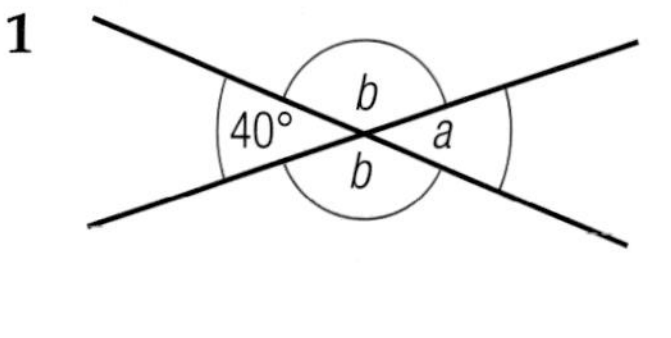

2

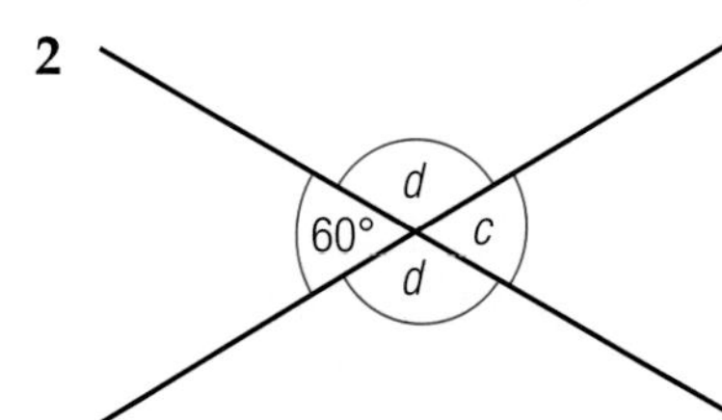

3

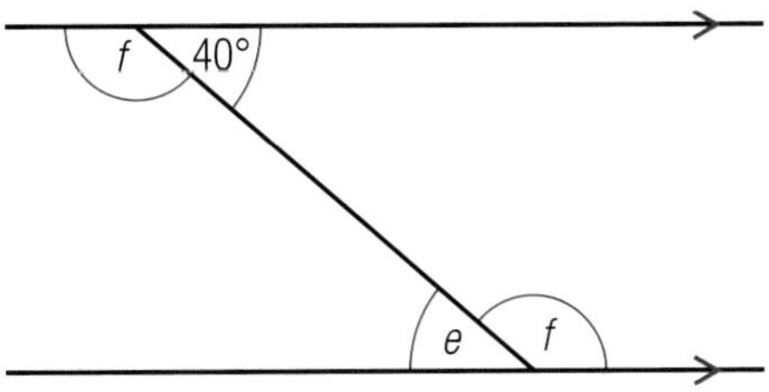

4

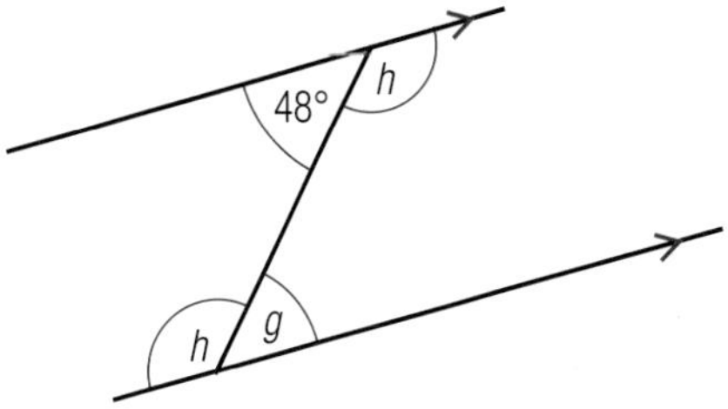

5

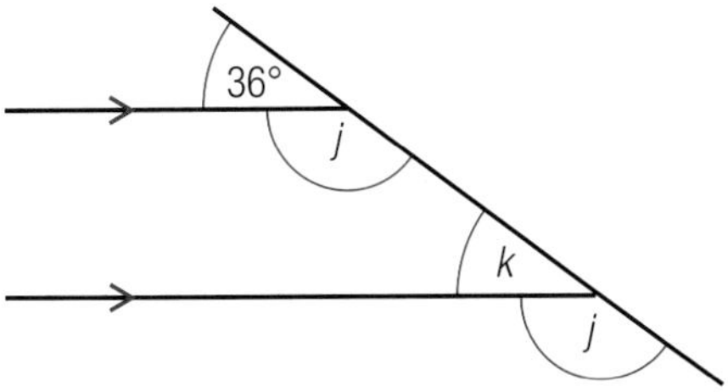

6

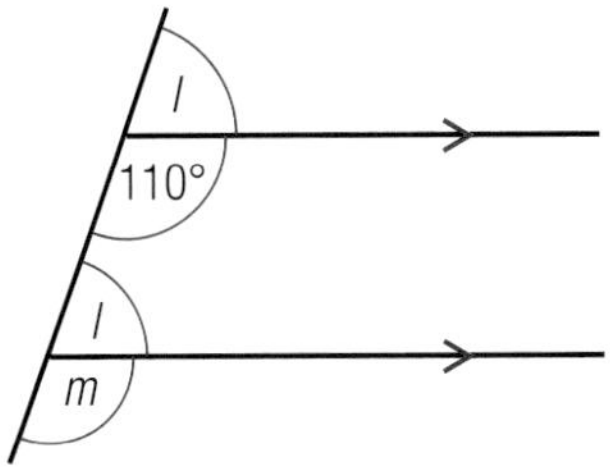

7

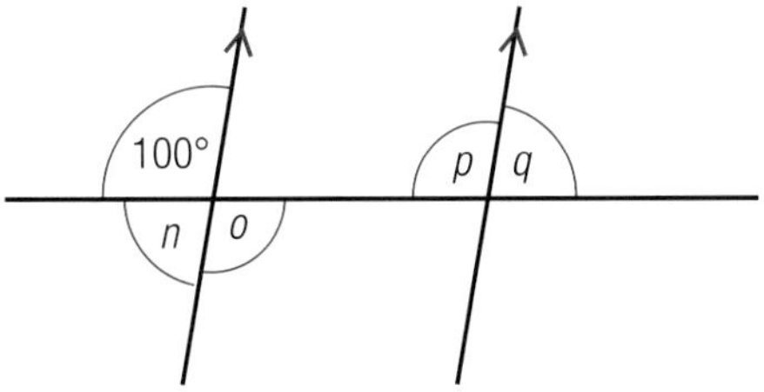

8

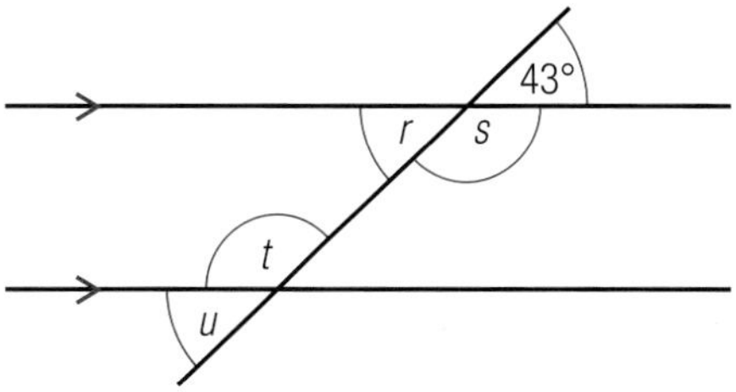

9

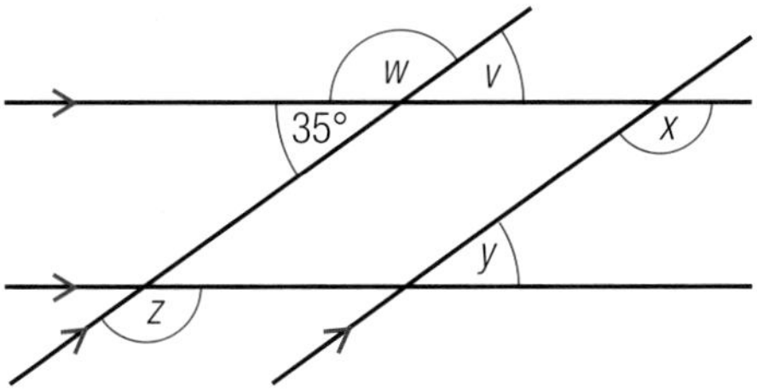

10

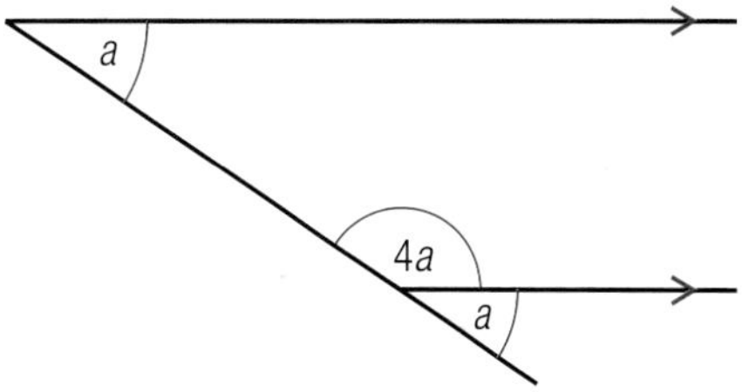

Angles of a triangle

A triangle has three angles as shown.

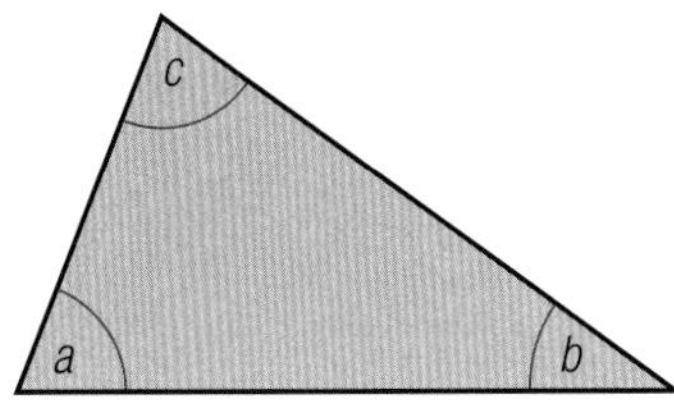

Although the sizes of the individual angles can vary, their total is always constant. The three angles always add up to 180°. In the triangle above,

$$a + b + c = 180°$$

Worked example

This triangle is isosceles. Calculate the size of each of the base angles.

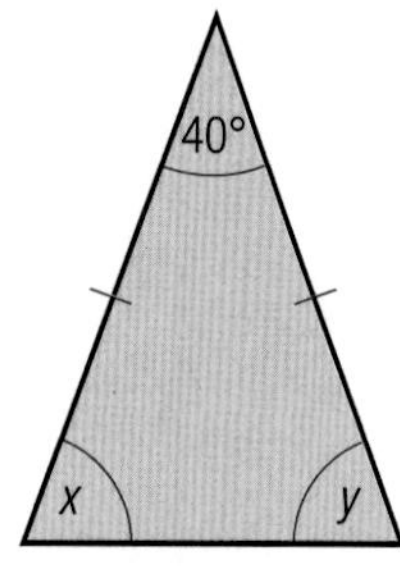

$x + y + 40° = 180°$ (angles of a triangle add up to 180°)

$x + y = 140°$

But $x = y$ (base angles of an isosceles triangle are equal)

Therefore $x = y = 70°$.

Angles of a quadrilateral

A quadrilateral has four angles as shown.
As with triangles, the sizes of the individual angles can vary, but the sum of the four angles is the same for any quadrilateral. The four angles always add up to 360°. In this quadrilateral,

$$a + b + c + d = 360°$$

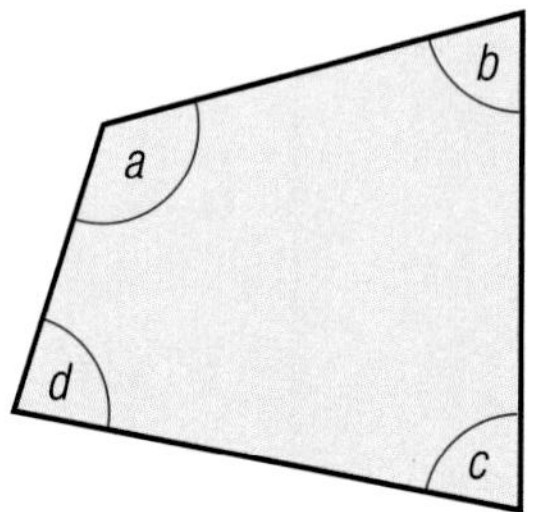

EXERCISE 17.4

Work out the size of each of the unknown angles in these diagrams. Give reasons for your answers.

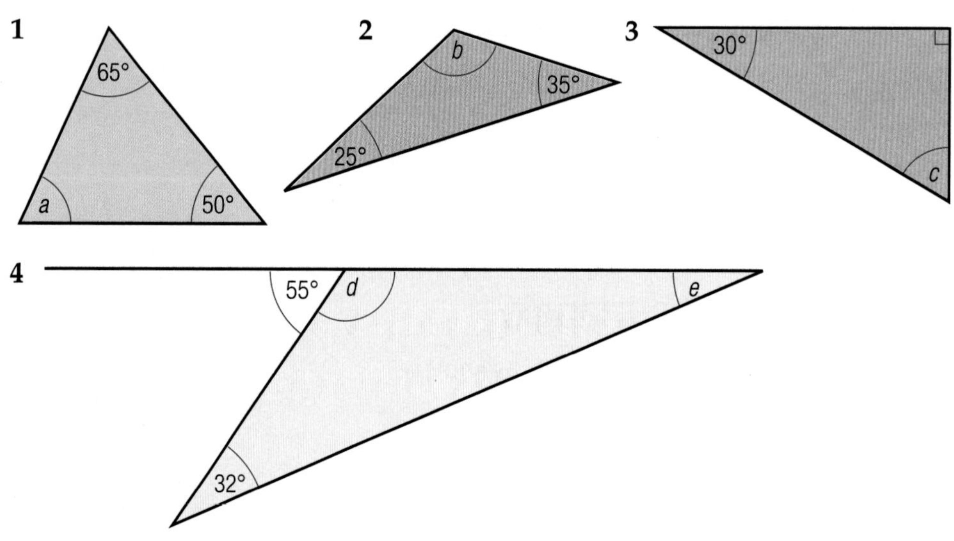

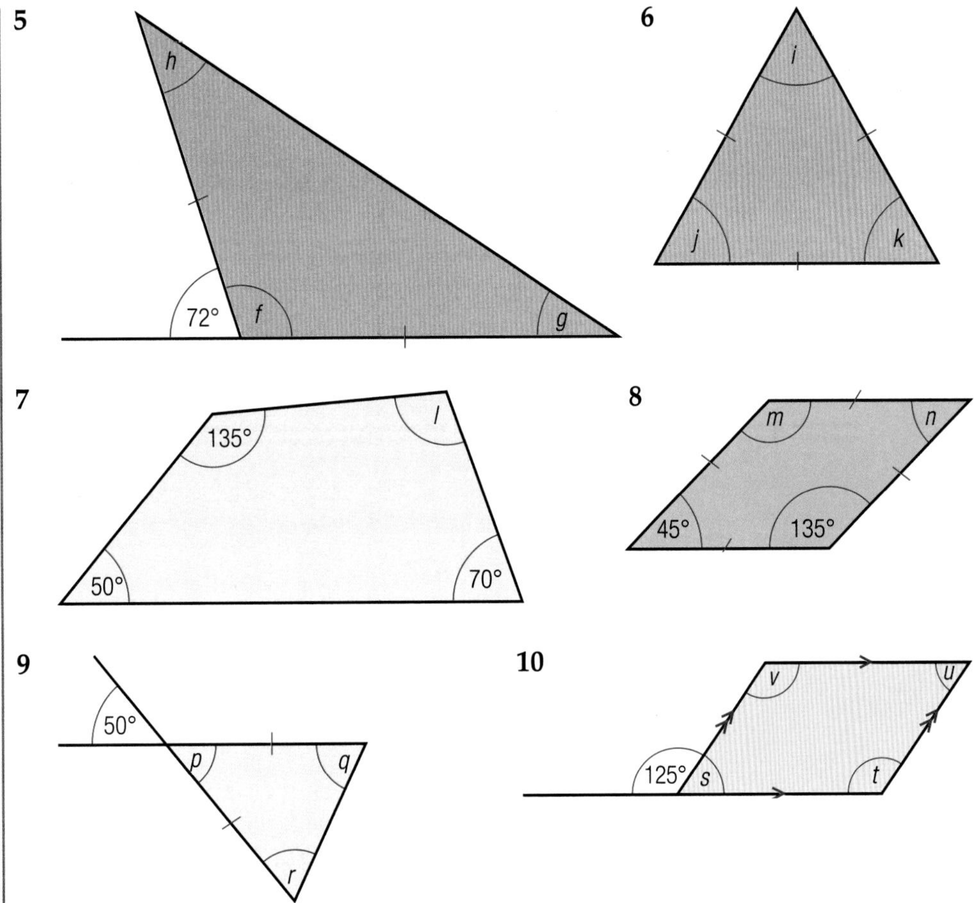
5
h
72°
f
g
6
i
j
k
7
135°
l
50°
70°
8
m
n
45°
135°
9
50°
p
q
r
10
v
u
125°
s
t

18 Area and perimeter of rectangles

- Know the abbreviations for and relationships between square metres (m^2), square centimetres (cm^2) and square millimetres (mm^2).
- Derive and use formulae for the area and perimeter of a rectangle; calculate the perimeter and area of compound shapes made from rectangles.

Area and perimeter

A **rectangle** is a two-dimensional shape with four sides. The four sides consist of two pairs of parallel sides as shown.

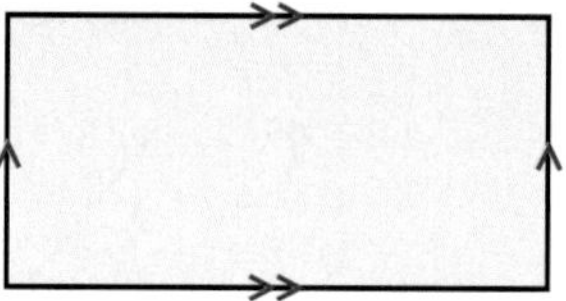

The **area** of a shape is the amount of *flat* space that it occupies.

This square is 1 cm long and 1 cm wide. Its area is **1 square centimetre** or 1 cm^2.

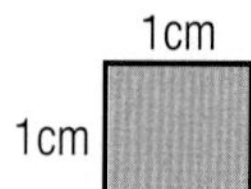

This square is 3 cm long and 3 cm wide. It has been split into centimetre squares.

We can see that a 3 cm × 3 cm square can be split into nine 1 cm × 1 cm squares.

The area of the 3 cm × 3 cm square is therefore 9 cm squares.

This is written as 9 cm^2.

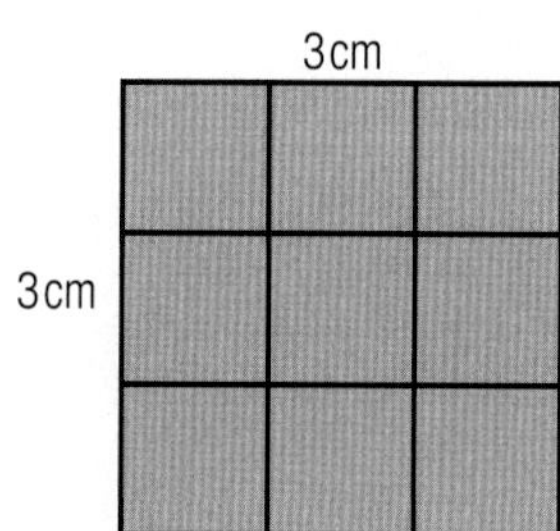

This rectangle is 5 cm long and 3 cm wide. It has also been split into centimetre squares.

A 5 cm × 3 cm rectangle can be split into fifteen 1 cm × 1 cm squares. The area of the 5 cm × 3 cm rectangle is therefore 15 cm^2.

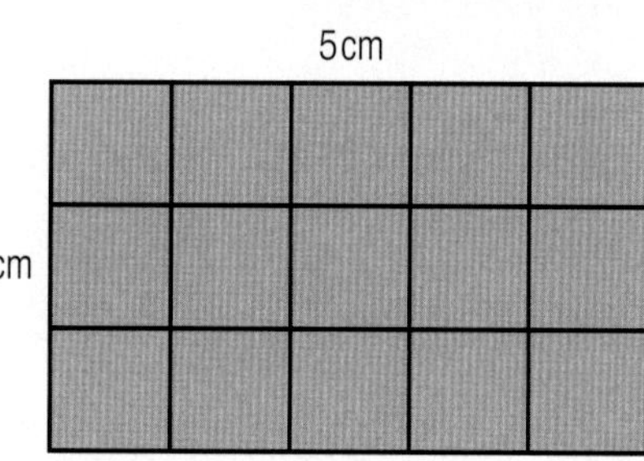

In general, therefore, the area of a square or rectangle can be calculated by simply multiplying the length by the width.

Area of a rectangle = length × width

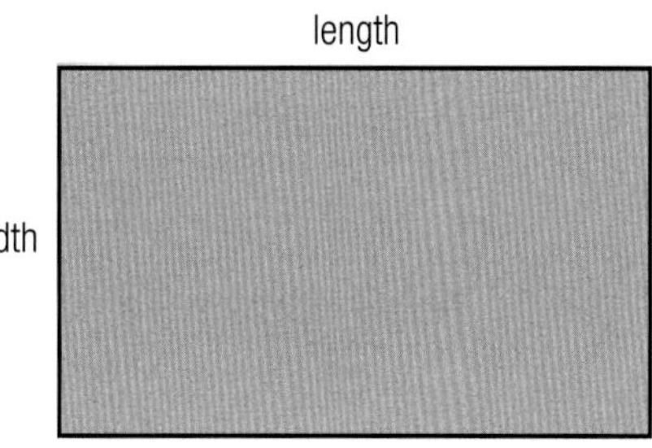

The **perimeter** of a shape is the distance around its edge. The words 'perimeter fence' refer to a fence enclosing a piece of land, i.e. a fence which runs around the edge of the land.

Worked example

A rectangle is 7 cm long and 3 cm wide.

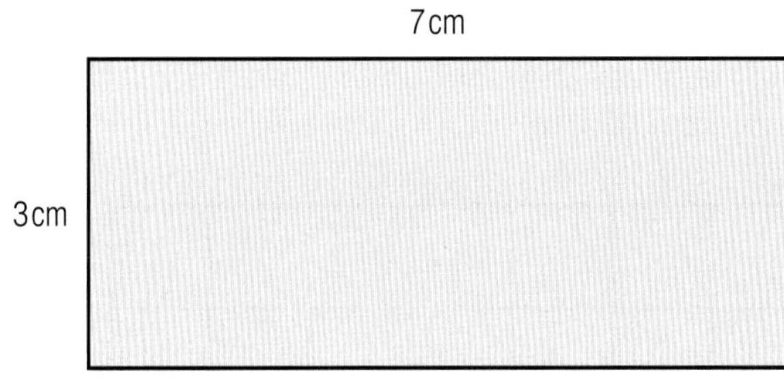

Calculate:

a) its area

b) its perimeter.

a) Area = length × width
= 7 cm × 3 cm
= 21 cm^2

b) Perimeter = 2 × length + 2 × width
= 2 × 7 cm + 2 × 3 cm
= 14 cm + 6 cm
= 20 cm

Different units

Most of the lengths that you work with will be measured in metres (m), centimetres (cm) or millimetres (mm).

Similarly, the units of area that you are likely to work with are square metres (m^2), square centimetres (cm^2) and square millimetres (mm^2).

In Chapter 4 you saw how to convert between the different units of length:

1 m = 100 cm **1 cm = 10 mm** **1 m = 1000 mm**

Worked example

A rectangle is 4 m long and 2 m wide.
Calculate its perimeter, giving your answer in centimetres.

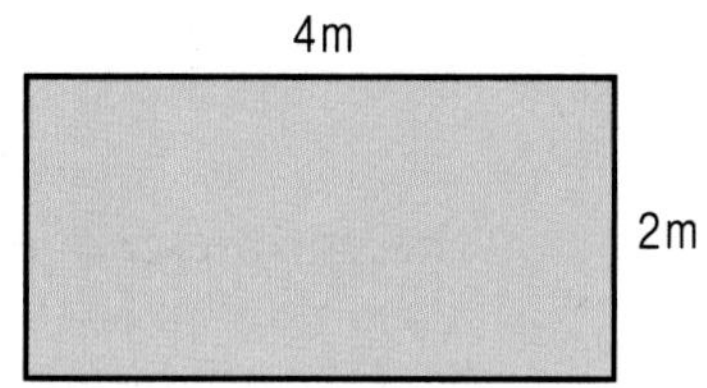

Perimeter = $2 \times 4\,\text{m} + 2 \times 2\,\text{m}$
$= 8\,\text{m} + 4\,\text{m}$
$= 12\,\text{m}$

But 1 m = 100 cm.

Therefore perimeter = $12 \times 100 = 1200$ cm.

It is also possible to convert between different units of area. This diagram is an enlarged picture of a 1 cm × 1 cm square.

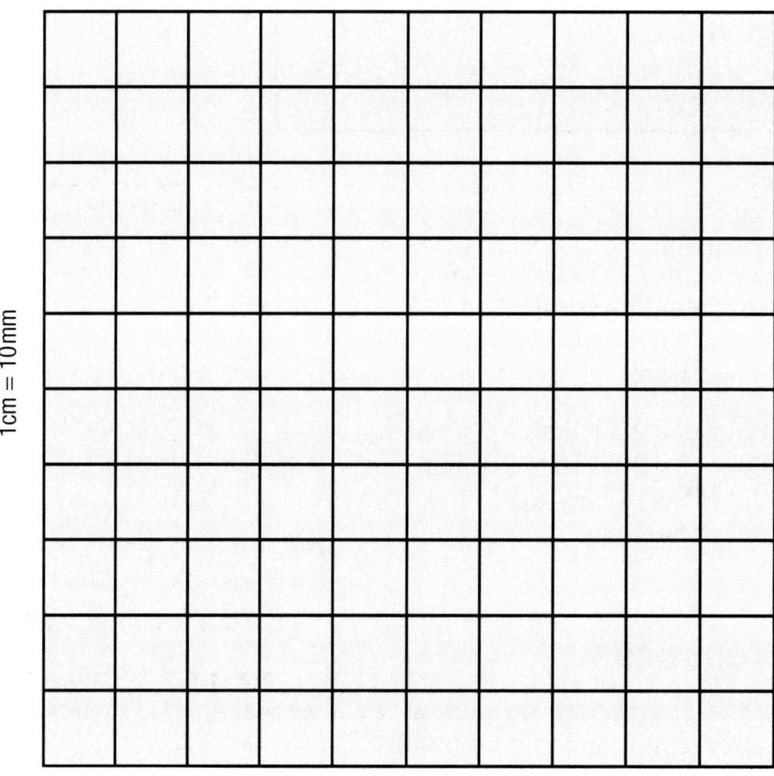

$$1\,\text{cm} = 10\,\text{mm}$$
$$1\,\text{cm}^2 = 1\,\text{cm} \times 1\,\text{cm}$$
$$= 10\,\text{mm} \times 10\,\text{mm}$$

Therefore $1\,\text{cm}^2 = 100\,\text{mm}^2$.

Similarly,

$$1\,\text{m} = 100\,\text{cm}$$
$$1\,\text{m}^2 = 1\,\text{m} \times 1\,\text{m}$$
$$= 100\,\text{cm} \times 100\,\text{cm}$$

Therefore $1\,\text{m}^2 = 10\,000\,\text{cm}^2$.

Also,

$$1\,\text{m} = 1000\,\text{mm}$$
$$1\,\text{m}^2 = 1\,\text{m} \times 1\,\text{m}$$
$$= 1000\,\text{mm} \times 1000\,\text{mm}$$

Therefore $1\,\text{m}^2 = 1\,000\,000\,\text{mm}^2$.

EXERCISE 18.1

1 Calculate the area and perimeter of each of these rectangles. Write the units of your answers clearly.

a) length = 12 cm width = 8 cm
b) length = 20 cm width = 3 cm
c) length = 8 m width = 2.5 cm
d) length = 15 mm width = 12 mm
e) length = 3 m width = 50 cm

2 A rectangle has length 8 m and width 6 m as shown.

Calculate:
a) the perimeter in cm
b) the area in cm^2.

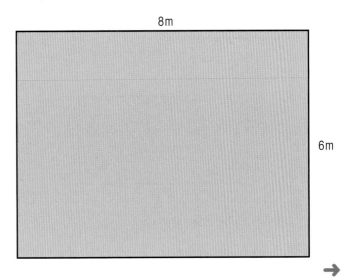

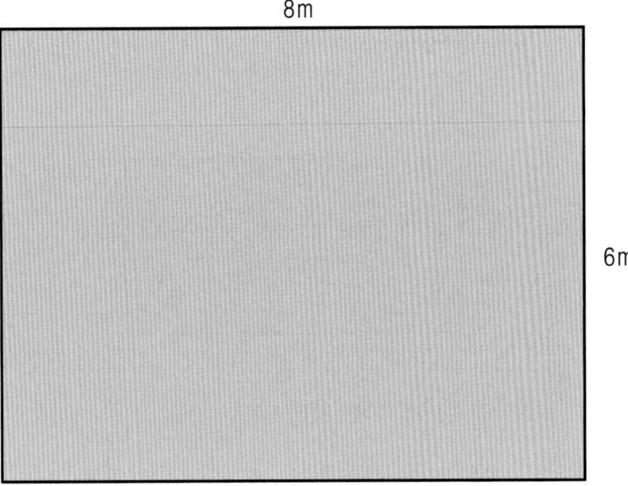

3 A rectangle has length = 4 m and width = 9 m.
Calculate:
a) the perimeter in mm
b) the area in mm^2.

4 A rectangle has area 48 cm^2. Its length is 6 cm.
Calculate:
a) its width
b) its perimeter.

5 A rectangle has perimeter 32 m. Its length is 9 m.
Calculate:
a) its width
b) its area.

6 A rectangle has area 50 000 cm^2.
Its length is 5 m.
Calculate its width.
Give your answer in metres.

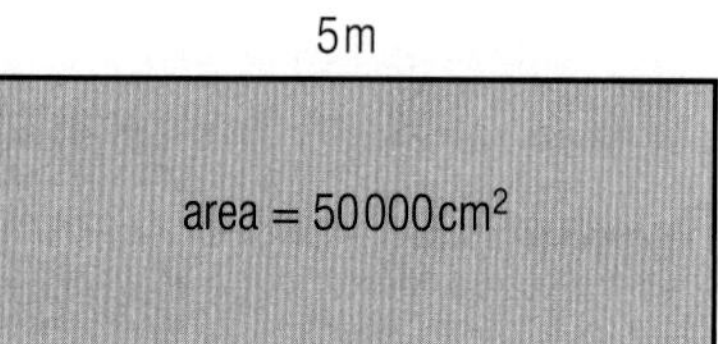

Composite shapes

A **composite** shape is one which is made from simpler shapes. To work out the area of a composite shape, it is often easier to work out the areas of the simpler shapes first.

Worked example

Calculate the area of this L-shape.

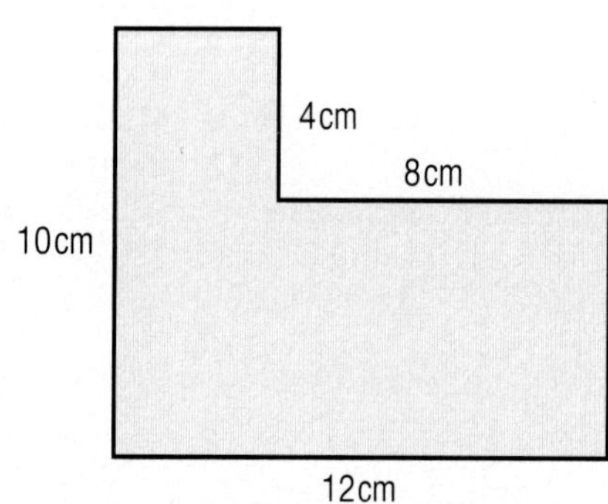

This can be done in two ways.

Method 1: By addition

The shape can be broken down into two rectangles, A and B.

Area of L-shape = area A + area B

Area of rectangle A = $10\,\text{cm} \times 4\,\text{cm}$
$= 40\,\text{cm}^2$

Area of rectangle B = $8\,\text{cm} \times 6\,\text{cm}$
$= 48\,\text{cm}^2$

Total area of L-shape = $40\,\text{cm}^2 + 48\,\text{cm}^2$
$= 88\,\text{cm}^2$

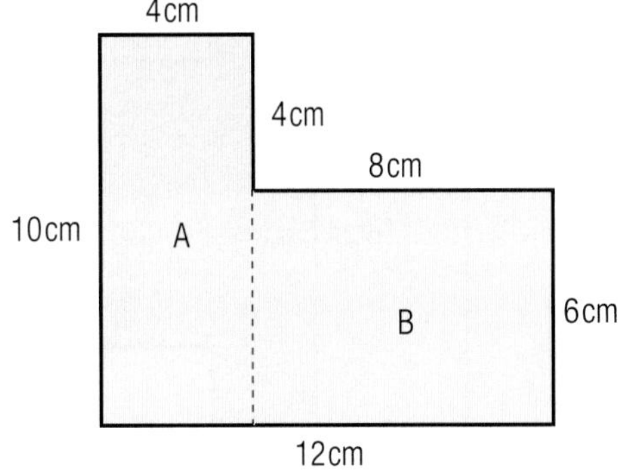

Method 2: By subtraction

Area of L-shape = area of large rectangle – area C

Area of large rectangle = $10\,\text{cm} \times 12\,\text{cm}$
$= 120\,\text{cm}^2$

Area of rectangle C = $4\,\text{cm} \times 8\,\text{cm}$
$= 32\,\text{cm}^2$

Area of L-shape = $120\,\text{cm}^2 - 32\,\text{cm}^2$
$= 88\,\text{cm}^2$

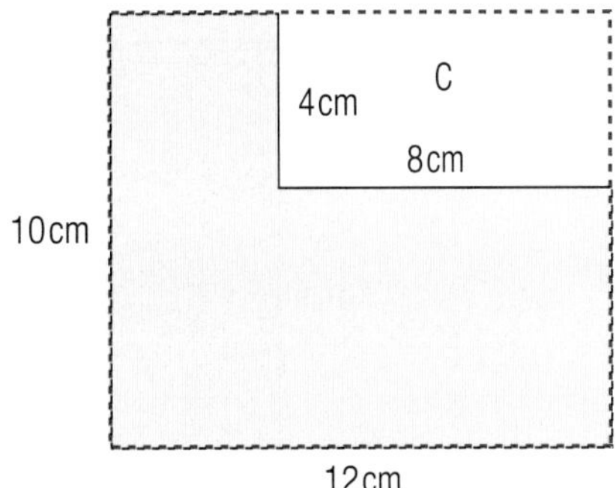

EXERCISE 18.2

Calculate the perimeter and area of each of these composite shapes.

1

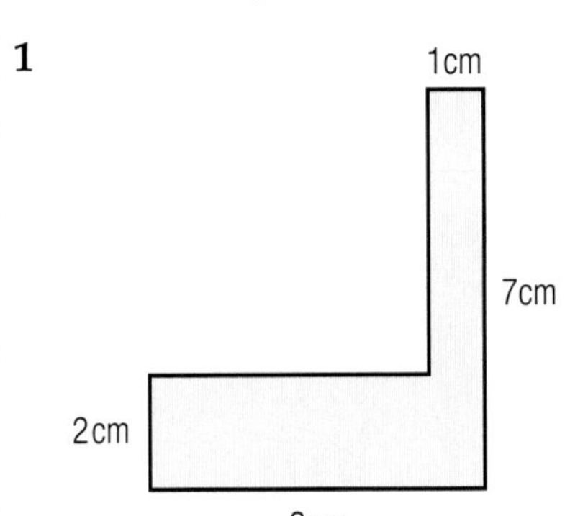

2

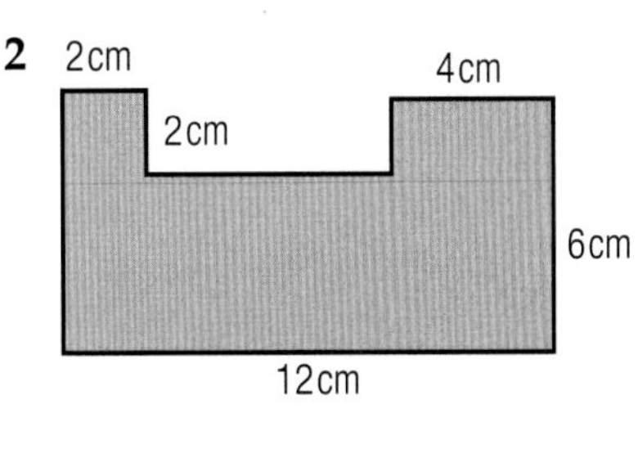

→

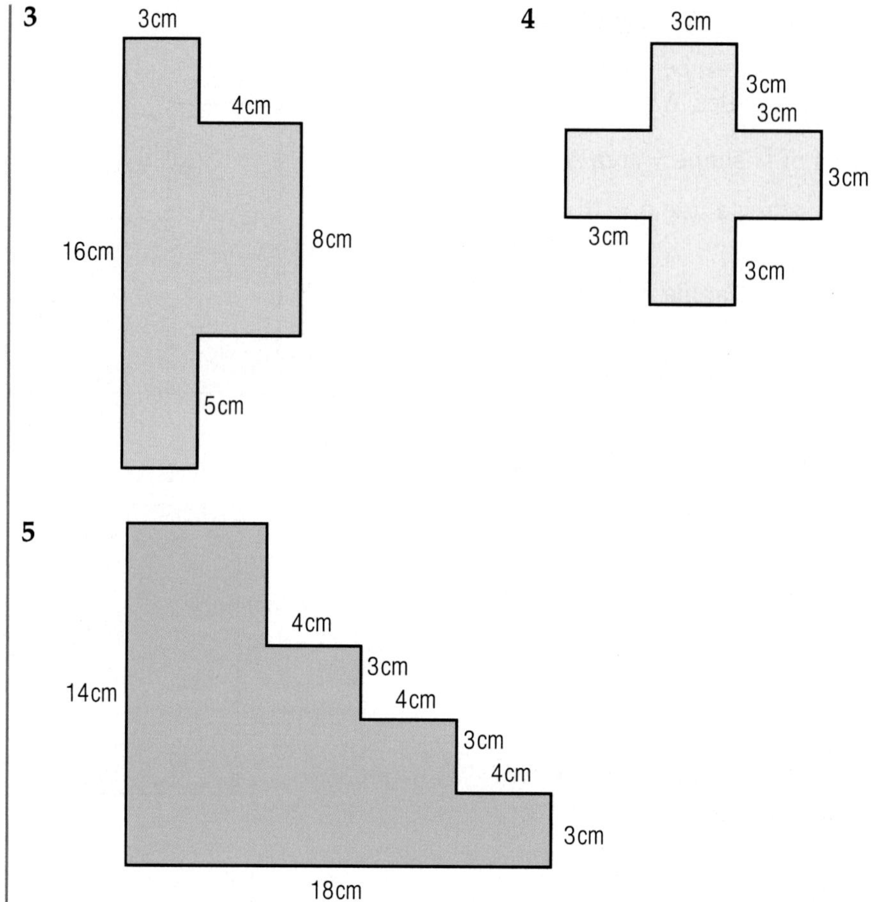
3
3cm
4cm
16cm
8cm
5cm
4
3cm
3cm
3cm
3cm
3cm
3cm
5
4cm
3cm
14cm
4cm
3cm
4cm
3cm
18cm

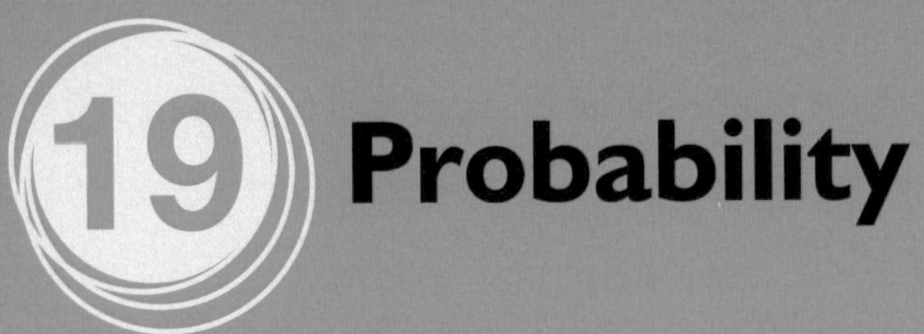

19 Probability

- Use the language of probability to describe and interpret results involving likelihood and chance.
- Understand and use the probability scale from 0 to 1.
- Find probabilities based on equally likely outcomes in simple contexts.
- Identify all the possible mutually exclusive outcomes of a single event.

Probability is the study of chance, or the *likelihood* of an event happening. In everyday language we use words that are associated with probability all the time. For example, 'I *might* see that film', 'I'm *definitely* going to win this race' or 'It's *unlikely* that I'll pass this test'.

In this chapter we will be looking at **theoretical probability**, i.e. what you would expect to happen in theory. But, because probability is based on chance, what should happen in theory does not necessarily happen in practice.

With an ordinary six-sided dice, there are six **possible outcomes** (six results that could happen). These are 1, 2, 3, 4, 5 and 6.

Each of these possible outcomes is an **equally likely outcome** if the dice is fair. This means that the dice is equally likely to show each of the numbers.

Each of these outcomes is **mutually exclusive**. This means they cannot happen at the same time.

The probability of getting a 2 when the dice is rolled is $\frac{1}{6}$.

The probability is $\frac{1}{6}$ because there is only one 2 out of six possible outcomes.

The probability of getting an 8 when the dice is rolled is $\frac{0}{6} = 0$.

The probability of getting either 1, 2, 3, 4, 5 or 6 is $\frac{6}{6} = 1$.

If an outcome has a probability of 0, it means the outcome is impossible.
If an outcome has a probability of 1, it means the outcome is certain.

The probability of an event can be placed on a probability scale from 0 to 1 like this.

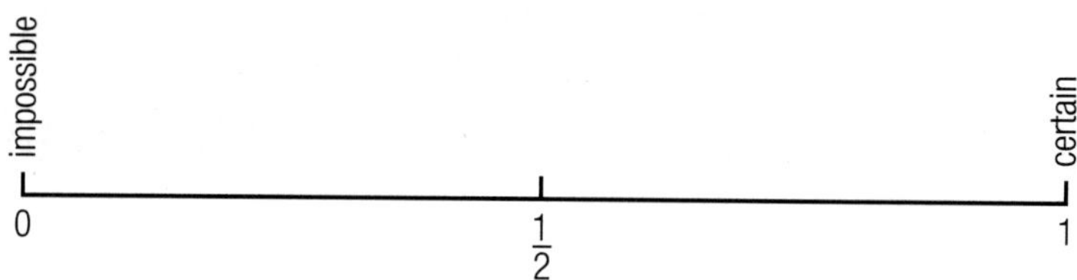

EXERCISE 19.1

1 Write down at least 15 words which are used in everyday language to describe the likelihood of an event happening.

2 Draw a probability scale similar to the one above. Write each of your words from question 1 where you think it belongs on the probability scale.

3

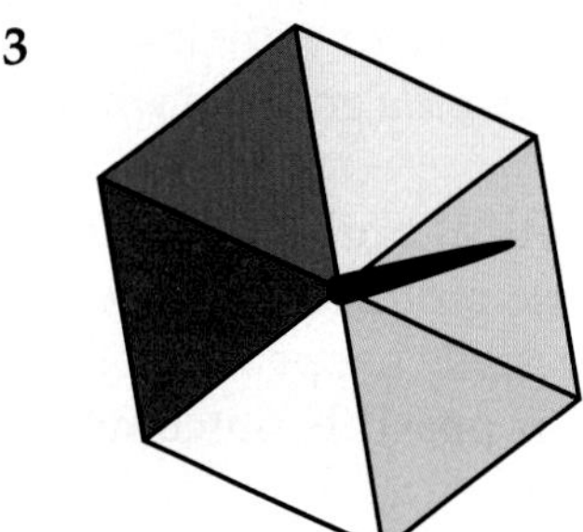

a) For the spinner shown calculate the probability of getting:
  (i) yellow
  (ii) light blue
  (iii) any blue.

b) The spinner is spun 60 times.
  (i) Estimate the number of times you would expect to get the colour red.
  (ii) Would you definitely get red that number of times? Explain your answer.

4 **a)** Calculate the probability, when rolling an ordinary, fair dice, of getting each of the following:
  (i) a score of 3
  (ii) a score of 4
  (iii) an even number
  (iv) a score less than 6
  (v) a score of 0
  (vi) a score greater than 0.

b) Draw a probability scale and place your answers to part **a)** on the scale.

5 **a)** Assuming that the chances of being born on any day of the week are all equal, calculate the probability of:

(i) being born on a Tuesday

(ii) not being born on a Tuesday.

b) Explain the result of adding the answers to **(i)** and **(ii)** together.

6 500 balls numbered from 1 to 500 are placed in a large container. A ball is picked at random.

a) Are the numbers an example of equally likely outcomes?

b) Calculate the probability that the ball:

(i) has the number 1 on it

(ii) has one of the numbers 1 to 50 on it

(iii) has one of the numbers 1 to 500 on it

(iv) has the number 501 on it.

'At random' or 'in random order' means that each choice is equally likely.

7 In a class there are 20 girls and 12 boys. The teacher collects all of their books in a random order. Calculate the probability that the teacher will:

a) mark a book belonging to a girl first

b) mark a book belonging to a boy first.

8 **a)** 26 tiles, each with one letter of the alphabet, are put into a bag. One tile is drawn out at random. Calculate the probability that it is:

(i) A or P

(ii) a vowel

(iii) a consonant

(iv) X, Y or Z

(v) a letter in your first name.

b) How could the outcomes *not* be equally likely?

9 **a)** Three red, ten white, five blue and two green counters are put into a bag, and one is picked at random. Calculate the probability that it is:

(i) a white counter

(ii) a red counter.

b) How could the outcomes *not* be equally likely?

10 The letters T, C and A can be written in several different orders.

a) Write the letters in as many different orders as possible.

b) If a computer writes these three letters in a random order, calculate the probability that:

(i) the letters will be written in alphabetical order

(ii) the letter T is written before both the letters A and C

(iii) the letter C is written after the letter A

(iv) the computer will spell the word CAT.

20 Multiplication and division 2

- Use known facts and place value to mulitply and divide two-digit numbers by a single-digit number, e.g. 45×6, $96 \div 6$.

In Chapter 6 you looked mainly at adding and subtracting numbers, including decimals, and in Chapter 13 you looked at basic multiplication and division facts.

This chapter looks mainly at written methods for multiplication and division, including decimals.

Mental skills

EXERCISE 20.1

Do these questions in your head, without looking at a multiplication grid or using a calculator. Write down your answers.

1 Multiply the following pairs of numbers.

a) 15×5 **b)** 14×7 **c)** 16×4 **d)** 13×5
e) 12×3 **f)** 18×7 **g)** 9×16 **h)** 7×33
i) 24×6 **j)** 16×8 **k)** 27×7 **l)** 24×9

2 Work out the following divisions.

a) $12 \div 4$ **b)** $16 \div 8$ **c)** $24 \div 6$
d) $32 \div 8$ **e)** $49 \div 7$ **f)** $56 \div 8$
g) $44 \div 4$ **h)** $36 \div 6$ **i)** $48 \div 8$

3 A child buys five packets of sweets each containing eight sweets. How many sweets does he buy in total?

4 A bar of chocolate is made of square-shaped pieces. The bar is four pieces wide and 12 pieces long. How many pieces are there in total?

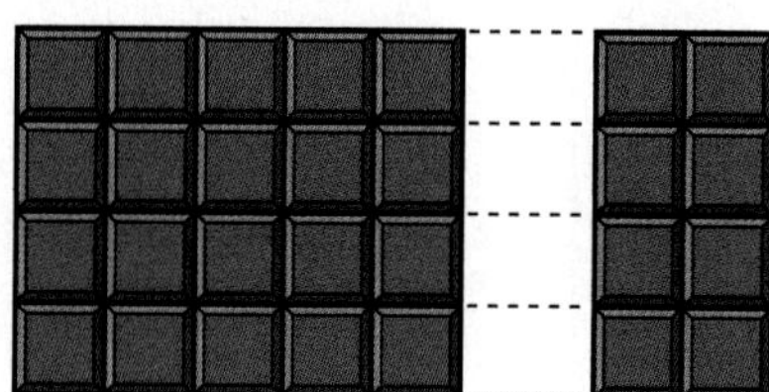

5 A tricycle is like a bicycle, but with three wheels. A shop has a stock of nine tricycles and 20 bicycles. How many wheels are there in total?

6 $36 is shared equally between four children. How much do they each receive?

7 A gardener plants three seeds in each plant pot.
She plants 27 seeds in total.
How many pots does she use?

8 45 chairs are arranged in rows of nine chairs.
How many rows are there?

Written methods for multiplication

To multiply larger numbers, we usually use a written method rather than trying to do the calculation mentally.

Worked example

Multiply 172 × 35.

- First write the numbers so that the units digits line up.

	Hundreds	Tens	Units
	1	7	2
×		3	5

- Multiply each of the digits in 172 by the 3 (which represents 3 tens, i.e. 30).

$$\begin{array}{cccc} & 1 & 7 & 2 \\ \times & & \mathbf{3} & 5 \\ \hline {}_{2}5 & 1 & 6 & \mathbf{0} \end{array}$$

*The **0** shows that 172 was multiplied by 30 rather than by 3.*

- Multiply each of the digits in 172 by the 5.

$$\begin{array}{cccc} & 1 & 7 & 2 \\ \times & & 3 & \mathbf{5} \\ \hline 5 & 1 & 6 & 0 \\ & {}_{3}8 & {}_{1}6 & 0 \\ \hline \end{array}$$

- Add the two results together.

$$\begin{array}{cccc} & 1 & 7 & 2 \\ \times & & 3 & 5 \\ \hline \mathbf{5} & \mathbf{1} & \mathbf{6} & \mathbf{0} \\ & \mathbf{8} & \mathbf{6} & \mathbf{0} \\ \hline {}_{1}6 & {}_{1}0 & 2 & 0 \end{array}$$

- The answer is 6020.

This method is called **long multiplication**. Another way of doing multiplications on paper is to use the **grid method**.

Worked example

Multiply 172 × 35.
172 is a three-digit number.
35 is a two-digit number.

- First draw a 3 × 2 grid and draw diagonals like this.

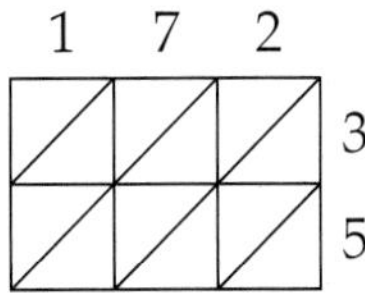

- Multiply each digit of 172 by each digit of 35 and enter each result in the corresponding part of the grid.

- Extend the diagonals.

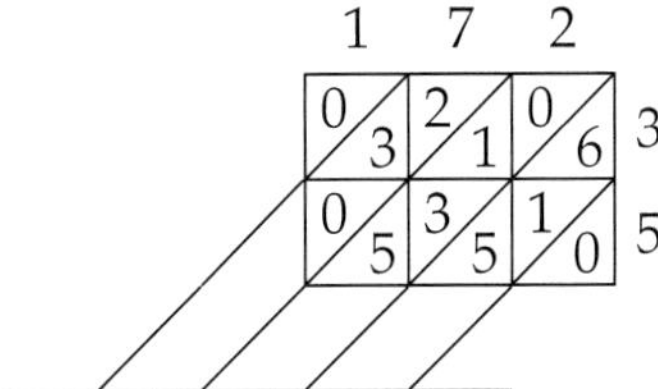

- Add all the digits along each diagonal.

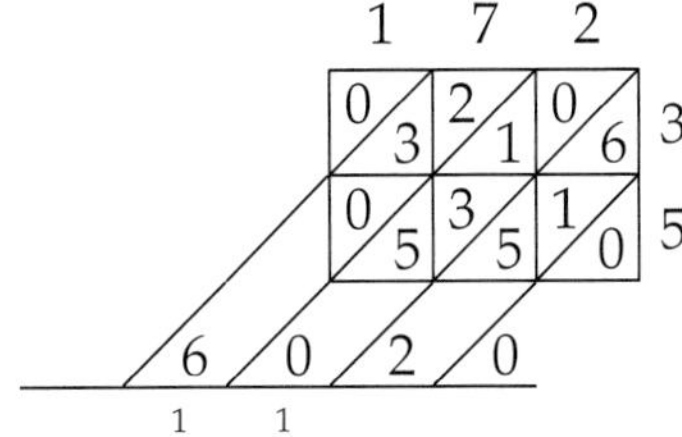

- The answer, as before, is 6020.

EXERCISE 20.2

Multiply each pair of numbers using either long multiplication or the grid method.

1 **a)** 27 × 31 **b)** 46 × 21 **c)** 57 × 69
d) 71 × 12 **e)** 89 × 64 **f)** 37 × 98

2 **a)** 361 × 21 **b)** 406 × 38 **c)** 62 × 592 **d)** 87 × 193

Written methods for division

Written methods are also used for division involving larger numbers.

Worked example

In other words, how many times does 23 go into 736?

Calculate 736 ÷ 23.

- First write the division like this:

$$23\,\overline{)\,7\;\;3\;\;6}$$

- Working from left to right, work out how many times 23 goes into each digit in turn.
  How many times does 23 go into **7**?

$$\begin{array}{rl} & \;\;\mathbf{0} \\ 23 & \overline{)\,7\;{}^{7}3\;\;6} \end{array}$$

0 times, with **7** left over (a **remainder**)

How many times does 23 go into **73**?

$$\begin{array}{rl} & \;\;0\;\;\mathbf{3} \\ 23 & \overline{)\,7\;{}^{7}\mathbf{3}\;{}^{4}6} \end{array}$$

3 times, with a remainder of **4**

How many times does 23 go into **46**?

$$\begin{array}{rl} & \;\;0\;\;3\;\;\mathbf{2} \\ 23 & \overline{)\,7\;{}^{7}3\;{}^{4}\mathbf{6}} \end{array}$$

2 times, with a remainder of 0

- Therefore 736 ÷ 23 = 32.

Multiplication and division are **inverse** (opposite) operations, just as addition and subtraction are. Suppose you are asked to work out the value of x when

$$17 \times x = 442$$

To find the number which 17 is *multiplied* by to give 442, the calculation can be rearranged like this:

$$442 \div 17 = x$$

This is now a *division*:

$$\begin{array}{rl} & \;\;\;\;\;\;2\;\;6 \\ 17 & \overline{)\,4\;\;4\;{}^{10}2} \end{array}$$

So $x = 26$.

EXERCISE 20.3

1 Work out the following divisions.

a) 525 ÷ 15 **b)** 960 ÷ 40 **c)** 935 ÷ 17
d) 972 ÷ 12 **e)** 726 ÷ 22 **f)** 918 ÷ 18

2 Work out the value of the letter in each of the following.

a) $31 \times x = 372$ **b)** $y \times 14 = 868$ **c)** $p \times 8 = 656$
d) $37 \times 123 = q$ **e)** $851 \div x = 37$ **f)** $833 \div a = 17$
g) $532 \div 14 = b$ **h)** $981 \div d = 9$

21 ICT, investigations and problem solving

1 Tile patterns

These diagrams show the first three patterns in each of three sequences of growing tile patterns.

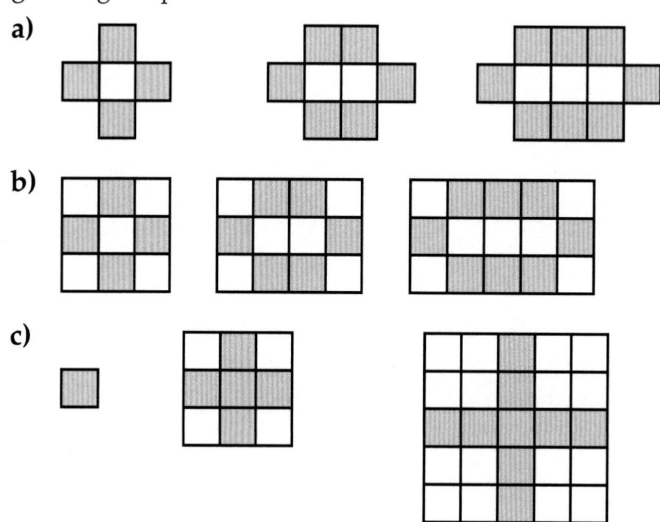

For each of these sequences of patterns:

(i) draw the next two patterns in the sequence

(ii) count the numbers of blue and white tiles in the pattern and enter the results in a table like this

Pattern	Number of blue tiles	Number of white tiles
1		
2		
3		
4		
5		

(iii) describe the relationship between the pattern number, the number of blue tiles and the number of white tiles

(iv) from your rules in part **(iii)**, predict the numbers of blue and white tiles in the tenth pattern.

Now design your own sequence of tile patterns and repeat parts **(i)** to **(iv)** for your own pattern.

2 Fraction triangle

In this triangle, a, b, c, d, e and f all represent fractions.

a $\quad$ b $\quad$ c

d $\quad$ e

f

$d = a - b$, $e = b - c$ and $f = d - e$.

a) Using this method of construction, copy and complete the fraction triangle below.

$1 \quad \frac{1}{2} \quad \frac{1}{3} \quad \frac{1}{4} \quad \frac{1}{5} \quad \frac{1}{6} \quad \frac{1}{7}$

$\frac{1}{2} \quad ? \quad ? \quad \frac{1}{20} \quad ? \quad ?$

$? \quad \frac{1}{12} \quad ? \quad ? \quad ?$

$? \quad ? \quad ? \quad ?$

$? \quad ? \quad ?$

$? \quad ?$

$?$

b) Describe the patterns you see in your completed fraction triangle.

3 Coats 'R' Us

You own a factory called 'Coats 'R' Us' which manufactures coats. This table identifies the raw materials needed for each coat and also their cost to the factory.

Material	Amount per coat	Cost
Cotton	3.8 m	\$200 per 100 m roll
Lining	2.3 m	\$120 per 100 m roll
Thread	180 m	\$7 per 2000 m reel
Buttons	8	\$6 per 50
Label	1	\$25 per 1000
Labour	20 minutes	\$8.50 per hour

You cannot buy parts of rolls or reels.

Your factory has received an order from a large retailer for 20 000 coats.

a) Set up a spreadsheet in order to work out how much of each raw material the factory will need to order.
b) Using the spreadsheet, calculate the cost of manufacturing one coat.
c) The factory wants to sell each coat for 50% more than it costs to manufacture.
Calculate how much each coat will cost the retailer.
d) The cost of labour increases to \$10.00 per hour. Use the spreadsheet to work out how much each coat will cost the retailer now.

A possible way of setting out your spreadsheet is given below.

	A	B	C	D	E	F	G
1							
2	Number of coats ordered		20000				
3							
4	Material	Amount of material/coat	Total amount of material needed	Cost (Dollars)			
5	Cotton (m)	3.8			←		
6	Lining (m)	2.3			←		
7	Thread (m)	180			←	Enter formulae in these cells in order to calculate amounts automatically	
8	Buttons	8			←		
9	Label	1			←		
10	Labour (hr)	1/3			←		
11							
12			Total cost		←		
13			Cost/coat		←		
14			Percentage profit	50	%		
15			Selling price/coat		←		
16							
17							
18							

4 Matchstick patterns

These diagrams show a sequence of matchstick patterns. In each pattern the matchsticks are arranged so that a line of squares is formed.

a) Draw the next two patterns in the sequence.

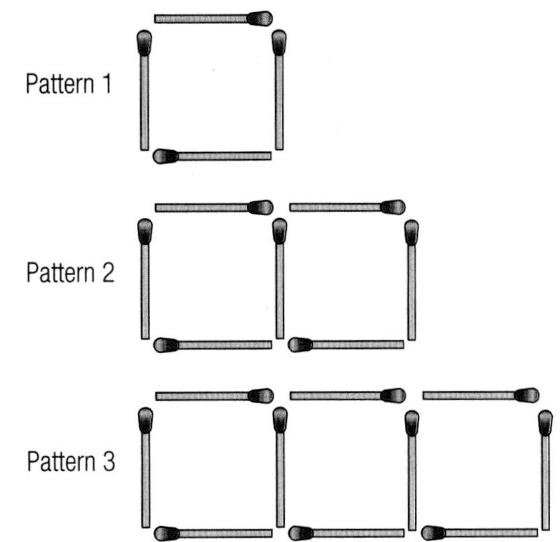

b) Count the number of matchsticks in each pattern and enter the results in a table like this.

Number of squares	Number of matches
1	4
2	
3	
4	
5	

c) Describe the rule linking the number of matches and the number of squares.

d) Without drawing, predict the number of matches needed for the pattern with ten squares.

e) Without drawing, predict the number of matches needed for the pattern with 100 squares.

f) If 121 matches are used for a pattern, how many squares will be in it?

5 Fenced off

A farmer has 64 m of fencing to make an enclosure. With the 64 m of fencing, she can make different-sized rectangles. An example of one is shown below.

31m

1m 1m

31m

a) Calculate the area of this enclosure.
b) Draw at least five different enclosures that the farmer could build, each with a perimeter of 64 m.
c) Calculate the area of each of the enclosures you have drawn.
d) Enter your results into a table like this.

Enclosure	Length	Width	Perimeter	Area
1	31	1	64	
2				
3				
4				
5				

e) What is the maximum area of enclosure you have found?
f) Compare your results with those of other students in your class. Has anyone found an enclosure with a bigger area? If so, what is it?
g) What shape of enclosure gave the maximum possible area?

Review 3A

1 Jamil spends $\frac{1}{3}$ of his pocket money on sweets. He saves $\frac{1}{9}$ of his pocket money. What fraction of his pocket money is left?

2 Convert these mixed numbers into improper fractions.

a) $3\frac{9}{11}$

b) $7\frac{6}{7}$

3 In a survey of 500 cars, 245 were white, 25 were blue and 130 were red. The others were silver. Express each of these numbers as a percentage of the total.

4 For each sequence below write down the next two terms and the term-to-term rule.

a) 7 12 17 22 27 ...
b) 31 24 17 10 ...
c) 24 12 6 3 ...

5 Work out the size of each of the unknown angles in these diagrams. Give reasons for your answers.

a)

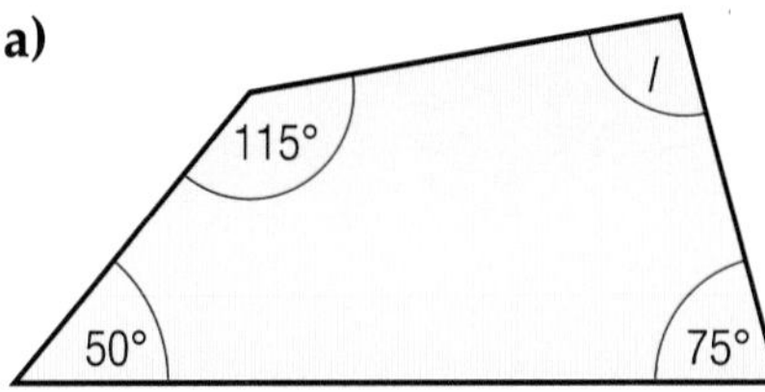

b)

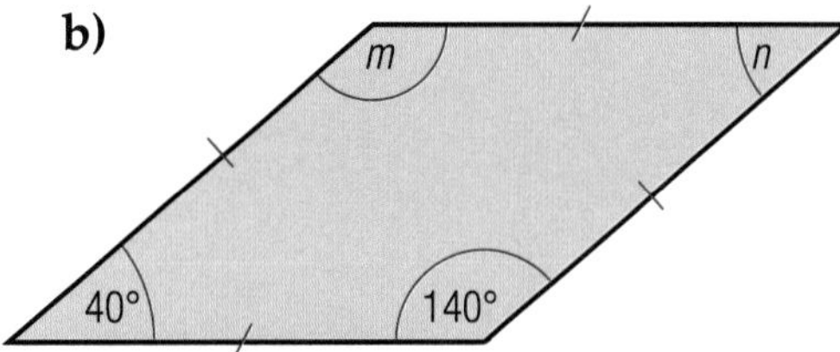

6 Calculate the area and perimeter of this L-shape.

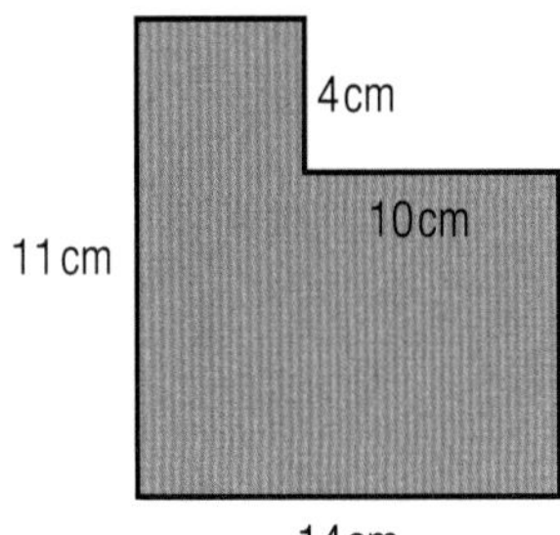

7 26 tiles, each with one letter of the alphabet, are put into a bag. One tile is drawn out at random. Calculate the probability that it is:

a) A, P or M
b) a vowel
c) a consonant
d) a vowel or a consonant
e) a letter in your last name.

8 *Without using a calculator,* work out:

a) 72×4
b) $91 \div 7$

Review 3B

1 A paint mixture is made up of $\frac{5}{12}$ red paint and $\frac{1}{12}$ blue paint, and the rest is white paint.

   a) What fraction of the mixture is white paint?

   b) The paint is sold in 6-litre containers.
   How many litres of red paint are needed for each container?

2 Evaluate the following.

   a) $\frac{2}{13} + \frac{3}{13} + \frac{5}{13}$

   b) $\frac{5}{18} - \frac{8}{9} + \frac{5}{6}$

3 Copy and complete this table.

Fraction	Decimal	Percentage
$\frac{1}{2}$		%
	0.25	%
		75%
$\frac{1}{8}$		%
$\frac{3}{8}$		%
		62.5%
$\frac{7}{8}$		%
	0.1	%
		20%
$\frac{3}{10}$		%

→

4 Work out the size of each of the unknown angles in these diagrams.
Give reasons for your answers.

a)

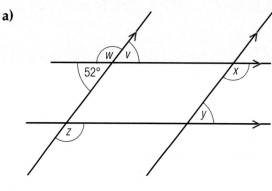

b)

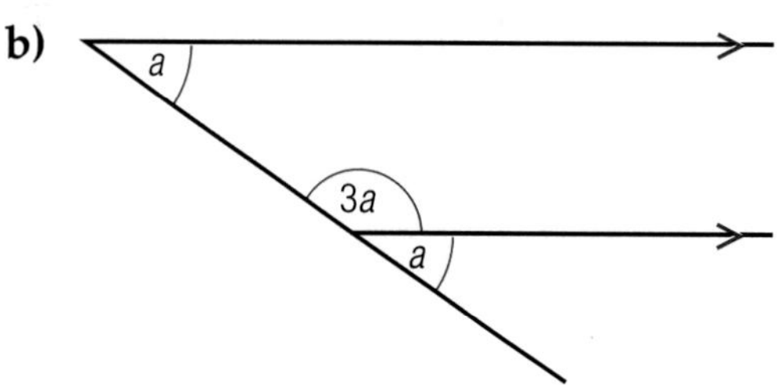

5 Calculate the area and perimeter of this shape.

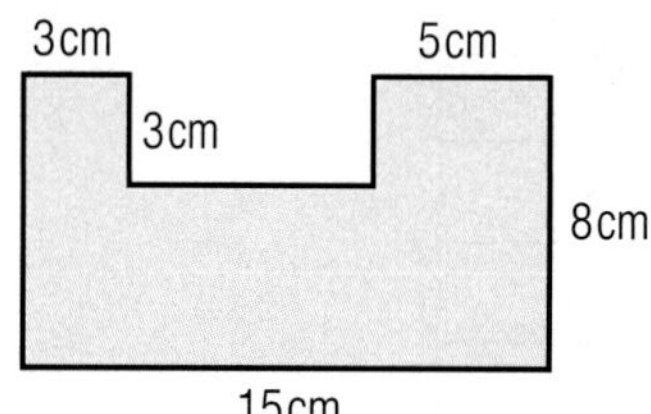

6 A six-sided dice is rolled.
Write down the probability of getting:

a) a 5

b) an even number

e) a number more than 3.

SECTION 4

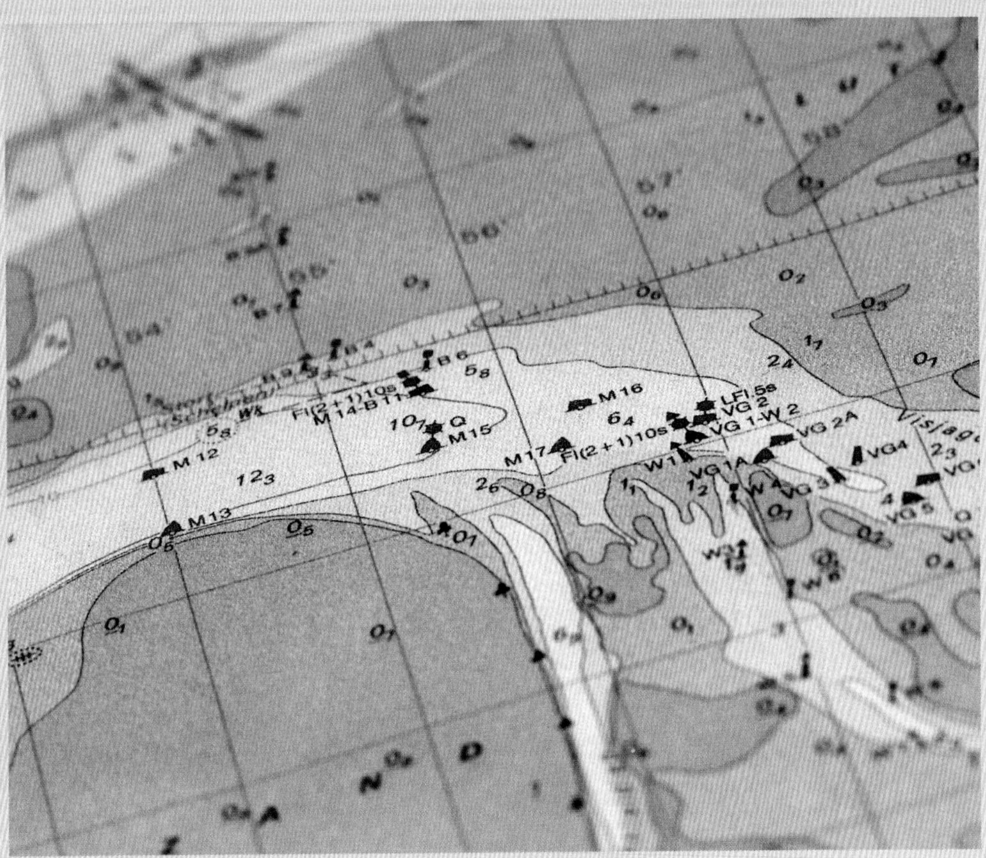

M 12
M13
M 14-B11
M15
M 16
M17
Fl(2+1)10s
LFl.5s
VG 2
VG 1-W 2
VG 2A
VG4
W1
VG 1A

22 Ratio and proportion

- Use percentages to represent and compare different quantitites.
- Use ratio notation, simplify ratios and divide a quantity into two parts in a given ratio.
- Recognise the relationship between ratio and proportion.
- Use direct proportion in context; solve simple problems involving ratio and direct proportion.

For a civilisation to endure and prosper, it must give its citizens order and fairness. The Chinese civilisation prospered for many centuries. Part of the fairness depended upon mathematics. Chapters 2, 3 and 6 of *Nine Chapters on the Mathematician's Art* were concerned with ratio and proportion so that 'rice and other cereals could be planted and distributed in the correct proportion for our needs' and 'so that the ratio of taxes could be levied fairly'.

Fractions and ratios

Equivalent fractions

We can see from the diagram below that $\frac{1}{2}$, $\frac{2}{4}$, and $\frac{4}{8}$ are **equivalent fractions**. They are called this because each fraction is worth the same amount. Similarly $\frac{1}{3}$, $\frac{2}{6}$ and $\frac{3}{9}$ are equivalent fractions, as are $\frac{1}{5}$, $\frac{10}{50}$ and $\frac{20}{100}$.

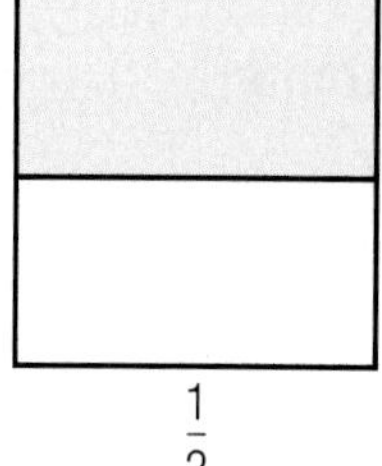

$\frac{1}{2}$

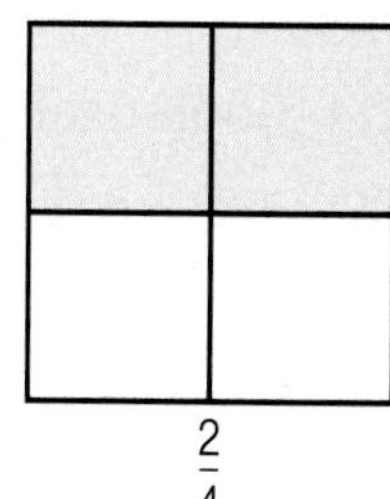

$\frac{2}{4}$

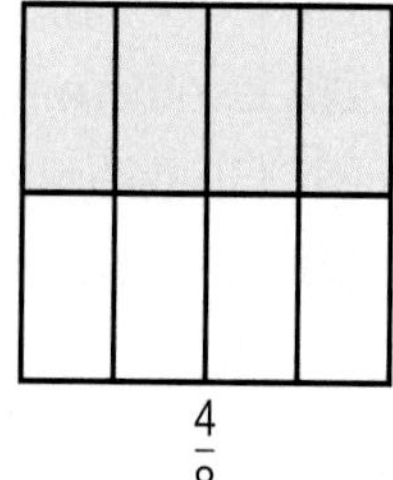

$\frac{4}{8}$

EXERCISE 22.1A

Copy these sets of equivalent fractions and fill in the blanks.

1 $\frac{1}{4} = \frac{2}{\square} = \frac{\square}{16} = \frac{\square}{64} = \frac{3}{\square}$

2 $\frac{2}{5} = \frac{4}{\square} = \frac{\square}{20} = \frac{\square}{50} = \frac{16}{\square}$

3 $\frac{3}{8} = \frac{6}{\square} = \frac{\square}{24} = \frac{15}{\square} = \frac{\square}{72}$

Equivalent ratios

Ratios behave in a similar way to fractions.

1:2 is equivalent to 2:4 or 35:70. In the same way, 15:5 is equivalent to 3:1 or 9:3.

EXERCISE 22.1B

Copy these sets of equivalent ratios and fill in the blanks.

1 4:5 = 8:$\square$ = $\square$:50 = 12:$\square$

2 7:2 = 14:$\square$ = $\square$:10 = 49:$\square$

3 8:5 = $\square$:50 = 32:$\square$ = 4:$\square$

Some ratios are written in the form 1:n, where n is a whole number or a decimal.

For example, in a school the teacher-to-student ratio may be given as 1:15. This means that for every teacher, there are 15 students. (It does not mean that every class has 15 students but that, if the number of students is divided by the number of teachers, the answer is 15.)

Worked example

a) A school has 40 teachers and 720 students. Write the teacher:student ratio in the form 1:n.

The teacher:student ratio is 40:720.

Therefore to write 40:720 in the form 1:n and keep the ratios equivalent, both sides must be divided by the same number.

Teachers : Students

40 : 720

÷ 40 ↓ ÷ 40

1 : n

Therefore $n = 720 \div 40$
$= 18.$

The ratio of teachers : students in the form 1 : n is 1 : 18.

b) The teacher : student ratio in a school is 1 : 18.
There are 25 teachers. How many students are there?

The ratio is given in the form 1 : n so the values need to be multiplied to keep the ratio constant.

Teachers : Students

Therefore the number of students $= 18 \times 25$
$= 450$

EXERCISE 22.1C

In questions 1–5, give your answers in the simplest form.

1 A school has 20 teachers and 480 students.
What is the teacher : student ratio?

2 A college has 250 staff and 3500 students.
What is the staff : student ratio?

3 A town in America has 2400 families and 4200 cars.
What is the family : car ratio?

4 In a batch of 10 dozen eggs, 25 are cracked.
What is the ratio of cracked eggs to un-cracked eggs?

A dozen is 12.

5 A ship has 300 crew to 750 passengers.
What is the ratio of crew to passengers?

6 The teacher : student ratio in a school is 1 : 21.
There are 24 teachers. How many students are there?

7 An alloy contains copper and tin in the ratio 3 : 1.
40 g of tin is used to make the alloy.
How much copper is used?

8 A nursery has an adult to child ratio of 1:4.
How many children can be looked after by 12 adults?

9 In a naval ship there are 12 crew to each officer.
There are 45 officers. How many crew are there?

10 At a concert, one free ticket is given for every 22 tickets sold.
16 free tickets have been given. How many tickets have been sold?

Direct proportion

Workers in a shop are paid for the number of hours they work. Their pay is in **direct proportion** to the number of hours they work – more hours, more pay.

Workers producing cups on a machine in a factory are sometimes paid for the number of cups they produce, not for the time they work. Their pay is in direct proportion to the number of cups they make.

Worked example

A machine for making bread rolls makes 1500 rolls in 20 minutes.
How many rolls will it make in 3 hours?

Let x be the number of rolls made in 3 hours.

The ratios have to be equivalent. You multiply the number of minutes by 9 to get 180 so you must also multiply the number of rolls by 9.
1500 × 9 = 13 500, so 13 500 rolls are made in 3 hours.

EXERCISE 22.2A

1 A heater uses 3 units of electricity in 40 minutes.
How many units does it use in 2 hours?

2 A machine prints 1500 newspapers in 45 minutes.
How many does it print in 12 hours?

3 A bricklayer lays 1200 bricks in an average 8-hour day.
How many bricks does he lay in a 40-hour week?

4 A combine harvester produces 9 tonnes of grain in 6 hours.
How many tonnes does it produce in 54 hours?

5 A machine puts tar on a road at the rate of 4 metres in 5 minutes.
a) How long does it take to cover 1 km of road?
b) How many metres of road does it cover in 8 hours?

When the information is given as a ratio, the method of solving the problem is the same.

Worked example

Copper and nickel are mixed in the ratio 5 : 4.
48 g of nickel are used. How much copper is used?

Let x grams be the mass of copper needed.

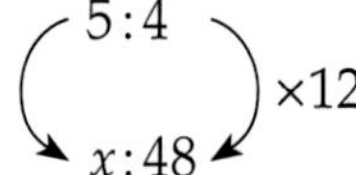

The ratios have to be equivalent. You multiply the mass of nickel by 12 to get 48 g so you must also multiply the mass of copper by 12.
$5 \times 12 = 60$, so 60 g of copper are used.

EXERCISE 22.2B

1 The ratio of girls to boys in a class is 6 : 5.
There are 18 girls. How many boys are there?

2 Sand and gravel are mixed in the ratio 4 : 3 to make ballast.
80 kg of sand is used. How much gravel is used?

3 A paint mix uses blue and white in the ratio 3 : 10.
6.6 litres of blue paint are used. How much white paint is used?

4 A necklace has green and blue beads in the ratio 2 : 3.
There are 24 green beads on a necklace. How many blue beads are there?

Dividing a quantity in a given ratio

Worked example

A piece of wood is 15 m long. It is divided into two pieces in the ratio 3 : 2.
How long is each piece?

A ratio of 3 : 2 means that you need to consider the wood as 5 parts. One piece of wood is made of 3 parts; the other piece is made of 2 parts.

3 : 2 gives 5 parts.

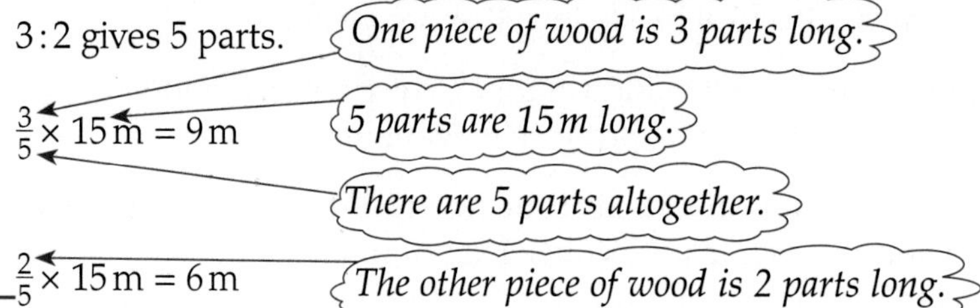

One piece of wood is 3 parts long.
$\frac{3}{5} \times 15\,\text{m} = 9\,\text{m}$
5 parts are 15 m long.
There are 5 parts altogether.
$\frac{2}{5} \times 15\,\text{m} = 6\,\text{m}$
The other piece of wood is 2 parts long.

EXERCISE 22.3

1 Divide 250 in the ratio 3:2.

2 Divide 144 in the ratio 1:2.

3 Divide 10 kg in the ratio 2:3.

4 Divide 1 hour in the ratio 5:7.

5 Divide 8 m in the ratio 3:13.

6 Divide 45 km in the ratio 7:8.

7 Divide 4 hours in the ratio 5:3.

8 Divide 2 kg in the ratio 3:7.

9 Divide 3 litres in the ratio 7:5.

10 Divide 1 cm in the ratio 2:3.

11 Divide 70 in the ratio 60% to 40%.

12 Divide 1 hour in the ratio 20% to 80%.

13 Express the ratio 3:17 as percentages.

14 Express the ratio 9:31 as percentages.

Using percentages to compare proportions

Sometimes it is not easy to compare ratios. If we change each ratio to a percentage, it is easier to compare them. If they are the same, they are said to be **in proportion**.

Worked example

Compare the ratios 3 parts in 10 and 12 parts in 40. Are they in proportion?

3 parts in 10 is $\frac{3}{10} \times 100 = 30\%$.

12 parts in 40 is $\frac{12}{40} \times 100 = 30\%$.

So the ratios are in proportion.

EXERCISE 22.4

Compare these ratios by changing them to percentages, and show that they are in proportion.

1 2 in 5 and 4 in 10

2 7 in 20 and 35 in 100

3 1 in 10 and 10 in 100

4 12 in 20 and 30 in 50

5 9 in 20 and 45 in 100

6 16 in 20 and 4 in 5

7 28 in 50 and 56 in 100

8 125 in 500 and 1 in 4

9 750 in 1000 and 3 in 4

10 50 in 200 and 1 in 4

11 2 in 5, 4 in 10 and 8 in 20

12 7 in 25, 14 in 50 and 280 in 1000

23 Formulae and substitution

- Derive and use simple formulae, e.g. to change hours to minutes.
- Substitute positive integers into simple linear expressions/formulae.

The formula $e = mc^2$ is one of the most well known formulae.

The formula $e = mc^2$ was worked out by a German mathematician who spent some of his working life as a clerk in a patent office. However, his work in mathematics made him a major figure of the twentieth century.

The man, as you might know, was Albert Einstein. Einstein's formula

$$e = mc^2$$

states that the energy, e, which can be released from matter is equal to the mass, m, multiplied by the square of the speed of light, c.

Other mathematical formulae you may have encountered are:

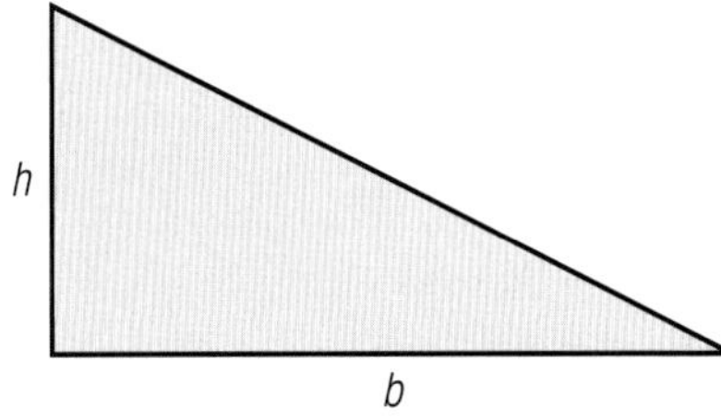

area of a triangle $= \frac{1}{2}bh$

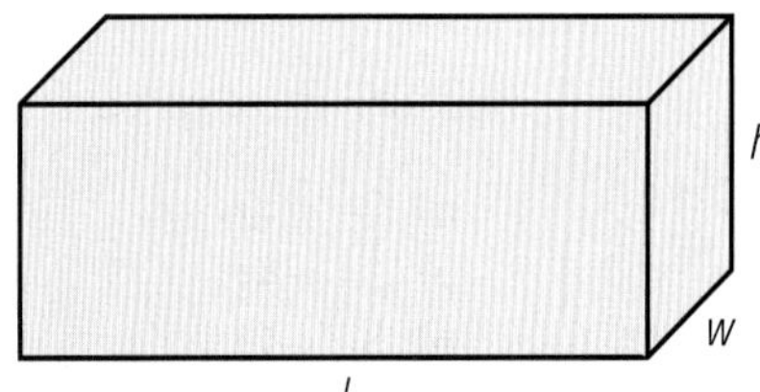

volume of a cuboid $= lwh$.

Substitution

$3p$ is an **expression**.
$3p = s$ is a **formula**.
$3p = 9$ is an **equation**.

It is important that you understand the differences.

A formula describes a relationship between different variables and can be used to calculate values. If $p = 5$, you can use the formula $3p = s$ to work out that the value of s is 15. If $p = 8$, then $s = 24$, and so on.

An equation, however, is only true for specific values of the variable. The equation $3p = 9$ is only true when $p = 3$.

Numbers can be **substituted** for the letters in both expressions and formulae.

Substitution into expressions

Worked examples

Evaluate (work out) the expressions below when $a = 3$, $b = 4$ and $c = 5$.

a) $2a + 3b - c$
$= (2 \times 3) + (3 \times 4) - (5)$
$= 6 + 12 - 5$
$= 13$

b) $3a(2b + 3c)$
$= (3 \times 3) \times ((2 \times 4) + (3 \times 5))$
$= 9(8 + 15)$
$= 9 \times 23$
$= 207$

EXERCISE 23.1A

Evaluate the expressions in questions 1–2 when $p = 2$, $q = 3$ and $r = 5$.

1 **a)** $3p + 2q$ **b)** $4p - 3q$ **c)** $p - q - r$ **d)** $3p - 2q + r$

2 **a)** $q(p + q)$ **b)** $2r(p - q)$ **c)** $3p(p - 3r)$ **d)** $4q(q - r)$

Evaluate the expressions in questions 3–5 when $p = 4$, $q = 2$, $r = 3$ and $s = 5$.

3 **a)** $2p + 4q$ **b)** $5r - 3s$
c) $3q - 4s$ **d)** $6p - 8q + 4s$
e) $3r - 3p + 5q$ **f)** $-p - q + r + s$

4 **a)** $2p - 3q - 4r + s$ **b)** $3s - 4p + r + q$
c) $p(q - r + s)$ **d)** $r(2p - 3q)$

5 **a)** $2s(3p - 2q)$ **b)** $pq + rs$
c) $2pr - 3rq$

Substitution into formulae

The perimeter, P, of a rectangle is the distance around it.

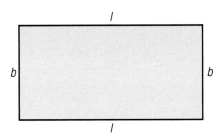

For this rectangle the perimeter is

$l + b + l + b$

or $2l + 2b$

or $2(l + b)$.

This can be written as:

$P = 2(l + b)$.

We obtained this formula from the diagram. This is one way to **derive** a formula.

The area, A, of the rectangle can be written as:

$A = l \times b = lb$.

EXERCISE 23.1B

1 Calculate the perimeter and area of each of these rectangles of length l and breadth b. Write the units of your answers clearly.

a) $l = 4$ cm, $b = 7$ cm **b)** $l = 8$ cm, $b = 12$ cm

c) $l = 4.5$ cm, $b = 2$ cm **d)** $l = 8$ cm, $b = 2.25$ cm

e) $l = 0.8$ cm, $b = 40$ cm **f)** $l = 1.2$ cm, $b = 0.5$ cm

g) $l = 45$ cm, $b = 1$ m **h)** $l = 5.8$ m, $b = 50$ cm

2 Find the perimeter and area of each of these rectangles.

a) the floor of a room which is 6.5 m long and 5 m wide

b) the floor of a sports hall which is 85 m long and 55 m wide

c) the lid of a CD case which is a square of side length 135 mm

d) a chess board of side length 60 cm

→

3 In physics this formula is used in calculations about electricity:

$$V = IR.$$

V is the voltage in a circuit in volts,
I is the current in amps,
R is the resistance in ohms.

Without using a calculator, calculate the voltage V when

a) $I = 7$ amps, $R = 60$ ohms
b) $I = 8$ amps, $R = 400$ ohms
c) $I = 0.3$ amps, $R = 2000$ ohms
d) $I = 80$ milliamps, $R = 5000$ ohms

The formula connecting the temperature in degrees Celsius (C) and the temperature in degrees Fahrenheit (F) is:

$$C = \frac{5}{9}(F - 32).$$

Worked example

What is the Celsius equivalent of 77 °F?

$$C = \frac{5}{9}(F - 32)$$

$$C = \frac{5}{9}(77 - 32)$$

$$C = \frac{5}{9} \times 45$$

$$C = 25$$

77 °F is equivalent to 25 °C.

EXERCISE 23.1C

1 What is the Celsius equivalent of each of these temperatures, given in degrees Fahrenheit?

a) 59 °F **b)** 104 °F **c)** 5 °F **d)** 212 °F **e)** 32 °F

2 The highest temperature created by humans is 950 million degrees Fahrenheit. It was achieved at the Tokamak Fusion Test Reactor in the USA on 27 May 1994.
Using the formula for converting degrees Fahrenheit to degrees Celsius, calculate the value of the highest temperature in degrees Celsius.

3 The lowest temperature possible is –459.67 °F.
Calculate the value of this temperature in degrees Celsius.

Deriving and using a formula

Earlier in this chapter you saw that the formula for the perimeter of a rectangle can be derived from a diagram.

It is also possible to derive a formula from written information.

Worked examples

a) In one year one dollar (\$1) could be exchanged for one euro and twenty cents (€1.20).

(i) Derive a formula to exchange dollars into euros.

(ii) Use your formula to work out how many euros you would receive for \$250.

(i) Let p be the number of dollars.
Let e be the number of euros.
From the information in the question, $e = 1.2$ when $p = 1$.
So the formula is:

$e = 1.2p.$

(ii) Substitute $p = 250$ into the formula:

$e = 1.2 \times 250$
$e = 300$

You would receive €300 in exchange for \$250.

b) An electrician charges a fixed fee of \$40 plus \$25 per hour.

(i) Derive a formula to show his charges, where C is the total charge and n is the number of hours.

(ii) What would the electrician charge for working 6 hours?

(i) $C = 40 + 25n$

(ii) $C = 40 + 25 \times 6$
$C = 40 + 150$
$C = 190$

The total charge is \$190.

c) A fitness club has a normal membership fee of \$36 per month.

As a special offer to encourage people to join, they give 3 months free membership to people who sign up for two years.

(i) Derive a formula for the cost, C, of a normal monthly membership, where n is the number of months.

(ii) Derive a formula for the cost, C, of a two-year membership with the offer.

(iii) Calculate the saving per month on a two-year membership.

(i) $C = 36n$

(ii) $C = 36(24 - 3)$
$C = 36 \times 21$
$C = 756$

(iii) The cost per month with the offer is $756 \div 24 = \$31.50$.
The saving per month is $\$36 - \$31.50 = \$4.50$.

EXERCISE 23.2

1 **a)** Derive a formula for converting the number of hours, h, into minutes, m.
b) Use your formula to convert $4\frac{1}{2}$ hours to minutes.

2 **a)** Derive a formula for converting the number of days, d, into hours, h.
b) Use your formula to convert 14 days to hours.

3 **a)** Derive a formula for converting the number of hours, h, into seconds, s.
b) Use your formula to convert $2\frac{1}{2}$ hours to seconds.

4 **a)** Derive a formula for converting the number of metres, m, into centimetres, c.
b) Use your formula to convert 3.3 metres to centimetres.

5 The cost of taking baggage on a low-cost airline is \$10 plus \$2 per kilogram.
a) Derive a formula for calculating the cost, \$$C$, of taking n kg of baggage.
b) Use your formula to calculate the cost of taking 23 kg of baggage.

6 The cost of a taxi fare is \$3 plus \$1.50 per kilometre travelled.
a) Derive a formula for calculating the cost \$$P$ of travelling n km.
b) Use your formula to calculate the cost of travelling 15 km.

7 A plumber charges a fixed fee of \$50 plus \$25 per hour.
a) Derive a formula for calculating the cost, \$$X$, of working Y hours.
b) Use your formula to calculate the cost of a job taking 3 hours 15 minutes.

8 An internet company charges its customers in the following way.
The internet is free for the first five hours each month and then is charged at a rate of 10 cents per hour.
a) Derive a formula for calculating the cost, \$$C$, of h hours of internet use.
b) Use your formula to calculate the monthly cost of 55 hours of internet use.

24 Coordinates

- Read and plot coordinates of points determined by geometric information in all four quadrants.

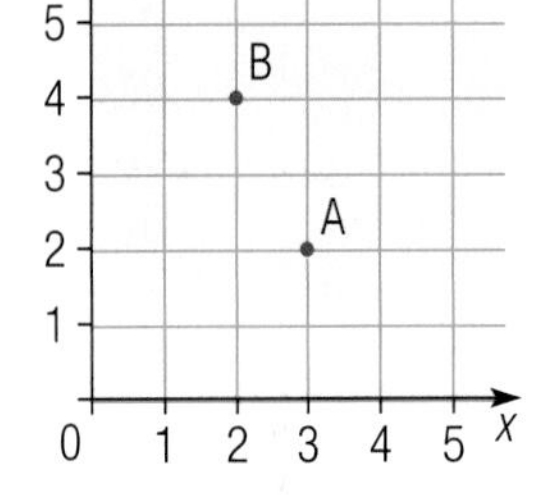

In order to fix a point in two dimensions (2-D) we give its position in relation to a point called the **origin**. We draw two axes at right angles to each other. The horizontal axis is called the ***x* axis** whilst the vertical axis is called the ***y* axis**. The *x* axis is numbered from left to right. The *y* axis is numbered from bottom to top.

The position of point *A* is given by two coordinates, the *x* coordinate and the *y* coordinate. So the coordinates of point *A* are (3, 2). Similarly, the coordinates of point *B* are (2, 4).

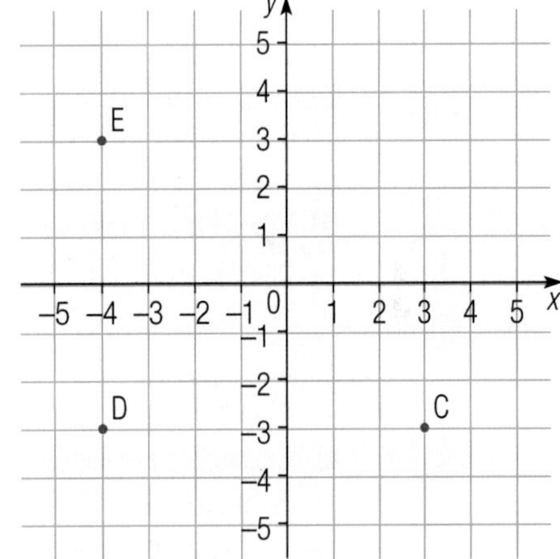

The axes can be extended in both directions. By extending the *x* and *y* axes below zero this grid is produced.

We can describe points *C*, *D*, and *E* by their coordinates.

Point *C* is at (3, –3).
Point *D* is at (–4, –3).
Point *E* is at (–4, 3).

EXERCISE 24.1A

1 Draw a grid with centre (0, 0), the origin, and mark the *x* and *y* axes with scales from –8 to +8. Mark these points on your grid.

a) $A = (5, 2)$ **b)** $B = (7, 3)$ **c)** $C = (2, 4)$
d) $D = (-8, 5)$ **e)** $E = (-6, -8)$ **f)** $F = (3, -7)$
g) $G = (7, -3)$ **h)** $H = (6, -6)$

→

For each of questions 2–4, draw a separate grid with x and y axes from –6 to +6. Plot the points, join them up in order and name the shape you have drawn.

2 $A = (3, 2)$ $B = (3, -4)$ $C = (-2, -4)$ $D = (-2, 2)$

3 $D = (1, 3)$ $E = (4, -5)$ $F = (-2, -5)$

4 $G = (-6, 4)$ $H = (0, -4)$ $I = (4, -2)$ $J = (-2, 6)$

EXERCISE 24.1B

Draw a grid with x and y axes from –10 to +10.

1 Plot the points $P = (-6, 4)$, $Q = (6, 4)$ and $R = (6, -2)$. Plot point S such that $PQRS$ is a rectangle.
- **a)** Write down the coordinates of S.
- **b)** Draw diagonals PR and QS. What are the coordinates of their point of intersection?
- **c)** What is the area of $PQRS$?

2 On the same grid plot points $M = (-8, 4)$ and $N = (4, 4)$.
- **a)** Joint points $MNRS$. What shape have you drawn?
- **b)** What is the area of $MNRS$?
- **c)** Explain your answer to part **b)**.

3 On the same grid plot point J where point J has y coordinate +10 and JRS forms an isosceles triangle.
- **a)** Write down the coordinates of J.
- **b)** What is the x coordinate of all the points on the line of symmetry of triangle JRS?

EXERCISE 24.1C

1
- **a)** Draw a grid with x and y axes from –10 to +10. Using a pair of compasses, construct a regular hexagon $ABCDEF$ with centre (0, 0), and where the coordinates of A are (0, 8). (See page 90.)
- **b)** Write down the coordinates of B, C, D, E and F.

2
- **a)** Draw a grid with x and y axes from –10 to +10. Draw an octagon $PQRSTUVW$ which has point $P = (2, -8)$ and point $Q = (-6, -8)$. $PQ = RS = TU = VW$ and $QR = ST = UV = WP$.
- **b)** Write down the coordinates of points R, S, T, U, V and W.
- **c)** What are the coordinates of the centre of rotational symmetry of the octagon?

EXERCISE 24.1D

1 The points A, B, C and D are not at whole numbers on the number line. Point A is at 0.7. Each small square represents 0.1.

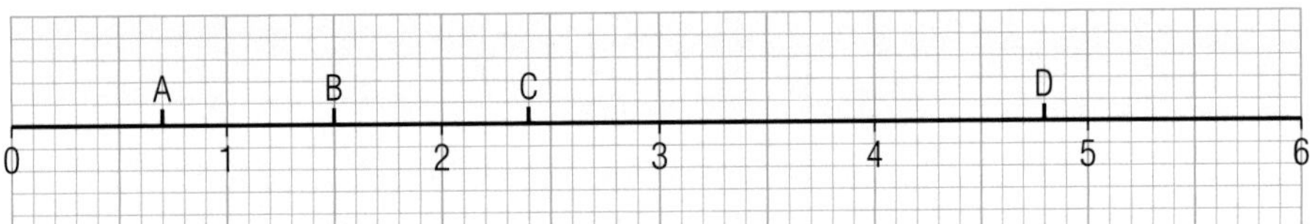

What are the positions of points B, C and D?

2 On this number line point E is at 0.4. Two small squares represent 0.1.

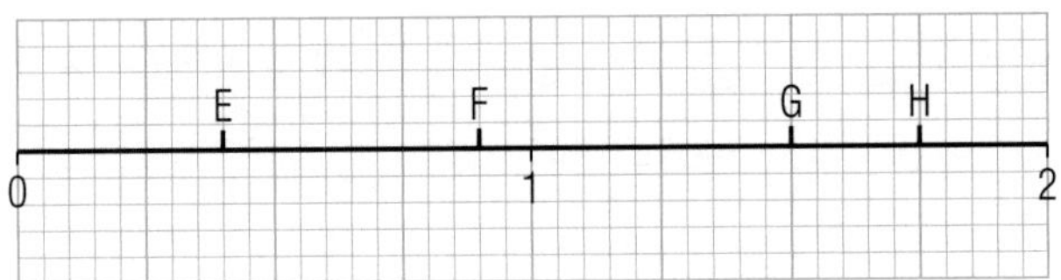

What are the positions of points F, G and H?

3 On this number line each small square represents 0.05, i.e. two small squares represent 0.1.

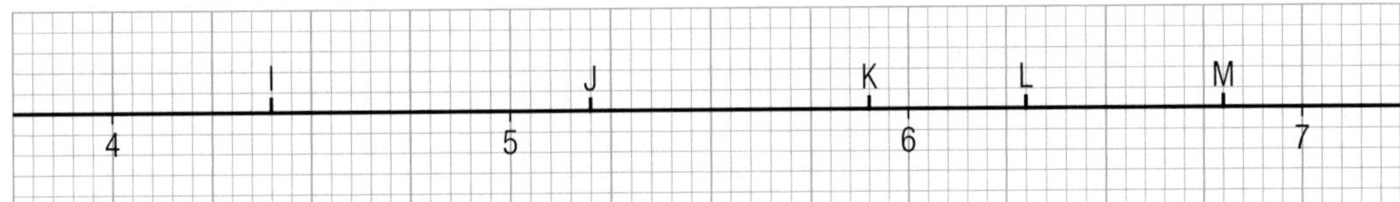

What are the positions of points I, J, K, L and M?

4 On this number line point P is at position 0.4 and point W is at position 9.8. Each small square represents 0.2.

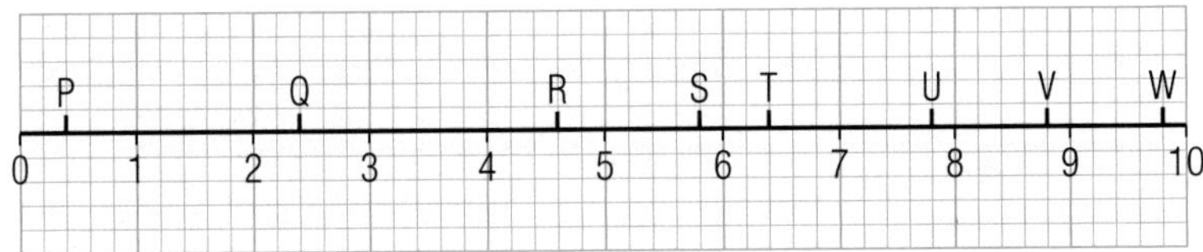

What are the positions of points Q, R, S, T, U and V?

EXERCISE 24.1E

1 Write down the positions of points A, B, C and D on this coordinate grid.

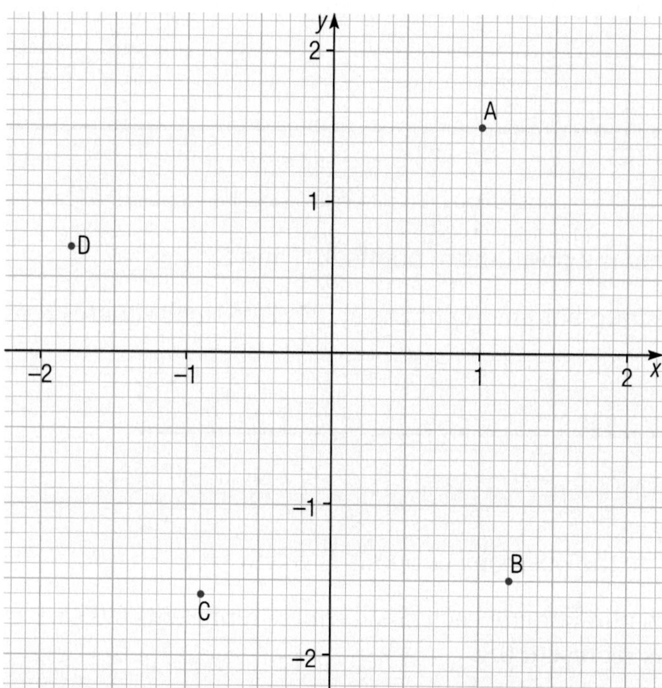

2 Write down the positions of points E, F, G and H on this coordinate grid.

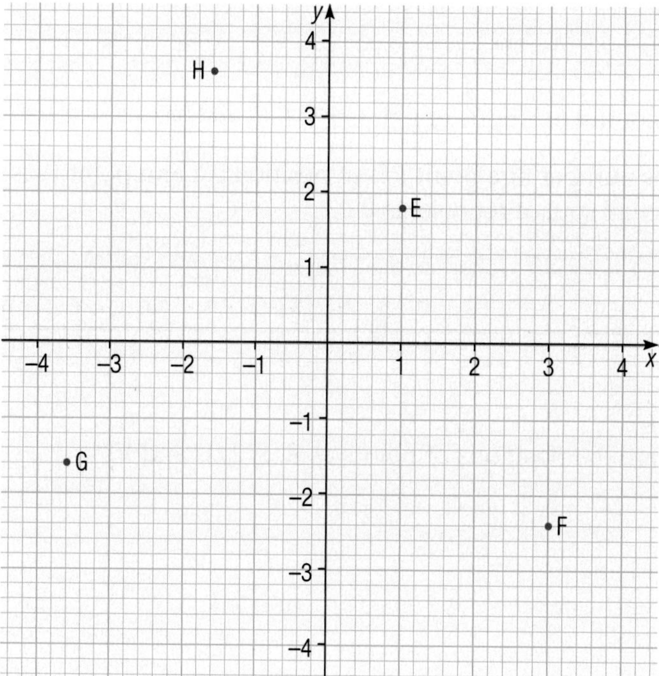

3 Write down the positions of points J, K, L and M on this coordinate grid.

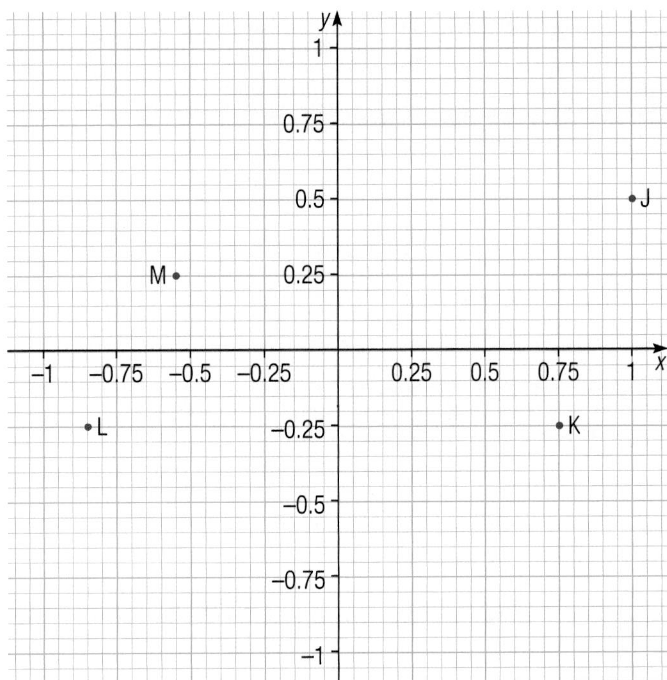

4 Write down the positions of points P, Q, R and S on this coordinate grid.

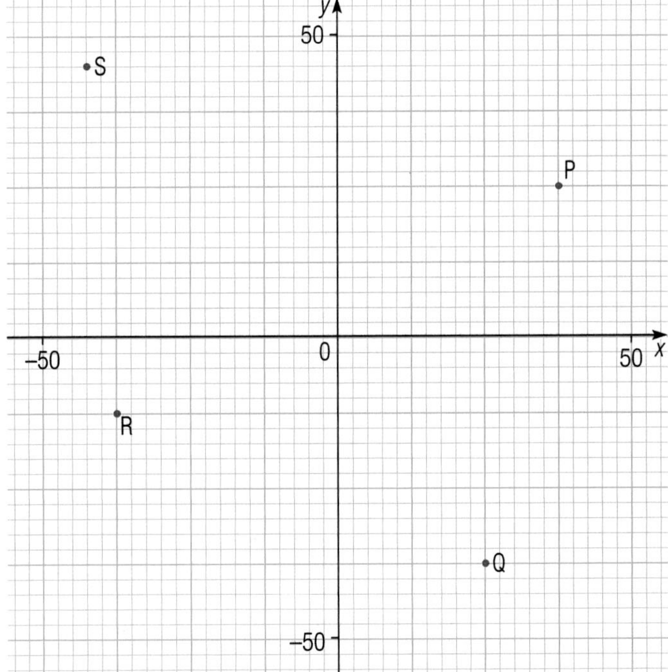

5 Weigh six different coins in grams and measure their diameters in centimetres (both sets of measurements should be correct to one decimal place).
Plot these measurements on a graph with axes the same as those below.

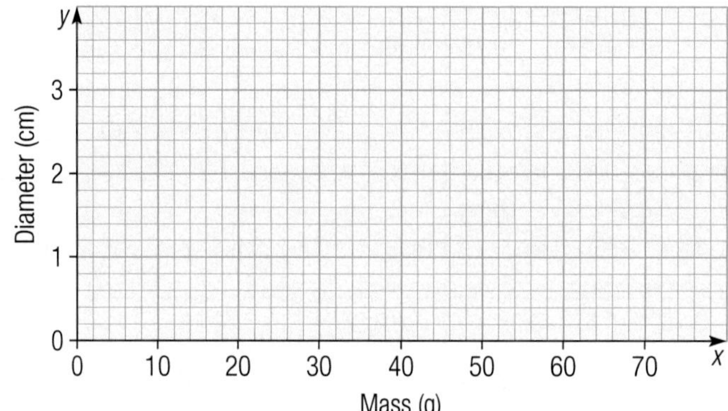

6 Draw a grid and choose a suitable scale for the points given below. Plot and label the points on your grid.

$A = (1.2, 2.8)$, $B = (2.5, -1.6)$, $C = (-2.8, -0.4)$, $D = (-2.4, 1.8)$

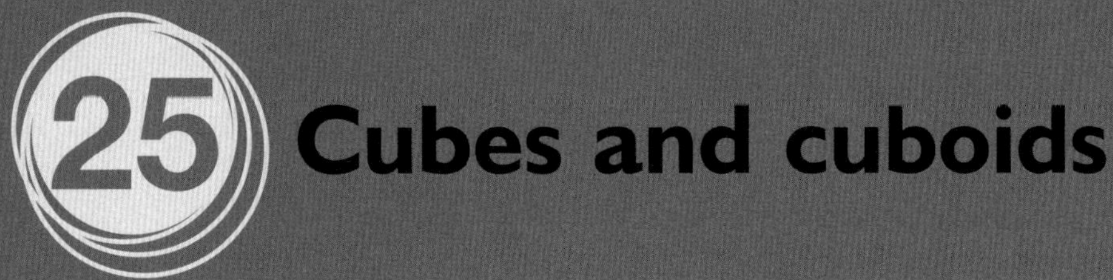

25 Cubes and cuboids

- Derive and use the formula for the volume of a cuboid; calculate volumes of cuboids.
- Calculate the surface area of cubes and cuboids from their nets.

Prisms

A **prism** is a three-dimensional (3-D) shape which has the same **cross-sectional** area all through it, i.e. if you were to cut slices through the shape, the shape and area of each slice would be exactly the same.

Here are some examples of prisms:

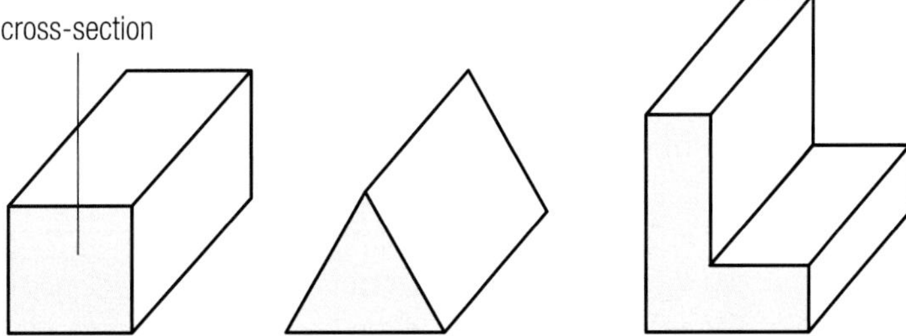

When each of these shapes is sliced parallel to the coloured face, the **cross-section** will always look the same. This means it is easy to calculate the volume of a prism.

Volume of a prism = area of cross-section × length

Cuboids

A **cuboid** is a type of prism in which all six faces are rectangular. A cuboid in which all six faces are square is called a **cube**.

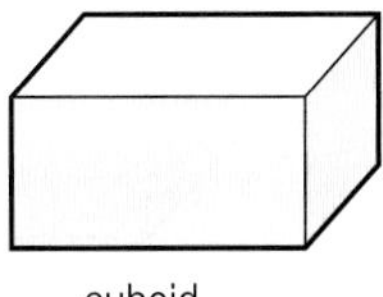
cuboid

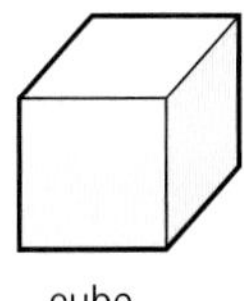
cube

It is easy to calculate the volume of a cube or cuboid.

Worked example

Calculate the volume of this cuboid.

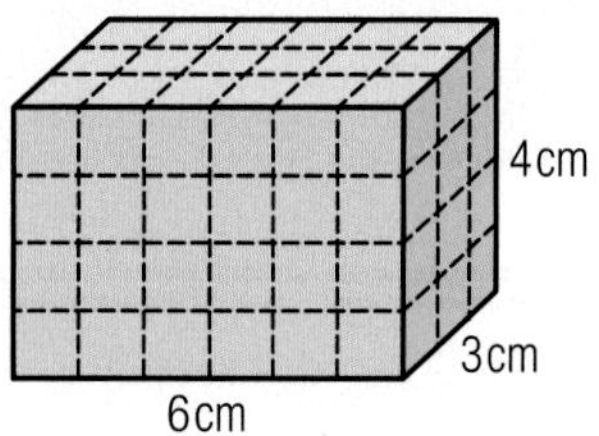

The cuboid is made up of 1 cm × 1 cm × 1 cm cubes.
Its volume (in cm^3) is the same as the number of 1 cm × 1 cm × 1 cm cubes it is made from.

There are 6 × 4 × 3 = 72 cubes.

Therefore the volume is 72 cm^3.

A simple way to calculate the volume of a cuboid is to multiply its length by its width and its height.

Volume of a cuboid = length × width × height

EXERCISE 25.1

1 Calculate the volume of each of these cuboids, where L = length, W = width and H = height.

a) $L = 4$ cm $W = 2$ cm $H = 3$ cm
b) $L = 5$ cm $W = 5$ cm $H = 6$ cm
c) $L = 10$ cm $W = 1$ cm $H = 4$ cm
d) $L = 40$ cm $W = 0.2$ m $H = 5$ cm
e) $L = 50$ mm $W = 30$ cm $H = 0.1$ m

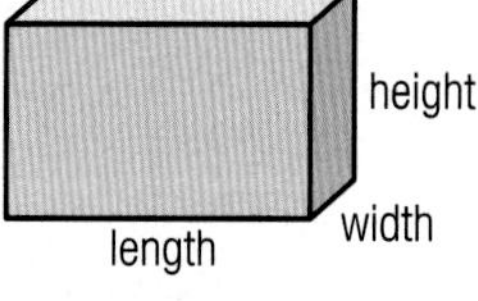

2 This cuboid has a volume of 360 cm^3.

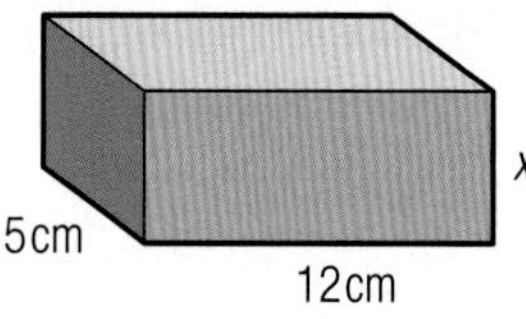

Calculate the length (in cm) of the edge marked x.

3 The volume of this cuboid is 180 cm^3.
Calculate the length (in cm) of the edge marked y.

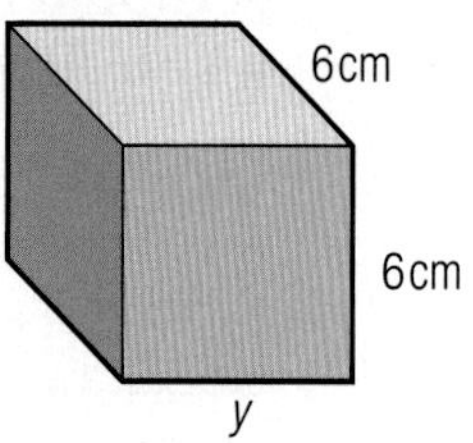

4 Calculate the length (in cm) of the edge marked p in this cuboid.
Its volume is $320\,cm^3$.

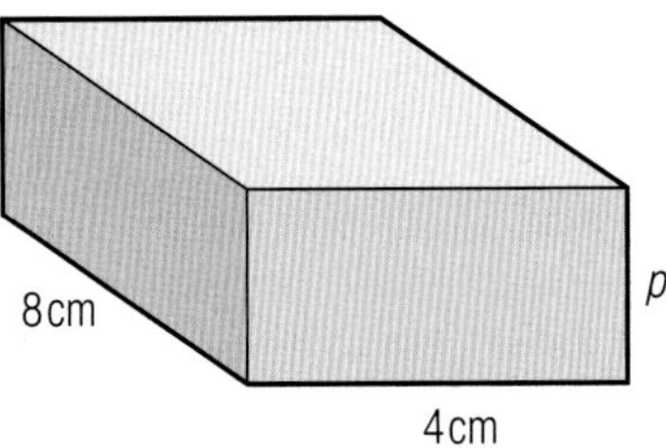

5 **a)** This cuboid has volume $768\,cm^3$ and the edges marked a are equal in length.
Calculate the value of a.

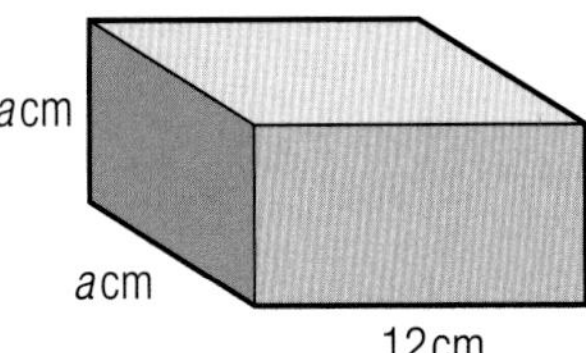

b) In another cuboid of length 12 cm and volume $768\,cm^3$, the width and height are *not* equal.
Give a pair of possible values for their length.

Surface area of a cuboid

In Chapter 18 you saw how to work out the area of a rectangle. The **surface area** of a cuboid is the total area of the six faces of the cuboid.

Worked example

Calculate the surface area of this cuboid.

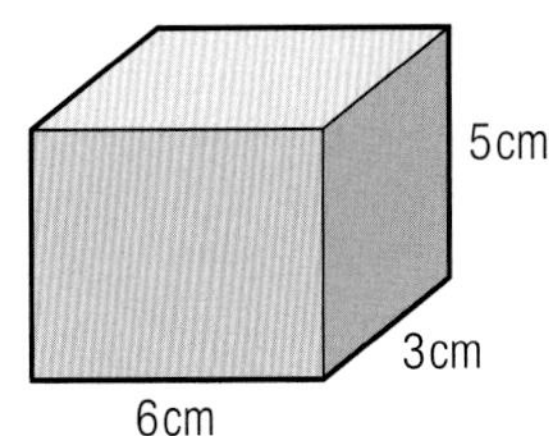

There are two ways of solving this problem.

Method 1: By calculating the area of each rectangular face

As the front is the same as the back, the top is the same as the bottom, and the two sides are the same as each other, the areas can be worked out in pairs.

Area of front and back = $6 \times 5 \times 2 = 60\,\text{cm}^2$

Area of top and bottom = $6 \times 3 \times 2 = 36\,\text{cm}^2$

Area of two sides = $3 \times 5 \times 2 = 30\,\text{cm}^2$

Surface area of cuboid = $60 + 36 + 30 = 126\,\text{cm}^2$

Method 2: By calculating the area of a net of the cuboid

A **net** of a cuboid is a two-dimensional shape which can be folded up to form the cuboid. For example,

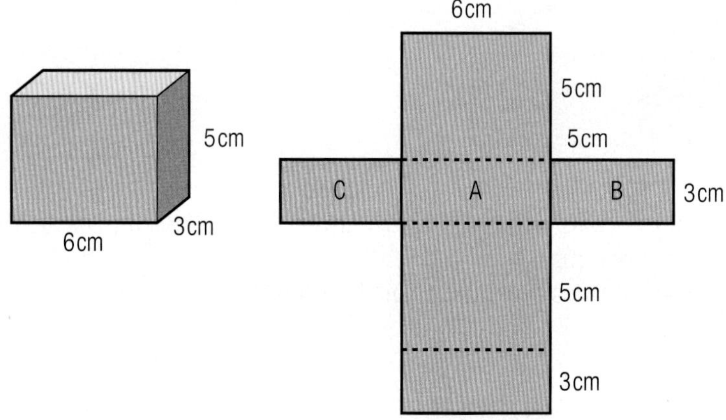

Its area is the same as the surface area of the cuboid.

Area of large rectangle A = $6 \times 16 = 96\,\text{cm}^2$

Area of rectangle B = $5 \times 3 = 15\,\text{cm}^2$

Area of rectangle C = $5 \times 3 = 15\,\text{cm}^2$

Total area = surface area of cuboid = $96 + 15 + 15 = 126\,\text{cm}^2$

EXERCISE 25.2

1 Calculate the surface area of each of these cuboids.

a)

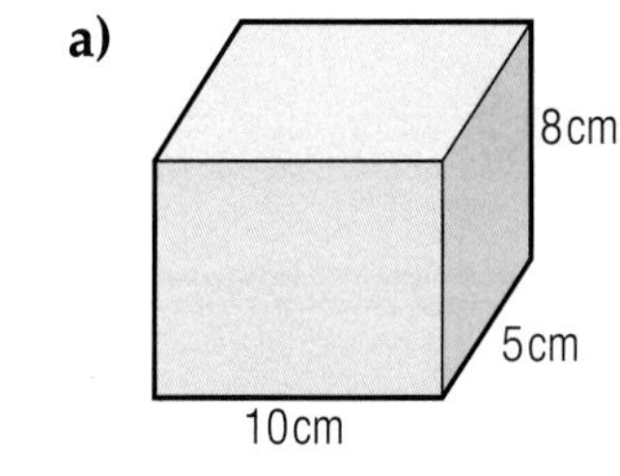

b)

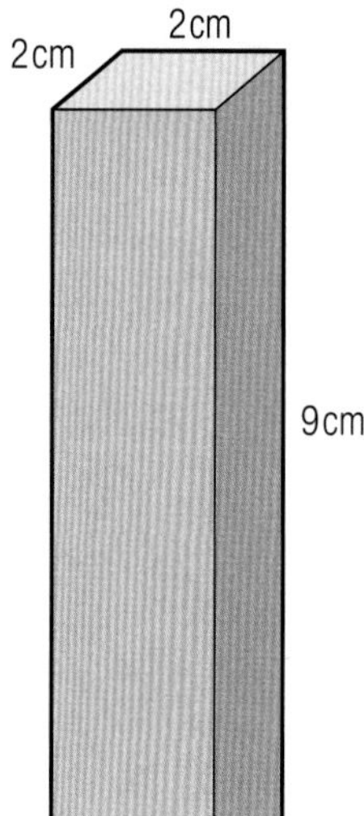

c)

25cm
1cm
1.5cm

2 A cube has edge length 3 cm.

a) Calculate its surface area.

b) A different cube has edges 2 times as long.
How many times bigger is its surface area?

c) A third cube has edges 3 times as long as the original cube.
How many times bigger is its surface area?

3 Here is the net of a cube.

Calculate:

a) the surface area of the cube

b) the volume of the cube.

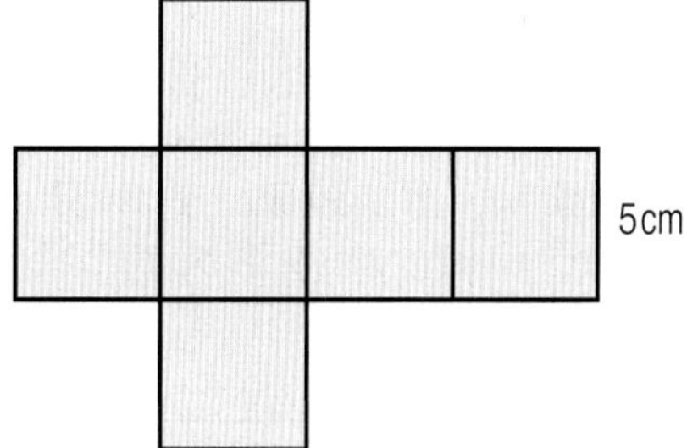

4 **a)** Draw two possible nets for this cuboid.

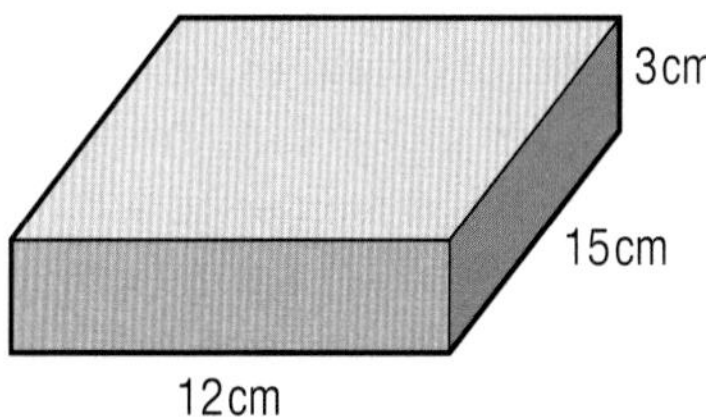

b) Calculate the total area of each net, showing clearly the dimensions of each part of the net.

c) Calculate the volume of the cuboid.

26 Experimental and theoretical probability

- Use experimental data to estimate probabilities.
- Compare experimental and theoretical probabilities in simple contexts.

In pairs or as a whole class, discuss the questions in this section.

The captain of a volleyball team always calls 'heads' when the coin is tossed to decide which way they play. She lost the toss the first five times. Her friend said, 'Don't worry, you will be right half of the time in the long run.'

Q What do you think she meant?

Q Do you think the coin will show heads or tails next time? Explain your answer.

'The long run' is sometimes called 'the law of averages' or, by mathematicians, 'the law of large numbers'. It says that, after a very large number of tosses (not just six or seven), the proportion of heads will be close to a half.

The law of averages was first described by the Swiss mathematician, Jacob Bernoulli (1655–1704) and is sometimes known as Bernoulli's theorem.

If the coin being tossed is misshapen it would be unfair or *biased*. The only way to find the probability of heads or tails with that coin would be by experiment.

If you toss the coin ten times and it shows heads four times, the **experimental probability** is $\frac{4}{10}$ or 0.4.

If you toss the coin 100 times and it shows heads 42 times, the experimental probability is $\frac{42}{100}$ or 0.42.

Q You toss the coin 1000 times and it shows heads 426 times.
What is the experimental probability?

Q Which of the three values do you think is the most accurate? Why?

EXERCISE 26.1A

1 Take a drawing pin and drop it on the desk 100 times.

a) Make a tally chart to record the number of drops and the number of times it lands point up.

b) Use your tally chart to estimate the probability of the pin landing point up.

2 Combine your results with nine of your friends, giving a total of 1000 drops. Estimate the probability of the pin landing point up.

This **two-way table** shows all the possible results of tossing two coins.

		Coin 1	
		Head	**Tail**
Coin 2	**Head**	head, head	tail, head
	Tail	head, tail	tail, tail

Because all four outcomes are equally likely, the **theoretical probability** of each outcome is 1 out of 4.

The probability of head, head is $\frac{1}{4}$.

The probability of tail, tail is $\frac{1}{4}$.

The probability of head, tail is $\frac{1}{4}$.

The probability of tail, head is $\frac{1}{4}$.

The probability of a head and a tail *in any order* is therefore $\frac{1}{2}$.

EXERCISE 26.1B

1 Toss two coins together ten times.

a) Record the results in a tally chart as HH, TT or HT (in any order).
b) Estimate the experimental probability of each.
c) How do your results compare with theoretical probability?
d) Combine your results with nine friends and estimate the new probabilities.
e) How do these results compare with theoretical probability?

2 **a)** Draw a two-way table to show the possible totals when two fair six-sided dice are rolled and their scores are added together.
b) Calculate the theoretical probability of throwing a total of 12 with two fair six-sided dice.
c) Calculate the theoretical probability of throwing a total of 7 with two fair six-sided dice.

3 **a)** Devise an experiment with two fair six-sided dice to determine the experimental probability of:
(i) throwing a total of 12 with two fair dice
(ii) throwing a total of 7 with two fair dice.
b) Comment carefully on your results and in particular how they compare with theoretical probability.

You may wish to involve others in the experiment to get a large sample.

4 From the experiments you have conducted, what do you think is the effect of the size of the sample on the result of a probability experiment?

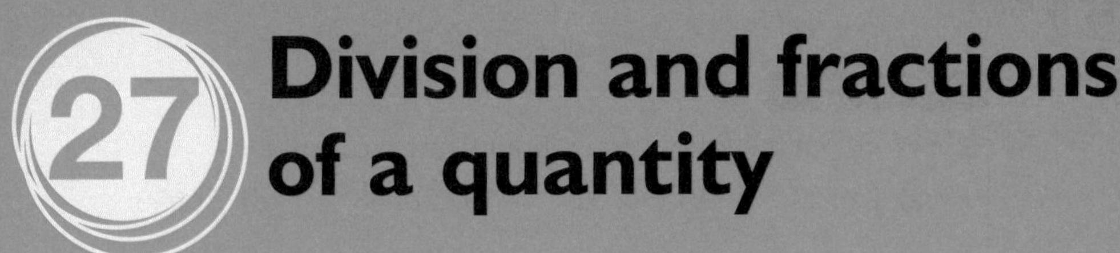

27 Division and fractions of a quantity

- Know that in any division where the dividend is not a multiple of the divisor there will be a remainder, e.g. $157 \div 25 = 6$ remainder 7. The remainder can be expressed as a fraction of the divisor, e.g. $157 \div 25 = 6\frac{7}{25}$.
- Calculate simple fractions and percentages of quantities, e.g. one quarter of 64, 20% of 50 kg.
- Know when to round up or down after division when the context requires a whole-number answer.

Calculating fractions and decimals of a quantity

In Chapter 15 you saw how to work out fractions and percentages of a quantity using a calculator. Many simple calculations can be done mentally or on paper instead.

Worked examples

a) Work out $\frac{3}{5}$ of 80.

$\frac{1}{5}$ of 80 is $80 \div 5 = 16$

$\frac{3}{5}$ of 80 is 3 times as much as $\frac{1}{5}$.

Therefore $\frac{3}{5}$ of 80 is $3 \times 16 = 48$.

b) Work out 30% of \$4.50.

10% of 4.50 is $4.50 \div 10 = 0.45$
30% of 4.50 is 3 times as much as 10%.

Therefore 30% of 4.50 is $3 \times 0.45 = 1.35$

30% of \$4.50 is \$1.35.

c) Work out 45% of \$60.

10% of 60 is $60 \div 10 = 6$
5% is 10% ÷ 2 and 40% is 4 × 10%.

Therefore 5% of 60 is $6 \div 2 = 3$ and 40% of 60 is $4 \times 6 = 24$

45% is 40% + 5%
Therefore 45% of \$60 is \$24 + \$3 = \$27.

EXERCISE 27.1

1 Work out the following without using a calculator.

a) $\frac{2}{5}$ of 20 **b)** $\frac{3}{8}$ of 32 **c)** $\frac{3}{4}$ of 48 **d)** $\frac{5}{6}$ of 30

e) $\frac{2}{9}$ of 81 **f)** $\frac{7}{20}$ of 60 **g)** $\frac{3}{16}$ of 32 **h)** $\frac{7}{10}$ of 25

2 Work out the following without using a calculator.

a) 20% of 50 **b)** 40% of 80 **c)** 25% of 60

d) 35% of 90 **e)** 11% of 50 **f)** 12% of 120

g) $17\frac{1}{2}$% of 200 **h)** $22\frac{1}{2}$% of 500

3 Work out one quarter of $60.

4 Work out 20% of 50 kg.

5 **a)** Work out 25% of $120.

b) A coat costing $120 is reduced by 25% in a sale. Work out its sale price.

6 **a)** Work out 30% of $80.

b) My electricity bill has increased by 30% when compared with last year. My bill last year was $80. Work out this year's bill.

7 **a)** Work out 5% of 70 kg.

b) Last year a man's weight was 70 kg. His weight has increased by 5%. Work out his current weight.

8 **a)** Work out 15% of $800.

b) An investor paid $800 for some shares. Their value has dropped by 15%. Work out their current value.

Division and remainders

In Chapter 20 you looked at a written method for dividing numbers. Here is a reminder of the method.

Worked example

Calculate 713 ÷ 23.

In other words, how many times does 23 go into 713?

- First write the division like this:

$$23 \overline{)\,7\ 1\ 3}$$

- Working from left to right, work out how many times 23 goes into each digit in turn.
  How many times does 23 go into **7**?

$$\begin{array}{r} \mathbf{0} \\ 23 \overline{\smash{)}\, \mathbf{7}\,{}^{7}1\;3} \end{array}$$

  0 times, with **7** left over (a **remainder**)

  How many times does 23 go into **71**?

$$\begin{array}{r} 0\;\mathbf{3} \\ 23 \overline{\smash{)}\, 7\,{}^{7}\mathbf{1}\,{}^{2}3} \end{array}$$

  3 times, with a remainder of **2**

  How many times does 23 go into **23**?

$$\begin{array}{r} 0\;3\;\mathbf{1} \\ 23 \overline{\smash{)}\, 7\;3\,{}^{2}\mathbf{3}} \end{array}$$

  1 time, with a remainder of 0

- Therefore 713 ÷ 23 = 31.

In the example above there was no remainder at the end, i.e. 23 went into 713 exactly. This is not always the case.

You know that 100 ÷ 25 = 4.
Therefore 700 ÷ 25 = 28
and 725 ÷ 25 = 29.
713 is between 700 and 725,
so 713 does not divide by 25 exactly.
There is a remainder.

Worked example

Calculate 713 ÷ 25.

- First write the division like this:

$$25 \overline{\smash{)}\, 7\;1\;3}$$

- Working from left to right, work out how many times 23 goes into each digit in turn.
  How many times does 25 go into **7**?

$$\begin{array}{r} \mathbf{0} \\ 25 \overline{\smash{)}\, \mathbf{7}\,{}^{7}1\;3} \end{array}$$

  0 times, with **7** left over (a **remainder**)

  How many times does 25 go into **71**?

$$\begin{array}{r} 0\;\mathbf{2} \\ 25 \overline{\smash{)}\, 7\,{}^{7}\mathbf{1}\,{}^{21}3} \end{array}$$

  2 times, with a remainder of **21**

  How many times does 25 go into **213**?

$$\begin{array}{r} 0\;2\;\mathbf{8} \\ 25 \overline{\smash{)}\, 7\,{}^{7}3\,{}^{21}\mathbf{3}} \end{array}$$

  8 times, with a remainder of 13

- Therefore 713 ÷ 25 = 28 with a remainder of 13 out of 25.
  This can be written as a mixed number, as $28\frac{13}{25}$.

EXERCISE 27.2

1 Work out the following, giving your answers as mixed numbers.

a) $157 \div 25$ **b)** $163 \div 20$ **c)** $172 \div 17$

d) $191 \div 30$ **e)** $72 \div 35$ **f)** $103 \div 4$

2 Work out the following, giving your answers as mixed numbers in their simplest form.

a) $124 \div 20$ **b)** $155 \div 15$ **c)** $310 \div 25$

d) $406 \div 10$ **e)** $250 \div 40$ **f)** $102 \div 100$

Rounding up or down

There are times when a division produces a decimal answer which in the context of the question needs to be rounded to a whole number. Sometimes, however, rounding to the nearest whole number may not be appropriate.

Worked example

A packet of sweets contains 58 sweets. This is shared between 6 friends. Calculate how many sweets each friend gets.

Using a calculator, the division $58 \div 6 = 9.\dot{6}$

$9.\dot{6}$ rounded to the nearest whole number is 10. However there are not enough sweets for each friend to have 10 sweets each. So the answer must be rounded **down** to give 9. Therefore each friend gets 9 sweets.

EXERCISE 27.3 

In each of the following round each answer to the most appropriate whole number.

1 64 sweets are shared between 11 people. How many whole sweets do they each receive?

2 A piece of metal rod 117 cm long is cut into smaller rods of length 15 cm. How many smaller rods can be cut from the larger one?

3 Cars each 3 m long are placed end to end into a container 50 m long. How many cars can be put into the container?

4 A piece of cloth 320 m long is cut to make dresses. If each dress uses 6 m of cloth, how many dresses can be made?

5 135 m of fencing is used to make 4 identical animal enclosures. The fencing can only be split into metre lengths. How many metres of fencing are used for each enclosure?

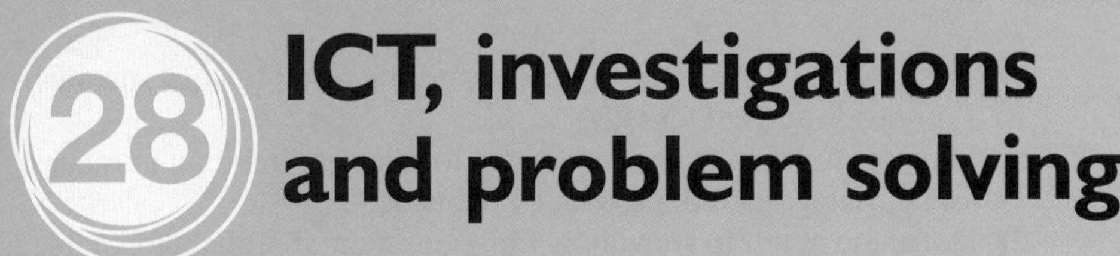

28 ICT, investigations and problem solving

1 Buy one, get one free

Shops and advertisers have different ways of promoting the sale of their products.

Look at these examples.

SALE
$\frac{1}{3}$ off all items.
Special offer
Buy 2 get 1 free
Final Reductions
40% off everything

Find as many different examples as you can of sale promotions. By carrying out calculations and showing your method clearly, decide which ones are better value.

2 Heads I win!

In this activity you will use a spreadsheet to analyse what happens to the results of an experiment, as you repeat it more and more times.

a) Set up a spreadsheet with headings as shown below.

	A	B	C	D	E	F
1						
2		**Spin number**	**Heads (1) Tails (0)**	**Total number of Heads**	**Proportion of Heads**	
3		1	1	1	1	
4		2	0	1	0.5	
5		3	0	1	0.33333333	
6		4	0	1	0.25	
7		5	1	2	0.4	
8		6	1	3	0.5	
9		7	0	3	0.42857143	
10		8	1	4	0.5	
11						
12						
13						
14						
15						
16–21		Continue the numbers to 100 using a formula	Record your results in this column	Use a formula to keep a running total of 'Heads'	Use a formula to calculate the proportion of 'Heads' after each spin	
22						

→

b) Toss a coin 100 times. Each time record the result in your spreadsheet. Use a 1 for heads and a 0 for tails.

c) Enter formulae in your spreadsheet to calculate the total number of heads and the experimental probability of heads.

d) Plot a line graph to show how the experimental probability of heads changes as the number of tosses increases.

e) Explain what your graph shows.

3 One hundred

a) Calculate the surface area of this cuboid.

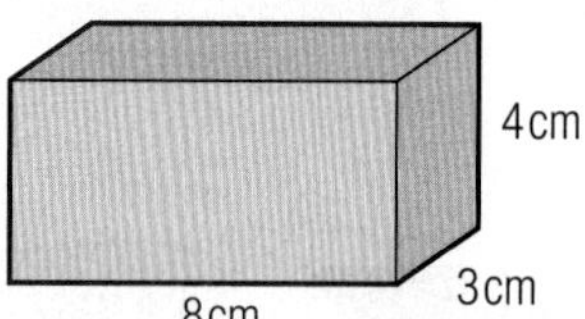

b) Another cuboid has a surface area of $100\,cm^2$.
Its edge lengths are all whole numbers of centimetres.
Work out possible values for the edge lengths.

c) Are there more possible values for the edge lengths?
If so, how many are there?
Try to give a reason for your answer.

4 Two-tone discs

These questions are about discs which have sides of different colours. One side is blue and the other is red.

a) If two of these discs are flipped at the same time, what is the probability that they both show the same colour, i.e. both blue or both red?

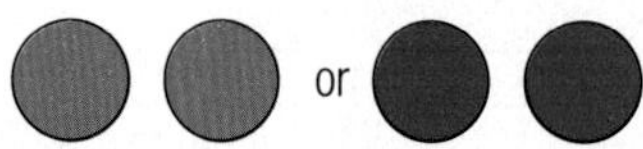

b) If three of the discs are flipped at the same time, what is the probability that they all show the same colour?

c) If four of the discs are flipped at the same time, what is the probability that they all show the same colour?

d) If five of the discs are flipped at the same time, what is the probability that they all show the same colour?

e) Put your answers from parts **a)** to **d)** into an ordered table.

f) Describe the relationship between the number of discs and the probability that they all show the same colour when flipped.

g) Use your rule from part **f)** to predict the probability that ten discs all show the same colour when they are flipped.

5 Coordinate patterns

The quadrilaterals drawn on this grid form a sequence.

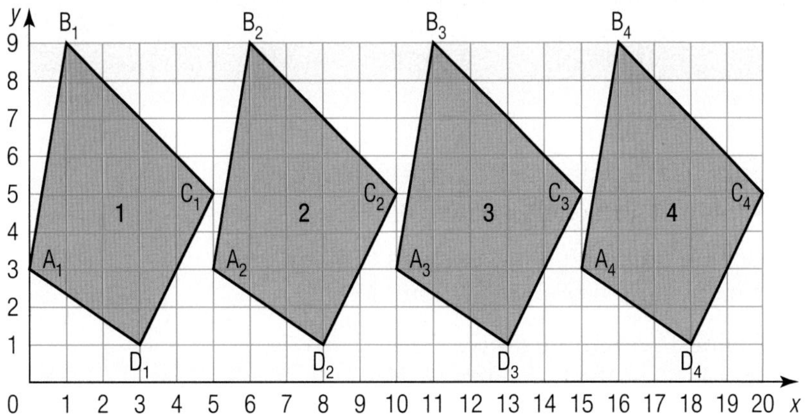

a) Write down the coordinates of the vertices A_1, B_1, C_1 and D_1 of quadrilateral 1.
b) Write down the coordinates of the vertices A_2, B_2, C_2 and D_2.
c) Record the vertex coordinates of the first four quadrilaterals in a table like this.

Quadrilateral	Vertex coordinates			
	A	*B*	*C*	*D*
1				
2				
3				
4				

d) Describe any patterns you see in your table.
e) Use your rules from part **d)** to predict the vertex coordinates of the tenth quadrilateral.

Review 4A

1 A heater uses 4 units of electricity in 30 minutes.
How many units does it use in 2 hours?

2 A machine prints 1200 newspapers in 40 minutes.
How many does it print in 12 hours?

3 **a)** Divide 10 cm in the ratio 2 : 3.
b) Divide 90 in the ratio 60% to 40%.

4 Evaluate (work out) this expression when $a = 3$, $b = 4$ and $c = 5$.

$$12a + 8b - 9c$$

5 In physics this formula is used in calculations about electricity:

$$V = IR$$

V is the voltage in a circuit in volts,
I is the current in amps,
R is the resistance in ohms.

Without using a calculator, calculate the voltage V when

a) $I = 2$ amps, $R = 60$ ohms
b) $I = 8$ amps, $R = 200$ ohms
c) $I = 0.5$ amps, $R = 2000$ ohms
d) $I = 80$ milliamps, $R = 2000$ ohms

6 Draw a grid and choose a suitable scale for the points given below. Plot and label the points on your grid.

$A = (1.8, 2.8)$, $B = (2.5, -3.6)$, $C = (-2.8, -0.4)$, $D = (-2.4, 3.8)$

7 Calculate the volume of the cuboid shown.

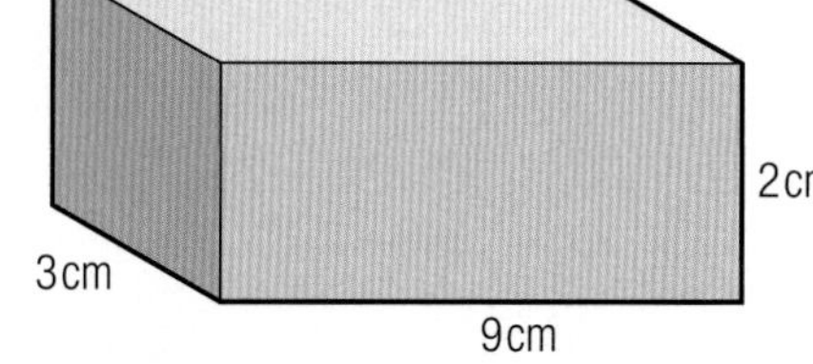

8 **a)** Make a spinner in the shape of a hexagon (see page 90). Label the sections 1 to 6.
b) Design an experiment to see if it is fair.
c) From your experimental results estimate the probability of getting:
(i) a 6
(ii) an odd number.
d) Compare your results with those expected by theory and explain what you notice.

Review 4B

1 A bricklayer lays 1100 bricks in an average 8-hour day.
How many bricks does he lay in a 44-hour week?

2 A combine harvester produces 7 tonnes of grain in 6 hours.
How many tonnes does it produce in 42 hours?

3 Divide 3 litres in the ratio 7 : 13.

4 Use percentages to compare the ratios 16 : 24 and 20 : 30.
Decide if they are in proportion.

5 Evaluate (work out) this expression when $p = 1$, $q = 2$, $r = 3$ and $s = 5$.

$$2s(5p - 2q) - 2r$$

6 An internet company charges its customers in the following way.
The internet is free for the first ten hours each month and then is charged at a rate of 12 cents per hour.

a) Derive a formula for calculating the cost, $C, of *h* hours of internet use.

b) Use your formula to calculate the monthly cost of 40 hours of internet use.

7 Write down the positions of points *E*, *F*, *G* and *H* on this coordinate grid.

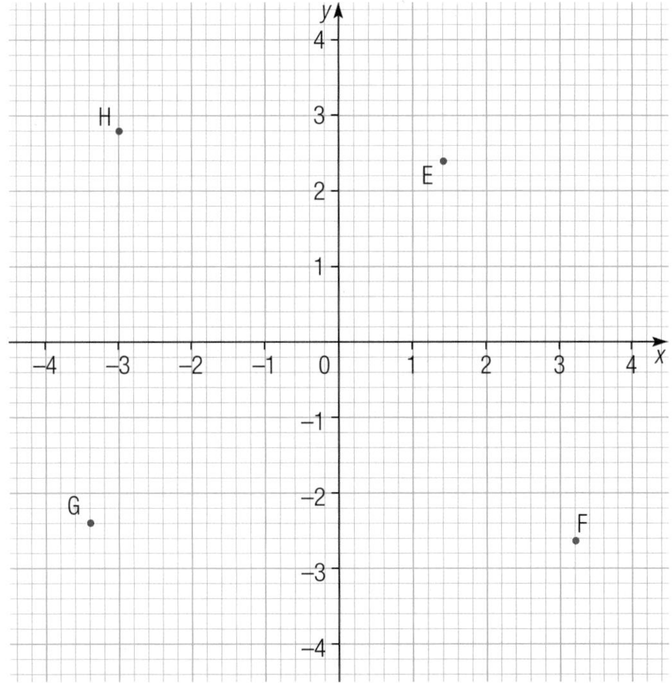

8 Calculate the volume of the cuboid shown.

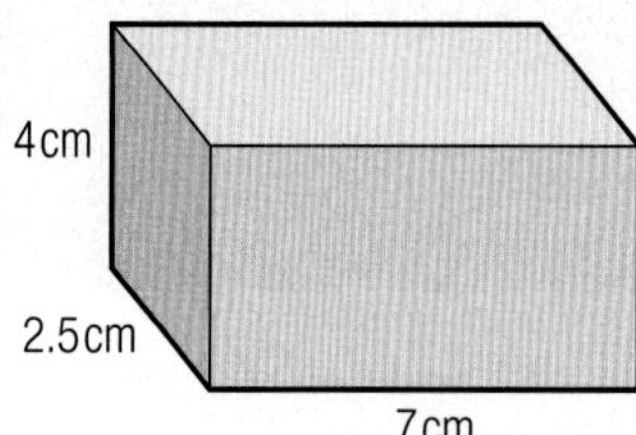

9 **a)** Devise an experiment to find the probability of throwing a 6 with a six-sided dice and getting heads when you toss a coin.
b) What is the theoretical probability of this outcome? Compare this with your experimental results.

Index